PUBLICATIONS OF THE INSTITUTE OF BUSINESS AND ECONOMIC RESEARCH

Recent publications in this series:

THE THEORY OF FISCAL ECONOMICS
by Earl R. Rolph (2d printing, 1956)

THE ROLE OF REGIONAL SECURITY EXCHANGES
by James E. Walter (1957)

ECONOMIC DEVELOPMENT OF COMMUNIST CHINA
by Choh-Ming Li (1959)

INTRODUCTION TO THE THEORY OF INTEREST
by Joseph W. Conard (1959)

ANTITRUST IN THE MOTION PICTURE INDUSTRY
by Michael Conant (1960)

ECONOMIC DOCTRINES OF KNUT WICKSELL
by Carl G. Uhr (1960)

A THEORY OF ACCOUNTING TO INVESTORS
by George J. Staubus (1961)

ORGANIZATION, AUTOMATION, AND SOCIETY

Publications of the Institute of Business and Economic Research
University of California

ORGANIZATION, AUTOMATION, AND SOCIETY

The Scientific Revolution in Industry

By ROBERT A. BRADY

UNIVERSITY OF CALIFORNIA PRESS 1963
BERKELEY AND LOS ANGELES

University of California Press
Berkeley and Los Angeles, California

Cambridge University Press
London, England

Library of Congress Catalog Number: 61-7535
Manufactured in the United States of America

Institute of Business and Economic Research
University of California, Berkeley

Preface

A host of new problems in organization is raised by the swift permeation of science throughout contemporary industrial societies, and conjointly by the cumulative momentum of industrialization throughout the shrunken space-time dimensions of the globe. Among these problems, one of critical importance for economic policy is the extent to which long-term and wide-range planning is required by both the structural layout and the operational conditions of the emerging technologies. To deal with this problem we shall require the development of an organization or systems theory which can cope adequately with the ever more complex issues of decision making in this transformed environment.

Policy and theory are here so closely interwoven that no one may tell where the one begins and the other ends. For both, the issue of centralization versus decentralization is being thrown directly to the forefront, and its importance is highlighted by the fact that two great contrasting ideological systems appear to divide the world. One champions (in theory at least) the highly decentralized American "free enterprise" system. The other promotes the highly centralized, "omnipresent," and "omnicompetent" planning mechanism associated with the U.S.S.R. (where, however, there is a trend toward decentralization).

On the fringes of the titanic struggle over both policy and theory are the underdeveloped countries. Virtually without exception these countries are now launched on long-range plans for accelerated economic development and social change. To implement vitally important parts of their plans, these same countries are borrowing, ad libitum, from many different sources, and what they imitate they are adapting to their own resources and to their cultural and national habit-patterns.

In all the borrowing, adapting, and welter of interchange, two indispensable components, those of science and industrial technology, seem increasingly—and in some respects to everybody's surprise—to rise above and beyond the sea of differences. As far as our evidence goes, to take the extreme case, it now seems clear that Soviet science in most fields is essentially like our own. In nearly all fields it is at grips with essentially the same fundamental problems; employs the same methodologies and techniques; combines postulation, deductive reasoning, and empirical verification in substantially the same ways; draws upon our research, our publications, and our discoveries and speculations as we in turn are learning to draw upon theirs. In each forward step, as scientists from different disciplines now testify, each body of workers evolves essentially the same types of natural-science laws, and comes up with identical or complementary inferences, proofs, and discoveries.

That this is so should surprise nobody. Such has been the history of both science and industrial technology over the past two hundred years. The interchange, however, is never merely two-way; it is generally an interchange in all directions at once: from the United States to or from the Soviet Union perhaps; but also from either or both of these to or from Britain, France, Germany, Japan, India, and so forth. It goes on wherever men work in laboratories or libraries, in research or design divisions, in mathematics departments, or in construction engineering.

As far as our evidence goes, here is the true universalism of modern times; here are the real, living, world-wide common beliefs, hopes, dedications, disciplines, values; here is arising the lingua franca which all peoples and tongues may understand; here also is the common pool from which any may draw the knowledge and devise the technologies upon which the material fates and fortunes of all mankind, in some general and uncertain way, seem to center.

The growing interdependence of science and technology necessarily results in the permeation of industrial processes with like points of view, like disciplines, like reference to objectively valid criteria, and like modes of making judgments. The evidence of such permeation crowds in from all sides. It shows up in the construction and layout of industrial plants and in the weaving of power, transport, and communications networks; in the operation and control of processes; in the analysis of problems raised by innovations; in the training, preparation, and approaches of management. To an increasing extent it is showing up in administration, and even in the shaping of various lines of policy decisions.

In science, universality is based on evidence of law, order, regularity—patterns of interdependence in nature. In technology, it is based on scientifically verifiable best methods of turning knowledge of these laws to human account. In management, and in at least the lower echelons of administration, it tends to become less clear, for here both are compelled, willy-nilly, to bridge the gap between technology and the highly volatile, almost endlessly complex "human factor" and the even more volatile and complex "social factor."

The trouble with both of these "factors" is that we still know so little about either, and that little which is, so to speak, "scientifically cleared up," still leaves us almost wholly in the dark concerning the relationship between the two. How much is man a mere biological specimen? How much a creature of culture? Who knows? Who can be sure?

The state of our "laws"—if, indeed, there be any—of personality and cultural change are more wrapped in mystery than is the secret of life itself. But of one thing we can be sure; and that is the kaleidoscopic swiftness with which environmental changes are taking place in contemporary times—not in the United States alone, but everywhere. The influences that from the time of Francis Bacon to the French Illuminati, made European intellectuals "furiously to think" have become the commoner's heritage today. Along with this have come more questionable yet also quite universal habits of "furiously to act" and "furiously to change"—to change attitudes, beliefs, hopes, wants, desires, institutions, social relations.

Part of this extraordinary and almost global cultural dynamism is traceable directly to the equally extraordinary dynamism of science and technology. Part of the dynamism of the latter is equally traceable to powerful stimuli coming from the former. They interact and react upon each other in an infinity of ways.

But also, paralleling this dynamism, it is everywhere evident that the need for more comprehensive and scientifically minded organization has arisen, prompted by the very nature of the phenomenal advances made by science and technology. How to preserve the cultural dynamism—or, at least, to recover what it may have to offer of value to human life, while effecting the necessary minimum degree of effective organization of scientific and technological resources—is probably the most difficult problem of history. It is rendered even more difficult by the built-in necessity of preserving the greatest possible capacity for change in science and technology themselves.

This need for flexibility in science and technology arises only in part from the nature of the driving forces which lend vitality to each. It is also, as may be shown, an indispensable condition to long-continued human life and culture on this planet.

The larger and more general problem was posed long ago by political theorists and historians. It is that of how to reconcile order and freedom; how to have the best and not the worst of both worlds. The growth of the new industrial technology has merely generalized the problem so as to encompass virtually all phases of life. It affects all aspects of contemporary civilized existence: politics and the state; education and the supply of public information; relations between rural and urban areas, and the organization of life in each; the comity of nations and the maintenance of peace. At all levels, the problem is how to combine coördination with individual initiative, organization with autonomy, effective interlacing of interdependent activities with flexibility and the need for change—irrespective of the source, whether from science, technological innovation, or cultural values.

This study is concentrated on industrial technology, with special attention to that level of development wherein the cleaning-up operations necessary to bring practice fully in line with scientific theory are already well along. It is essentially a sort of ground-clearing study. It stops short of any attempt to draw many conclusions. It seeks merely to answer one type of question, namely, what, in the light of certain well-accepted criteria, is the best way to organize the productive resources of an economy when decision makers are prepared to make full use of the potentialities opened up by advances in science and engineering.

It consists, so to speak, of a series of "stills" depicting the implications of what may, without exaggeration, be referred to as "the scientific revolution in industry." No attempt to cope with the problems of organization now, or for a long time in the future, will get very far unless it begins by taking these "stills"— either in their present form, or as they may be altered by further innovations in science and technology—as given and irreducible components.

But so to accept them carries some rather far-reaching implications for the manner in which most problems of organization in both economic and noneconomic affairs are formulated. It is my belief, as indicated in both the first and last chapters of this study, that what is involved for the social sciences is no less revolutionary in scope and method than those developments in quantum theory, relativity, and the like which led to the revolution in physical theory of the 1930's, and which were brought to the notice of a startled world by the explosion of the first atomic bomb.

As far as academic halls are concerned, the conventional divisions of subjects into political science, economics, sociology, business administration, and history—not to mention psychology, anthropology, and possibly even much of philosophy—may now well be as obsolete as the medieval division into the trivium and quadrivium after the Renaissance, and as cumbersome in coping with the problems which now crowd upon scholars for solution.

My debts for assistance in this study are too numerous, many of them of too long standing, and at many points too difficult to identify clearly, for full and adequate acknowledgments.

I am, however, under especially heavy obligations to several institutions and persons whose assistance it would be ungrateful not to acknowledge in full. First of these is the late President

xii   *Preface*

Keppel of the Carnegie Corporation, who made available from
that organization funds to finance two years of field investigations in Europe studying industrial organization. Subsequent by-
product studies were made of emerging power configurations
(*Business as a System of Power*, Columbia University Press,
1943), and of the program of the first postwar Labour government in Britain (*Crisis in Britain*, University of California Press,
1950). Those studies were primarily concerned with the problems of bureaucracy and power, and their implications for organization and decision making. Complete listing of further aid by
assistants, colleagues, students, and critics within business and
governmental circles would run into hundreds of names. For
reading and criticisms of the entire manuscript at one stage or
another I am especially grateful to Mr. Morris L. Cooke, of the
Public Affairs Institute, Washington, D.C.; the late Professor
Dickson Reck, School of Business, University of California,
Berkeley; Professor Hugh Hansen, Department of Economics,
University of Iowa; Professor Warren Gramm, Department of
Economics, University of California at Davis; Mr. L. L. Howell,
of the Harry Cooper Stores, Pasadena; and several dozen students
at the University of California.

Especially valuable have been many of the additional—and at
one point or another—detailed criticisms and suggestions by
chapters. Amongst those to whom grateful acknowledgments
should be made are:

For chapter i: Professor S. V. Ciriacy-Wantrup, of the Giannini
Foundation, University of California; Mr. Leslie C. Edie, Port
of New York Authority; Professor Corwin Edwards, School of
Business Administration, University of Chicago; Professor
Andreas Papandreou, Department of Economics, University of
California; and Professor Paul Baran, Department of Economics,
Stanford University.

For chapter ii: Professor Ciriacy-Wantrup; Professor Erich
Zimmermann, University of Texas; and Professor Baran.

For chapter iii: Professor Robert Brode, Department of Physics,
University of California; Professor Tom S. Kuhn, Department of
Philosophy, University of California; Mr. Lauriston Marshall,
Director of Research, Link-Belt Company, Indianapolis; and Mr.

C. E. Sunderlin, Deputy Director, National Science Foundation, Washington, D.C.

For chapter iv: Admiral George F. Hussey, Jr. (retired), Secretary of the American Standards Association, New York; Mr. Willis McLeod, Chief, Standards Division, G.S.A., Washington, D.C.; Mr. Richard Bergmann, Vice-President and Chief Engineer, Link-Belt Company; Mr. Tom Davis, Link-Belt Company; and Mr. Marshall.

For chapter v: Professors Ravitz, Schaffer, and Somerton, all of the Department of Mineral Technology, University of California.

For chapter vi: Professors Varden Fuller and James J. Parsons, respectively of the Giannini Foundation and the Department of Geography, University of California; and Mr. Robert Enochian, of the Department of Agriculture, Washington, D.C.

For chapter vii: Mr. Marshall; Mr. Charles O'Connor, President of Reichhold Chemicals, Inc.; and Dr. Charles Thomas, Professor of Physics, University of Michigan.

For chapter viii: Professor Cyril Atkinson, Engineering Design, University of California; Mr. Marshall; and Professor Baran.

For chapter ix: Professor Harmer E. Davis, Mr. Richard Carll, and Mr. Richard M. Zettel, of the Institute of Transport Engineering, University of California; Mr. Arthur Grey, Department of Economics, University of Southern California; Mr. Edie; and Mr. R. S. Henry, Vice-President, Association of American Railroads.

For chapter x: Mr. Marshall, Professor Hansen, and Professor Gramm.

For chapter xi: Professor Theodore Hawkins, Department of Political Economy, Johns Hopkins University; and Professor David Revzan, School of Business, University of California.

For chapter xii: Mr. Edie; Professor Dallas Smythe, of the Institute of Communications, University of Illinois; Mr. M. H. Cook, of the Bell Telephone Company; and Mr. Robert Walsh, of the International Telephone and Telegraph Company.

For chapter xiii: Professor Papandreou, Mr. Edie, Professor Baran, and a dozen or so others.

For financial assistance I am further indebted to the Bureau of Business and Economic Research of the University of California, which supported the British study, and which has given continuous and generous support for research and clerical assistance since that time.

For research assistance I have an especially deep obligation to Professor Norman Bursler, now of the Law School, University of Chicago; to Dr. William Taylor, now of the International Monetary Fund, Washington, D.C.; to Professor John Dalton, now of the Department of Economics, University of Maryland; and to Mrs. Caroline Webber and Miss Ruth Rappaport, both of Berkeley, California.

Throughout all phases of this study my wife, Mildred Edie, has given invaluable advice and criticism—particularly pointed in chapter xi. Needless to add, errors of omission and commission must of necessity be mine alone.

Which latter comment, however, may deserve another few lines. At all points the material has been sifted for the homeliest and most familiar illustrations possible. Every bit of superfluous data or process of reasoning has been cut away. The first effort throughout has been to achieve the maximum of communication in general clarification of what quickly becomes, even to the expert, almost infinitely complex.

Berkeley, California   Robert A. Brady

Contents

PART I

Variables Which Condition Success

I

Introduction: Characteristics of the Scientific Revolution in Industry

Clearly the facts of the much-publicized scientific revolution in industry are of overwhelming interest in the commanding heights of polity throughout the world. Wherever we look, it is seen now to contain one of the indispensable keys to success in defense and war, to the realization of hopes of mass prosperity, and hence to the spread of democratic cultures. This is true whether we have in mind the multifarious, piecemeal, and day-by-day adaptations of older industrial countries such as the United States and Britain, or any of the vast areas just beginning efforts at accelerated economic development throughout the length and breadth of the world.

The new patterns of industrialization, like the spread of Christianity under the Caesars or of democracy after the Illuminati, are everywhere the order of the day. On all sides they are in the ascendant; with objections in the minor key duly allowed for, the new scientific-minded industrial technology is everywhere both generally sought after and, once begun, irreversible. On its account most developed and underdeveloped countries alike seem prepared to modify, alter, or, *in extremis,* sacrifice whatever stands in the way in the forms of law and custom, politics and religion, economics and standards of living.

By it most of life is bound to be altered in detail, when not wholly transformed. While the older industrial countries are constantly altering the life styles of their own peoples and institutions in keeping with the lines of force traced out by this continuing revolution, the newer are faced with the possibilities and the hazards of adaptation en masse at the latest levels of invention, technique, science, and "know-how." In either environment, the new developments confront, or will soon confront, society with the ultimate problem: the rational organization of production on the most comprehensive and technically efficient basis possible.

That this *ultimate* problem should confront us now, with the stamp of "urgent business" on it, is due to two closely related sets of reasons. The first has to do with the new and sobering view of natural resources. Here the old cornucopian view is gone. The unlimited "fullness of the earth" is no longer with us. On every side modern industrial technology, like the older, starvation-level agricultural societies, is now faced with the ironclad necessity of becoming resource-conscious. Even the most lavishly endowed nations of the earth are being forced, as the monumental reports of the Paley Commission for the United States have made abundantly clear,[1] to consider prospects of numerous, and in some cases critical, materials shortages. The United States itself is swiftly becoming a major "have-not" nation. Most of the older industrial countries reached this stage a long while ago.[2]

The second set of reasons for the urgency of the problem of rational organization in production is found in the very nature of the scientific revolution in industry itself. Up to a certain point, the issues have little to do with ideologies or social programs. The inner logic of the newer technology sets certain broad limits on how it may be most efficiently managed and directed. Through its application, processes are being linked to processes, plants to plants, firms to firms, and even industries to industries in such a way, and under such ordering disciplines of integration and synchronization, that the relating plans and management procedures must keep in step on pain of crippling breakdowns, any one of which may threaten to ramify endlessly throughout the system.

The integrating plans must everywhere take cognizance of the strict limits imposed by the structure of limited natural resources, and at the same time manage so to guide and rationalize production processes that output may yet be expanded indefinitely. The two interact continually. The more severely limited the natural resources, the greater is the emphasis upon more rational, economical, and efficient industrial organization. At the same time, the more complete the resort to the newer industrial technologies, with their protean productive power and consequent mounting draft on resources, the greater is the concern over conservation.

Over half a century ago, Thorstein Veblen referred to "this concatenation of processes" by way of which "the modern industrial system at large bears the character of a comprehensive, balanced mechanical process." [3] Viewing the problem of the intricate technology of the future, when based on massive use of low-grade natural resources—long after high-grade deposits will have been exhausted everywhere—the California Institute of Technology finds that because of the huge increases required in energy resources simply to keep the whole process going, there might, following any major catastrophe, actually be a "point of no return." [4] Once, that is to say, major breakdown occurred, the combination of intricate integration of the industrial system at large with the necessarily gigantic minimum requirement of energy to keep the system going might foredoom the possibility of any regeneration of the system at all.

Without regard to any such possible future denouement of so dramatic a character, the facts behind the speculation may be seen to render an understanding of the scientific revolution in industry one of the most important and pressing needs of contemporary times. It will quickly be apparent that the new order differs radically from that celebrated by the elder Arnold Toynbee in his famous pioneering study of the eighteenth- and nineteenth-century industrial revolution.[5]

To be sure, the new grew out of and is linked with the old. The line of inheritance is direct. Yet even a quick glance at its specific differentia will show how this revolution within a revolution has qualities and characteristics that set it off as something distinct and different in its own right.

It has four general aspects. Each is closely related to the others and is, in fact, heavily dependent upon them. First is the chemical revolution in the materials foundation of industry. Second is the standards and specifications revolution in the criteria for selecting the best methods, processes, products, and the like. Third is the electronics and automation revolution in the processing methods of industry. And fourth is the revolution (at the moment, primarily atomic) in the systems of energy supply.

The revolutionary impact of each of these lines of development is not confined to any single line of industry. Each in a different way affects, or promises eventually to affect, nearly every level of production from raw-materials extraction to final use by the ultimate consumer. They then promote, singly and in concert, reconstruction of transportation and communications networks, and they lay heavy emphasis upon fundamental reorganization of goods distribution.

As a further consequence, they encourage reëxamination of a wide range of basic postulates in related fields of science. How far, may be appreciated by a brief summary of the leading aspects of the scientific revolution as indicated above.

THE CHEMICAL REVOLUTION

The physical-chemical revolution is slowly enveloping the raw-materials base of the industrial system as a whole. It is of comparatively recent origin. Aside from metallurgy (technically a chemical process), chemical processing on an industrial basis is about 100 years old. But *permeation* of chemical processing throughout the industrial system is far more recent still. For Germany, the great pioneer in this field, it dates back mostly to the turn of the century. For the United States it dates back to the First World War. It is built squarely on detailed, fundamental laboratory research.

The spread of physical-chemical analysis (or transmutation) of a widening range of complex raw materials has opened the way to extensive and flexible substitution of materials in field after field. One of the largest chemical companies in the United States estimates that more than half of its range of products and volume of output is in products which were unknown before World War II. Another estimates that more than half of its output in 1965 will be in products which are unknown in laboratories today. In field after field, this rapidly spreading chemical revolution adds to materials substitution the broad use of wastes and otherwise underutilized by-products. For some substances, such as petroleum, natural gas, coal, and, more recently, wood products, virtually all physical-chemical components can now be used.

At the same time, the similarly flexible synthesis of such components makes possible the production of a bewildering variety of both new and substitute end-products.

From beginning to end of both analysis and synthesis, this chemical revolution of the industrial raw-materials base rests upon, and is further accelerated by, the revolution in standards and specifications.

THE STANDARDS AND SPECIFICATIONS REVOLUTION

It may readily be seen that "chemicalization," as it is sometimes called, of raw materials depends upon the evolution of comprehensive and exacting systems of nomenclature, formulas, process and equipment controls, and precise standards for guiding each and every step in production in keeping with the scientific facts regarding inherent physical-chemical properties in processes of analysis and synthesis. With and upon these are then built further systems of precise specifications on the use or function of each segregated or recombined set of such physical-chemical components. Each step in chemical processing taken in this direction has thus reënforced a separately originating, but also swiftly spreading, system of specifications and standards which is similarly based upon the achieving of comprehensive sets of objectively determined requirements for the adequate performance in use of each and every material, machine, component, process, and finished goods. This might properly be termed the "specifications revolution."

Though difficult at first for the layman to understand,[6] the long-run implications of such standards and specifications are quite revolutionary. A "specification," MacNiece has written, "is the definite, particularized, and complete statement of qualities, characteristics, and requirements of materials, processes, and procedures," and it rests throughout on the preëxistence of careful, systematically worked-through, and scientifically valid systems of standards.[7] The results of a systematic carrying-through of these specifications techniques upon all phases of materials supply, production processes, and methods of distribution (e.g., elimination of meaningless product differentiation) of both producers' and consumers' goods are extraordinary, and in the main are as little understood in theory as they are revolutionary in practice.

THE ELECTRONICS AND AUTOMATION REVOLUTION

Such systems of specifications and standards, when fully carried through, make possible rigorous control over all phases of quantity and quality variation. The way is thereby cleared for completely mechanical or other types of continuous-flow coupling of all, or at least the bulk of, previously discrete steps in processing. With this interlinkage is then combined both temporal and volumetric adjustment from machine to machine (and from equipment to equipment) of loads and capacities. The whole is further supplemented by adequate devices to secure quality control at each separate step in processing. The way is then prepared for application of electronically operated, automatic, self-correcting ("feedback") control devices. When this is done, the plant becomes fully automatic. "Automation," as this end product of converging efforts at technical plant-rationalization is currently termed, has already come to dominate many branches of the heavy chemicals industries, and is rapidly spreading throughout various lines of manufacture.

The Council for Technological Advancement suggests that full automation comes in three major steps: (1) automatic handling of materials, as illustrated by packing plants in the "disassembly" of hogs, or the assembly line as introduced by Henry Ford in automobile production; (2) the integration of production or processing equipment, already rendered automatic, with automatic handling, wherein the separate processing, if guided by "built-in devices such as cams, templates or limit stops" to follow a pattern, may be controlled by a mechanism having a physical analogy to the machinery or processes controlled—i.e., the "analog type of automation"; and, finally, (3) the addition of automatic computers which "read" the production record and use this information to "correct" the process automatically. This last is the feedback which results in full automation. Information, as in the simple device of the home thermostat for controlling room temperature, is supplied which "automatically influences the end result." [8]

How far can automation go? Today we are entering the era of automation—where machines and other equipment, under push button control, will turn out almost any kind of product with wizard-like precision in huge quantities and at low cost . . . not only glassware, light bulbs, automobile engines, and radio and television tube assemblies, but also canned foods, beverages, and pharmaceuticals are being . . . processed automatically.[9]

In this type of production, the entire factory becomes, in effect, "a machine with integrated parts." So far-reaching are some of the technical, economic, and managerial implications of a systematic reworking-through of the principles of automation—derivable ultimately from the much-heralded new developments in information theory, and viewed by some as the most significant scientific development since Max Planck introduced the Quantum Theory[10]—that Norbert Wiener and others think that taken by itself it may properly be termed the "Second Industrial Revolution." [11]

Under the regime forecast by this "revolution," a factory becomes capable of continuous operation 24 hours a day and 365 days a year—at least theoretically and with due allowance being made for breakdown, repair, and maintenance. Only one technical limitation then stands in the way of universalization of automation throughout the leading industrial processes of the globe. That is, energy supply. Energy is probably the most important single limiting factor to the utilization of resources. "What constitutes an available mineral resource" a California Institute of Technology report found, "is essentially a question of energy." [12] Generally speaking, if given ample and readily available energy supplies at any and all desirable locations, it will be found that (see chap. ii) most problems of resource supply are, in effect at least, solved.

THE ENERGY REVOLUTION

The problem of energy supply has been solved with a further "revolution," that of atomic energy.[13] It affords the following advantages.

With respect to supply, Palmer C. Putnam, a consulting engineer for the Atomic Energy Commission, has estimated that the known world reserves of fossil fuels would last, at the calculated consumption level of the year 2000, some 80 years, whereas the amount of uranium and thorium already in sight would provide energy at the same rate for 1,700 years.[14] There are excellent reasons for believing that new finds will soon outdistance those already known. Success in the breeder process multiplies the use of any given supply of fissionable material. The addition of light metals, as suggested at the Geneva Conference,[15] is theoretically possible. But the possibility of using the fusion process (as in the hydrogen bomb) and heavy water (deuterium) opens the prospect of limitless energy resources for the future.

With respect to cost, by current methods cost is almost wholly in the engineering facilities required to turn atomic into electric energy, and this is believed to be already within striking distance of all but the most economical hydroelectric power. (See, however, chaps. ii and x below.)

Finally, *with respect to location,* since one pound of uranium is about the fuel equivalent of 1,300-1,500 tons of standard bituminous coal, the cost of transport to the energy generating site is negligible. The startling result is that no region of the world, however well or poorly endowed with the older sources of power and energy, need any longer be limited in its economic development by shortages of this sort.

IMPACT UPON TRANSPORTATION AND COMMUNICATION

Ample, flexible, and universally available power within raw-materials plants and processing plants makes possible the permeation of automation throughout the central industrial phases and aspects of production. Consequently, the whole concert of such processes may now be organized on a mass-output basis. Furthermore, just as internal reorganization replaces previously discrete processing steps or batch operations with continuous self-correcting flows, so the external conditions to the efficient and unbroken operation of the "automated" plant call for continuous, evenly spaced flows of materials to its doors and of finished products away from the ends of its production lines. Heavy emphasis is then placed upon two complementary developments external to the plant, the over-all effect of which is to generalize the operating conditions and, so to speak, the "life style" of the new industrial technology throughout the industrial system.

These complementary developments are of the utmost importance for an understanding of the problem dealt with in this study. They may only be briefly stated here. The first is actual, direct interplant synchronization. This originates from the effort to achieve an appropriately exacting timing and volumetric adjustment of capacities and output of all plants thus brought together in synchronized chains of successive steps from the raw materials to the finished products. The second complementary development is based partly on the first, but it is also partly of independent origin. A series of related changes has culminated in the reduction of interplant transport facilities to the close equivalent of intraplant flows.

That is to say, transport and communication media come to operate as synchronized automatic or semiautomatic networks. Advance along either line tends further to encourage, and in part rests upon, advance along the other. Some of the effects already achieved are quite remarkable.

In a few cases direct physical interplant synchronization, perhaps best illustrated by some of the new gas and petroleum refining plants in Texas, is so nearly complete that the principles of "automation" may be said to govern at once both the bulk of interplant materials flows and the over-all functioning of the complex of the several related plants involved. In subsequent chapters (e.g., chaps. vii and viii), examples will be given which will show how far the movement has already gone.

The second complementary development is more familiar, but possibly of even greater importance. Two broad levels may be distinguished. First are certain cases where transport media are already completely "closed" in the sense of being automatically operated and automatically controlled systems virtually in their entireties. And second are cases where operating changes, while making possible some approximation to those typical of closed systems, are still (and may, indeed, always remain) some distance removed from the first level.

On the first level are grid power systems, pipeline networks, and (least important at present) continuous-belt interplant connections. All three systems "transport" materials or energy supplies which alternatively would have to be carried by rail, water,

or highway media. In these cases all or at least the bulk of interplant production processes, from the raw-materials stage on, are
synchronized in comprehensive, instantaneously adjustable, automatically controlled, and completely interdependent networks.
Control of these transport networks is effected by use of private,
or public, specialized communications facilities which are precisely analogous to those which interconnect and maintain continuous running adjustment within plants fully oriented to "automation."

On the second level are the rail, highway, waterway, and airway transport systems where internal pressures for technical rationalization—especially when combined with the increasing reorganization of the multitudes of plants and business operations
duly serviced by these transport media on the basis of continuous,
evenly flowing production processes—serve to promote the closest
possible approximation to the operational conditions holding for
transport systems on the first level. In effect, this means that, by
freight cars, trucks, etc., materials "flow" over these media
to and from plants in such a way and on such schedules that,
at both the beginning and the end of freight movements, storage
and warehousing are minimal or, ideally, nonexistent. Every move
made in this direction through scheduling and routing of freight
carriers, and in the required management of the details of movement over tracks, highways, etc., promotes further approximation
to the conditions of internal plant transport where the handling
of materials has been put, or may be put, on a completely automatic basis.

On this second level the necessary supply of intelligence at
decision-making and coördinative points of linkage is handled
through resort to a communications system which may be either
wholly or partly private, or wholly public. In any case, however,
the principle holding for the communications system is that
ideally it shall be as comprehensive in geographic coverage as the
transport media and the location of all the users thereof, and that
it shall be capable of automatic, instantaneously self-correcting
adjustment to varying loads at all times and at all points throughout the system. This principle holds not only for each separate
strand of communication—telephone, telegraph, cable, wireless

facilities—but also, as will be shown, for the system as a whole.

Two things have been happening. First, transportation and communication networks are in process of being unified and streamlined to the point where they are subject to nearly complete automation. Second, these networks, as they link plants similarly automated, become, in effect, components of much larger technically unified systems.

When these two complementary technical developments are taken together with the four aspects mentioned above—chemicalization of the raw-materials base, permeation of systems of standards and specifications, plant automation, and atomic energy—we see the principal characteristics of the dawning scientific revolution in industry. Consideration of its conditions for effective operation, and of its current lines of growth, indicates the emergence of an industrial order which may well differ as radically from the regime of the "dark Satanic Mills," of which Carlyle spoke with such violent condemnation, as did the latter from the era of medieval handicraft. The implications for the related bodies of theory are apt to be far reaching and fundamental.

THE GROWING NEED FOR "RETHINKING THROUGH"

In discussing that specialized portion of the scientific revolution in industry called "automation," Diebold has made the point that, in every instance, carrying it into practice encourages, when indeed it does not demand, the "rethinking through" of each relevant process from beginning to end.[16] This holds, as the automation reports testify, at once for the nature of the materials entering the plant, for all the machinery linked in successive steps in processing and manufacture, for the types of jobs and the training of the staff, for management control, for the types and uses of end products or services, and for most, if not all, of the routine office accounting and record keeping.[17]

Diebold cites steelmaking to illustrate the need for "rethinking through." Here automation has clearly conquered in only two cases, continuous casting and continuous rolling of tin plate. Steelmaking as a whole—materials to blast furnaces, thence blast furnaces to open-hearth furnaces, to soaking pits, and finally to rolling mills—seems, on the best evidence, *not* suited to continuous-flow processes. Yet he sees the possibility that here, as in many similar cases, such a "rethinking through" might reveal automation potentialities which have already been developed, or at least foreshadowed, by current advances in steel metallurgy. One convincing example may be offered in evidence: continuous casting has already eliminated a previously discrete soaking-pit stage which had long been regarded as an unavoidable breaking-point in flow production.

Far more important is the "rethinking" of both the possibilities and the implications of generalizing the new scientific revolution in industry throughout, so to speak, the central trunk and main branches of the industrial system. This calls for (1) reëxamination of the entire structure of available raw materials and of the manifold and increasingly more urgent problems of conservation; (2) reconsideration of the technical and economic implications of universalization of systems of specifications and standards; and (3) reformulation of the supply and cost allocation problems at the numerous points where—as in chemical analysis and synthesis, or in unified grid power systems—facilities are of the multiple-purpose, multiple-function, or multiple-product types. It calls also for (4) new inquiries into the bearing of interconnections among plants enmeshed in such patterns of directly linked, continuously flowing production upon plant agglutination and, alternatively, upon possibilities of plant relocation and scattering; and (5) new lines of inquiry into the supply, cost, and pricing problems involved in plant investment and in the marketing and distribution of, and the consumer demand for, the commodities and services made available through these vastly altered methods of production.

"RETHINKING THROUGH" ON THE TECHNICAL SIDE

"During the last century," wrote Sir W. C. Dampier of the "scientific age" of the nineteenth century, in contrast to the manner in which "the great inventions of former ages" occurred, "we see scientific investigation in the laboratory preceding and suggesting practical applications and inventions." [18] Since he wrote (1910), this statement might better be rephrased to read that "scientific research has already so far permeated the industrial system that

we can no longer tell where the one begins and the other ends."
The "scientific age," that is to say, has truly arrived when not
only invention but also the entire round of productive operations
has been organized along scientific lines. Nobody, of course,
claims that such a picture holds for the contemporary industrial
system in its entirety. But the intention to bring it about does hold
for swiftly expanding sectors, and from the principles evolved
in these sectors it now seems possible to foresee some, if not most,
of the principles, problems, and solutions which are apt to be
characteristic of such a consummation.

For one thing, given any structure of demand, science—theoretical and applied (engineering)—clearly holds the principal
key to adequacy of resources. With minor exceptions, and
whether one has in mind the agricultural, mineral, or energy
resources of land, sea, or air, both the *discovery* and the *best use
over time* (conservation) of known types of resources depend almost entirely upon the most carefully planned scientific exploration and scientifically directed exploitation. As for the *new types*
of resources, such as uranium and thorium for atomic energy,
these are now wholly a product of scientific research (chap. ii).
The scale of "additions" made to resources in the last 30 years by
scientific research—including the discovery of new methods of
utilizing otherwise waste products—may well be in excess of all
previous discoveries of minerals, fuels, and other materials.

Resources and their conservation, however, are only the beginning of the burden placed upon science by its wedding with
industry. The problems faced by the scientific staffs involved tend
to become coextensive with the entire concert of industrial operations.

To put the matter somewhat more explicitly, theoretically the
"chemical revolution" extends the range of problems so as to
encompass the physical-chemical properties of all possible alternative and substitute materials in nature; the "specifications revolution" so as to encompass the properties, design, performance, and
use of all products—whether as raw materials, component parts,
or assembled products—for both producers' and consumers'
goods; the "automation revolution" so as to encompass all technical processes, along with the interlinking networks of power,

transport, and telecommunication, from the raw-material stage to the point of distribution for purposes of final consumption; and the "energy revolution" so as to promote the new scientific revolution in all areas and regions of the earth which possess adequate resources for development on a long-term basis.

Each advance along these lines introduces into industrial technology at least some of the patterns of complexity, interdependence, and order characteristic of the changing view of the nature of the world held by science itself. By the same token, it also adds further to the growing need for a more effective organization of scientific efforts, long felt to be an increasingly more important precondition to further advance in each of the various branches of science. From the time of the founding of the great national academies of the seventeenth and eighteenth centuries, but increasingly with the cumulation of scientific information, this need has grown.

It is an axiom that the problems and the laws of science are a "seamless web"; that chemistry is interrelated with physics, atomic research with astronomy, the physical sciences with the biological sciences, and both of the latter with the social sciences. But from the same axiom it also follows that advance in the principal segments or spheres of scientific research is dependent, to some extent, upon advance elsewhere.

The ever closer working-alliance between research and technology is adding a new note of urgency to the recognized need for organization, mobilization, and pooling of scientific research among the hundreds of public and private research institutes and academies scattered throughout the world. The very sustenance of life itself, the possibility of maintaining or further raising material standards of living, and—at least currently—the chances of securing sufficient military security to escape total annihilation, all alike depend directly and with increasing weight upon the effectiveness with which the organization of science is carried through on the most comprehensive basis possible. The data brought together in chapter iii will illustrate how important this new emphasis has become.

Along with this acute rephrasing of the need for better and

more comprehensive organization of scientific resources themselves, the growing fusion between research and industrial practice brings into sharp focus new problems which are of an unprecedented difficulty. The central and obvious fact must be faced that in strong contrast with the situation which obtains when science is mostly preoccupied with the facts of nature per se, the shifting of focus to include, or at least directly link up with, problems of industry serves inevitably to confront science with a greater and more commanding sense of the facts of human purpose.

From time immemorial productive operations have been undertaken to achieve ends, to fulfill aims, to reach goals, to satisfy objectives, to express interests, and to subserve values. Science, in its new role of master of the secrets of instrumentation, however motivated by pure research interests in its more remote depths, is now in process of being made, on a vastly expanded scale, a direct working party to the patterns of human ends as well as of industrial means. It then follows that unless both means and ends make some sense to the scientist, through him industrial technology may be faced with a new dry-rot capable not only of crumbling the edge of scientific and engineering advance, but also of disturbing the day-by-day functioning of the system as a going concern.

Three new sets of problems—old in terms of human life, but lent a new meaning in this setting—immediately face the scientist and the engineer, and require of them a new concern for the problems of human society.

The first set of problems is associated with redirection of research and reformulation of plans for technological changes in terms of overriding considerations of conservation. As mentioned above, conservation is now more than coextensive with natural resources; it is coextensive with the methods of using these resources. Its problems, that is to say, extend from the mine, forest, or field through all uses involved in the processes of production and onward to the ultimate consumer. Wastages may occur at any point; *conservation is a problem at all points.* Put differently, the scientist and the engineer are now concerned with the problem of efficiency under the regime of *generalized mass production*. They must, accordingly, face the problem of efficiency at all points of the system.

The problems of conservation and efficiency are no sooner faced on this comprehensive footing, than it must be realized that concepts of engineering efficiency in the larger frame of reference lack a general common denominator, and have no alternative but to seek expression by and through money equivalents. Efficiency becomes transmuted in terms of economy, and economy is a problem of costs. But to resolve efficiency factors into "cost" factors confronts the affected sciences with a second set of problems, i.e., with those associated with the *meaning and validity of costs*, their incidence upon individuals and groups, and the social as well as the technical conditions for their minimization in the supply, not of goods in general, but of all the requirements for the eventual delivery of ultimate consumers' goods and services which themselves are looked upon as means for fulfilling human aspirations. Cost is the most important technical clue to both internal and external economies (in the Marshallian sense), and alternatively to the preventable waste of productive resources. It becomes, accordingly, immediately evident that the technical "rethinking through" of which we have been speaking is heavily dependent upon and closely tied up with the need for a further "rethinking through" on the economic side (chap. xiii).

The elements of this latter need already are evident throughout the economic literature, and have confronted economic science with a number of problems which it cannot handle alone. Great significance inheres in the fact that economics is a social, not a natural science. But as a social science its concerns are more intimately tied up with those of the other social sciences than are those, say, of physics with chemistry, astronomy, and the biological sciences. The engineer and the scientist, and along with them more clearly than heretofore the economist, are then faced with a third set of problems which may be broadly designated as "cultural" in the sense understood by sociologists, historians, and especially anthropologists. These problems have to do with the individual and social values that motivate economic action in the face of the astounding potentialities of the scientific revolution in industry on the one hand, and on the other with the swiftly changing structures and disciplines of organization required to realize these potentialities without subordinating all ends to means.

This third set of problems will be generally ignored in this study—not because they are considered to be of minor importance, but because, contrariwise, they seem (at least to the writer) of such transcendent importance for both economics and all the other social sciences that it is best to postpone even a preliminary consideration of the new types of problems arising from the emerging scientific revolution in industry until a reasonably clear picture may be had of just what this "revolution" actually means for the productive apparatus. They are, so to speak, temporarily impounded in a Marshallian *ceteris paribus*, the better to undergo more searching analysis later.

The second set of problems, centered in the meaning of costs, however, is of vital importance to this study; throughout it the proposition will be maintained that they call for a continuing "rethinking through" which has far-reaching implications for the scope and method of the science of economics.

"RETHINKING THROUGH" ON THE ECONOMIC SIDE: A PRELIMINARY PROBLEM

There is a view of science which denies the need of "rethinking through" the basic propositions and methods of economics on any occasion other than the appearance of a new and startling theory, as in the case of quantum mechanics. This is the position of logical positivism, which defends its approach on the grounds of temporal universalism of relevant scientific propositions. This position holds that economics is, or at least should be, developed as are physics, chemistry, and mathematics, on the assumption that basic data with respect to human nature and fundamental relations in society do not change. Its premises, propositions, inferences, conclusions, and laws would then not be subject to historical change. Accordingly, whatever the impact on society of the new industrial revolution, to logical positivists it would not change either fundamental data or underlying law.[19]

It would lead too far afield to explore here the reasons that render this position wholly inadmissible in the social sciences. However, it is important to note that, with respect to the *data of explication* (Carnap's phrase for the data which science is to examine with a view to explaining relations having the force of law)[20] and in sharp contrast with the natural sciences, the facts of technology and the social sciences are undergoing perpetual, irregular, and highly discontinuous (yet also cumulative) change. The industrial revolution and the decline of feudalism are examples. Furthermore, most of the data are rarely subject to experimental segregation, and then but very imperfectly and crudely—mainly by way of rough analogy. Actually, all the data in the hands of human beings are throughout, but also with infinitely varying differences in both detail and intent, oriented to purpose.[21]

In the second place, with respect to method, social-science data are only in rare instances subject to commensuration. Most economic data cannot readily be categorized. We cannot devise a thoroughly defensible index of production for most individual commodities, let alone for a major industry or society as a whole. Even the precision of the statistical data published by the highly competent Bureau of Labor Statistics involves qualifications which frequently, if not generally, render the classification meaningless for purposes of useful application of strict logical or mathematical reasoning. In the simpler cases where the data are relatively easy to categorize, as with costs and prices, the parameters are themselves as much, if indeed not more, functions of policies —the determinants of which are themselves rarely commensurable with respect to even the more obvious minor details—than policies are of them.

When one turns finally to *empirical verification*—the accord of theory with the facts which is confessedly the test of the validity of the processes of logical positivism, or for that matter of any type of scientific thinking—the data to which conclusions, theorems, etc. must allude and with which they must be squared are once again inconstant and undergoing rapid changes, in both quantities and qualities. With social-science data, in short, *temporal universality is impossible and meaningless*. As Alfred Marshall recognized long ago, both human nature and human societies in the long run change to such an extent that principles and laws must change, too. The scientific revolution in industry has served, at times, to shrink the "long run" from centuries or decades to weeks or days.

There are numerous reasons beyond these which call for rejection of the position of logical positivism. The most powerful reasons are found in the direct examination of problems raised by the scientific revolution in industry, which the positivistic school seems unable even to see. Two illustrations may be cited at this point. The first has to do with the vagueness surrounding the nature and meaning of cost itself; the second, with the closely related problem of least cost associated with the central controversy over competition versus monopoly.

PROBLEMS ASSOCIATED WITH THE INDETERMINANCY OF COSTS

Economics has long been faced with a strange dilemma. Clearly the concept of cost is central to the whole of its subject matter, and probably more attention has been paid to its meaning, determination, and measurement than to any other aspect of its chosen terrain. At least in the early classical days, the problem of cost to economists occupied a position similar to the principle of gravitation in astronomy and physics. Given the principles governing the one, the remainder of the dependent phenomena might be known. But the closer the phenomena of cost were examined, and the more clearly these costs had to be dealt with in the context of mass production, the less simple and determinate cost appeared to be.

Once the labor theory of value, or its somewhat attenuated variant, the psychological (pain-cost) theory of value, was given up, then cost to economists became, in effect, indeterminate. And it became indeterminate precisely at the time—from the middle of the nineteenth century on—when the private need for a valid and defensible pricing policy in the swiftly expanding mass-production industries was matched by the equally strong public need for a solid basis from which to launch control over the newer public utilities and to curb the feared manufacturing monopolies. Private and public price strategy, that is to say, sought to gain greater knowledge about the precise meaning of data whose materiality had meanwhile been questioned.

Two examples may be cited. The first concerns the allocation of known cost totals; the second is concerned with the very meaning of the concept itself. As for the first, around the turn of the century Schmalenbach and others working with the problems of rate regulation of public utilities and the costing and pricing policies of mass-production industries began efforts to reduce concepts regarding different classes of costs—fixed, sunk, circulating, prime, etc.—to workable form for direct industrial use. In the main their efforts had little effect upon economic theory— although consideration of the problems had already worked a veritable revolution in the handling of business costs—until J. M. Clark wrote his great book on *The Economics of Overhead Costs* in 1923.[22] The real originality of Clark's pioneering study did not consist of significant new ideas advanced by the author. The book was quite frankly a digest of an enormous mass of more or less empirically evolved practices in such fields as railroading, communications, the iron and steel industries, and engineering. But Clark amassed a powerful weight of evidence, which could no longer be ignored, to the effect that costs were meaningless except in the context of policy; and policy depended upon purpose, intent, interests—in short, upon individual and group interests and, ultimately, upon social philosophy.

Furthermore, in effect Clark presented economists with the conclusion, which has not been effectively challenged since, that the more completely industry moves over to a mass-production basis, the clearer it becomes that cost is a function of policy as much as the reverse. Putting the matter somewhat differently, the parameters of costs are those set by policy, and policy itself is rarely, and at very few significant points, subject to objectively valid determination. Cost, in other words, is indeterminate except in the context of policy; it is policy which gives meaning to accounting classification, and it is from policy that accounting axioms derive whatever content they may be said to possess.

Thus what is to be regarded as an overhead cost, varying in some fashion inversely with output, is a matter of policy. Similarly, what is to be classed as a variable cost (such as wage payments or materials costs), varying in some fashion directly with output, is a matter of policy. How the cost aggregates of either or both general categories are to be allocated to individual units of output are also matters of policy. Whether the costs of investment, or financing, or management, or labor, or research, or selling and distribution are high or low, and whether they are distributed over output in one way or another, are equally matters where the elements and the amount of cost *per unit of output,* regardless of the types of goods or services involved, depend upon policy, and they cannot be fixed or allocated until policy is known. Virtually every step leading up to the new industrial revolution has tended further to underscore this interdependence of cost and policy. But this latter revolution has universalized the problem. It now reaches from raw materials to finished goods, and from the processes of production to the supplying of all financing and public-utility services.

Subsequently, Clark, Copeland, Kapp, and others have raised the issue of social costs, an idea closely related to Marshall's concept of costs and gains (economies) external to the firm. There can be no question but that each new advance along the lines of the scientific revolution in industry heightens the importance of social costs. A strong case might be made that the possibilities open to the ordinary business firm are now mainly to be found in external economies. More important, it is now clearly impossible neatly to separate the one from the other. The maneuvers of private enterprise are now largely taken up with designs to shift costs to the general public—to get their "share" of social and external economies which they have had no direct hand in creating.

At this point the second example, that of the meaning of cost itself, takes on a new significance. The problem as such is very old. What, under the feudal system, one might ask, was the cost of a bushel of wheat which might find its way to local markets from the manorial estate? Should it include the *corvée,* the taille, the salt, and other taxes—whether in money or in kind? Should it include the entire range of feudal dues, taxes, tolls, and other exactions? Should any payment made be included whether it yielded little or no output; whether it forestalled production and technological advance or even cut off innovation entirely; whether the central purpose of production was ostentatious consumption (in which case it would be heavily directed away from investment and expansion), or the promotion of war, or anything else?

In the contemporary environment, are taxes business costs? What of lobbying, political graft, wages paid to racketeers? What of high-pressure salesmanship, of the losses and gains of the gaming tables to which responsible officials might resort betwixt and between? Inclusion of items such as these brings one directly to efficiency-frustrating and resources-wasting acceptance of Davenport's famous statement:[23]

All labor, therefore, that commands a price, though it be the poisoning of a neighbor's cow or the shooting of an upright judge, all durable goods commanding a rent or affording a valuable service—lands, machines, burglars' jimmies, houses, pianos, freight cars, passenger cars, pleasure boats—all patents, privileges, claims, franchises, monopolies, tax-farming contracts, that bring an income—all advertising, lying, earning, finding, begging, picking, or stealing, that achieve a reward in price, or a return which is worth a price—are productive by the supreme and ultimate test of private gain. The meaning of product is *proceeds.*

A startling, but logical, conclusion follows:

It will then be manifest that each distributed cost is merely the market price of a productive efficiency; and that just as the market price of a consumption good neither expresses its utility nor measures it, and is neither determined by it nor measured by it, so the market price of each productive efficiency cannot express the quantum of that efficiency, is not equal to it, is not determined by it, does not measure it, and is not measured by it.

Efficiency, it is important to note, is "productive of proceeds." This is precisely what is meant by the expression widely employed in contemporary economic theory, "the marginal efficiency of capital." It has nothing to do with output efficiency of men, resources, or processes of production, or with the quality of goods.

However pleasant and secure it may have seemed to proceed in this cavalier fashion in the past, such a view makes no sense at all in the face of the scientific revolution in industry. The new industrial processes cannot be made to function *efficiently* and *economically*—which is to say, with the least means in the form of capital, materials, labor, and other inputs—without resort to the practice of always looking behind every cost classification for the variables determining its classification as a cost per se: its scale and proportions, its allocation, its bearing upon prices and the bearing of prices on it. The close interdependence now called for between technically related industries, as well as the normal functioning of the intricate control-devices now rapidly coming into use for effecting interplant synchronization, means that wastes and inefficiencies introduced at any one point tend to ramify endlessly and with widening destructiveness.

The general problem may be put this way: assuming as given the general objective of the fullest and most feasible utilization of the newer mass-production methods under the terms and conditions imposed by the exigent values of contemporary society, what is the pattern of organization of productive resources which makes the best use of the scientific-engineering "know-how" now available? Every cost, cost classification, operation, activity, or function which is not instrumentally *necessary*, which is not positively and (given the individually and socially validated policy) objectively needed in order to make such best use of this "know-how" may thus either be identified as unnecessary or dispensable. This is frankly evaluative, and is to be carried through with the belief that it is the clear, positive, canonically proper, and necessary task of the economist; that it constitutes his essential part of the conduct of scientific research into the problems of society as a whole. Perhaps even more important is the injunction now laid on all industrial use of science—that of conserving resources to the maximum. From this there is now no possible escape.

Such a "rethinking through" of the meaning of costs must postulate initially the *possibility* that the most thoroughgoing organization of the productive apparatus of society along the lines made feasible by the new industrial revolution *may* be held generally valid by society as a whole. It may further be supposed at least *possible* that such a scientific reorganization of the productive apparatus of this country—of any country for that matter, or even of the world as a whole—may be carried out in such a way that it does not destroy or require abandonment of the essential values of contemporary civilization, but may, contrariwise, as well be organized to provide both institutional support and material sustenance to its life processes. The problem will be, first, how to trace out the most promising and feasible lines of reorganization of productive processes warranted by the leading facts of the continuing revolution in industrial technology. The following step will be to see how far either the organization of technology or the governing institutions of society, or both, may need to be altered to effect a workable synthesis between the two.

The caveat, however, must be entered at this point with all possible emphasis, that *it does not follow that rational organization,* as made possible and promoted by the inner logic of the new industrial revolution, *will actually be carried out, or that if carried out it will yet be managed so as to be generally consonant with democratic institutions and the cultural values of Western society.* On the contrary, the societies of the United States and of the Soviet Union alike, as well as of their numerous imitators over the rest of the globe, are one and all threatened with the complete dwarfing of the individual; with the rise of vast, unwieldy, personality-destroying, and irresponsible blocs of privately administered power; with huge cities, gigantic organizations of production, complex and rigidifying bureaucracies which can really be "understood" by nobody and called to account by no one. Where, also, are the "principles of transcendence"—the systems of values by which human beings may rescue themselves from the spreading "trivialization" of life[24]—to be found in the dull routines of the clerk if workaday disciplines within these overshadowing organizations are permitted to freeze in the image of the anthill or the colony of termites?

However important the technical and quasi-technical problems dealt with in this volume may be, for human affairs they are reduced to insignificance by the new problems of bureaucracy and motives which with every step in the new direction rise ever more insistently. Carelessness about the nature and import of the scientific revolution in industry has been general throughout the social-science literature. Yet it is impossible to be sure just where, and how far, the new problems are inherently a part of the possible new order of things, and how far a dispensable carry-over from the past, without being quite sure just what this "new order" may be. A reëxamination of the possible implications of thoroughgoing "scientification" of the industrial system is inescapable at this point. With such a reëxamination before the social sciences, it may then be possible to cope with the increasingly important issues of individual and social policy with a much firmer and more realistic grasp.[25]

Proceeding on this first preliminary level, then, there is a great deal to discover which may give the investigator a sense of pioneering new territory. Throughout, in connection with the problem of the meaning of cost, it may quickly be seen that there has been carried over from the past or invented *de novo* what amounts in the aggregate to a rank and tangled undergrowth of countless unnecessary duties, jobs, functions, offices, and operations. It might well be that a careful working-through of the relevant data might show that in many basic production operations "waste motions"—jobs which in relation to getting out the product and delivering it to the ultimate consumer are actually superfluous —absorb upwards of half, or maybe more, of all the factory and office space, the paper work, and the various functions connected with management and administration. Comparable waste might be found also in the ancillary and supplementary services which go along with production in the form of banking, insurance, brokerage, publications, etc., and in the systems of goods distribution and servicing—still almost unbelievably clumsy—which stand intermediately between the productive plant and the consuming public.

To illustrate, although the statistics are imprecise, somewhat more than one million able-bodied workers in the United States are employed in house-to-house selling although there is no rational ground for one such person (chap. xi). Whatever the amount of manpower unnecessarily employed here in the supplying of goods and services (the probable amount doubtless varying with time and place), it functions not to enhance the volume of output and facilitate the forwarding of goods from the plant but, rather, unnecessarily to absorb the labors of vast numbers of human beings, to clog the smooth running of operations and to fill the desks, the mails, and the minds of operative personnel with the performance of tasks which are superfluous and hence dispensable to the eventual net gain of all.

All this is not a product of mere "bureaucracy." Of uneconomical bureaucracy, of course, there is a great deal, which in itself is bad enough. But worse is the fact that vast, energetic, and enormously ingenious efforts are being made which have the overall effect of building into the economic system inefficiencies which threaten at many points to offset the extraordinary efficiencies introduced by the scientific revolution in industry.

The second step referred to above involves far more significant social issues. But both steps also raise an additional question, concerning the economist as social scientist, which further illustrates the revolutionary implications of the portentous changes under review. This is the question of the efficiency (least means) criteria in the conflict between "monopoly and competition" as alternative forms of economic organization.

Monopoly appears to the economist primarily as a problem of costs, and is, hence, a special case of the generalized problem of indeterminacy of cost under conditions imposed by the scientific revolution in industry. But to political science, monopoly is essentially a problem of power, linking the problems of the engineer and business administrator directly to the values and institutions of democratic society.

REËXAMINATION OF "COMPETITION VERSUS MONOPLY"

This issue has absorbed a great and increasing portion of economists' time and attention. The literature assumes some definite relationship to exist between the facts of technology and the capacity of the reigning scheme of things (competition, monopoly, or some variation of either) to bring about some given degree of socially satisfactory efficiency in production. With the general exception of the so-called "natural monopolies," and the partial exception of vertical integration in the heavy metallurgical industries, however, references to technological developments are exceedingly rare. Most of the generalizations made would, or at least could be made to, apply equally well to a primitive industrial system or even to a handicraft society.

Typically, discussion of the merits or demerits of any given competitive scheme, or of any given departure from such a scheme (clear up to the limiting case of complete monopoly power), proceeds almost wholly with reference to a given scheme of motives and an acknowledged distribution of power. The terms of reference are, accordingly, those that would seem to lie most properly in the fields of psychology and philosophy on the one hand, and of political science on the other. They are not based on the facts of changes in the engineering data of industrial growth or of scientific organization, and they are typically treated without significant reference to either.

Two examples may be cited. In *The Political Economy of Monopoly* Fritz Machlup finds that

. . . most of the growth of corporate empires during the last fifty or sixty years was not a matter of technological integration of production but rather financial integration of control. . . . There was nothing "natural" about this growth of business firms into corporate giants. It was merely a matter of shortsighted legislatures and courts, and ingenious lawyers, promoters and businessmen.[26]

This judgment is offered as a self-evident truth, fully borne out by a historical record which is readily available to any critic. No proofs, except of a negative sort, are submitted in evidence.

The negative proofs consist of a review of the well-known and more fully substantiated facts about the collusive devices and maneuvers of firms engaged in consolidating—through merger or other devices, including the cartel type of interfirm compacts or understandings—an expanding economic power. But whether or not there existed supplementary, or even merely parallel, economies which were directly or indirectly associated with technological advance, or with new and bold ways of accomplishing economic ends, remains unknown to the reader and to Mr. Machlup—unknown for the simple reason that the investigation was not made, and because the data are not available. From the sometimes quite scholarly mass of federal, state, and private investigations of the "power trust," for example, one would never have guessed that such a multiple-purpose scheme as the Tennessee Valley Authority was even possible. Its advantages would have escaped attention because the subject would have escaped scrutiny. In the whole history of antitrust legislation hearings,

and of regulatory activity, no one has ever found what constitutes
an optimum-efficiency production unit.

A second example is provided by Fellner's book, *Competition
Among the Few.*[27] This study represents a rather bold attempt
to assimilate to the theory of competition all the bits and pieces
of theory regarding monopoly, oligopoly, imperfect competition,
and the like, which have grown up alongside, but have never
been effectively absorbed into, the organon of either the old Austrian or the Marshallian systems. His argument may be summarized as follows: (1) Prices are at once determinate, stable,
and fair, and the best allocation of resources in the usual case
obtains only under conditions approximating pure competition.
(2) Criteria may be set up which individually or in combination make possible the determinate degree of departure by which
actual prices may deviate from competitive prices, and competitive conditions of production from those organized on a more
monopolistic footing. (3) These departures then can be attributed
either (*a*) to technological factors, in which case they may be
allowed as necessarily unavoidable and (possibly) advantageous,
or (*b*) to collusive manipulations, in which case they become fit
subjects for antitrust or similar types of restraining action. The
whole of economic behavior may then be assimilated to the
underlying theory of pure competition.

But Fellner seems impelled by these conclusions to investigate
the exceptions, and hence leaves his readers without (*a*) any
usable criteria for determining the case for exception, and (*b*)
any notion of how large a segment of the industrial system may
fall into this class. Yet, as will be pointed out in subsequent pages,
there is virtually no industry, trade, medium of transport or communication, or even service where technological and organizational desiderata do not encourage some degree of abandonment
of the competitive norms of behavior. Indeed, as has frequently
been well argued, the shoe seems now to be on the other foot; the
exceptions are the rare cases where competition is sufficiently
close to any of the well-established or more commonly accepted
"models" to merit any serious attention at all.

But "monopoly" fares no better. Nobody knows whether it is
generally or necessarily efficient or not. Indeed, it may well be

that virtually all of the important changes wrought in the fabric of production by the scientific revolution in industry, as the following chapters will outline them, favor bypassing the controversy as though it did not exist—bypassing, that is to say, on the grounds that the mechanics of profit maximization, however competitive or monopolistic the industry, are no longer capable of shedding much light on the efficient organization of economic activity, when industry is structured along the lines to be traced out below.

Such a possibility need not be modified by consideration of the subject matter of what has, in academic circles at least, come more recently to be known as "industrial organization." As commonly taught, this field is concerned with neither industry nor organization, but with the catallactics of profits maximization under varying degrees of market control, with size and efficiency correlates based on plant-cost curves which are not directly subject to inspection, and with the manner in which power will be directed and distributed under stimulus of univocal motivational drives. Here again there is no recognition of the need for squaring either the motivational drive or the organizational problems with psychological or organizational theory. Simple acquisition in a simple (small-scale, individualistic, competitive) economy is transposed to a complex, rapidly moving, and large-scale industrial economy. Every interest and motive in such a complex cultural milieu has come to play a part in the determination of decisions, and the simple facts of each cost and price situation rarely provide the investigator with unquestionably valid raw-cost and price data upon the basis of which he can erect a solid structure of valid resource-allocation theory.

First, the changed motives change decisions, and second, the effect and the meaning of efficiency in the uses of resources in the altered power-structure of monopoly change the results even more. Hence, "industrial organization" in this new context becomes, in effect, a pseudo subject with pseudo problems which are solvable with the benefit of false or, at best, simple-minded analogies. At few if any points are they capable of delivering valid opinions regarding the over-all economically most efficient disposition of resources. Nor do they seem able to provide reliable guides for the formation of policies regarding even conspiratorial behavior in the complex of cultural currents and power eddies which are common characteristics of this new industrial milieu.[28]

Very clearly, this suggests further reasons for undertaking a more or less complete "rethinking through" of the entire range of facts bearing upon economic motivations in the setting of the scientific revolution in industry and of the sizes and types of economic organization and control within society, which encourage or retard its expansion. While the space limitations of the following chapters will not permit paying much attention directly to this range of problems, for present purposes it will do to assume (*a*) that the problem of motivational drives in the type of economic system foreshadowed by this technological revolution must be handled as a separate and independent (though closely related) problem on its own merits, and (*b*) that the same holds for problems of the appropriate forms of human organization in this milieu—with its tendency to promote a seemingly inevitable and massive bureaucratization of virtually the entire range of functions, in detail and at large, throughout the economic system as a whole—regardless of whether its several more strategic segments are publicly or privately owned, and whether the immediate unit of reference be small or large in scale.

To repeat, in the setting of the astounding changes forecast by the new industrial revolution, a prior condition to reëxamination of these and similar problems is a reasonable degree of clarity as to the precise nature of the revolution itself. Search for such clarity has provided the *raison d'être* of this study. In making the study it has been found that while in any given case the details are intelligible only to the specialist, and to the layman may seem endlessly complex, yet the broad outlines of the changes visible on the industrial horizon are relatively easy to perceive.

FURTHER REASONS FOR STUDYING THE SCIENTIFIC REVOLUTION IN INDUSTRY

Wherever one looks—whether at fact and opinion in America, Britain, Russia, Germany, or elsewhere—the main outlines of the new scientific and engineering developments appear to be envisaged in essentially the same terms. The problems associated with them, however, are not confined to the older industrial systems, and are apt, in fact, shortly to be experienced in common by all regions of the earth.

Most countries have already undertaken national programs for rapid economic development. Most are also coöperating with other countries for mutual acceleration of common programs. We have long recognized this to be true of the nations in the Soviet block. Currently, most Southeast Asian countries are participating in the coöperative ventures originally outlined in the Colombo Conference of 1950. Most Western European nations are members of the European Coal and Steel Community, the European Economic Community, and the Common Market, which contain elements of further large-scale industrial development.[29]

The British Colonial Development schemes have succeeded in launching long-range and centrally planned development programs in most of Britain's colonial territories. The United States, principally through Marshall Plan and Mutual Security aid, has given massive support to development programs throughout the non-Soviet world. All these efforts have been paralleled at some point by United Nations programs—mostly under the auspices of the eleven "Special Agencies" such as FAO, WHO, UNESCO, the International Bank, and the International Monetary Fund— having similar objectives.

The conditions under which such plans are being conceived and carried on tend generally to promote ever more insistent attention to the problems taken up in this study. For one thing, the planners are generally compelled to move with maximum *speed*. A pamphlet dealing with development in the British colonial areas comments:

The pressure of ideas, which are themselves the natural product of the education we provide, and the passionate enthusiasm of emergent peoples for all the magic of a "Brave New World," have between them forced the pace to a speed which has turned ordered development into a breakneck race against time.[30]

But the reasons cited in this passage for the "breakneck race" are only a small part of the causes for the mounting pressure for rapid change. The internal popular demands for development are being fanned to white heat by the play upon them of nationalistic leaders trained in Western industrial countries, and imbued with their material standards of living. They are at all important points further stimulated by an omnipresent, ingenious, many-faceted, and steadily mounting propaganda emanating from the prosperous "developed" countries which is without parallel in the history of the world.

This propaganda is lent unusual penetrating power by the intensity of the "cold war" global rivalry of the Great Powers to marshal behind them the interest and ideological support of peoples everywhere. Furthermore, it is directed not merely toward achieving some definite level of material improvement in the distant future; it is also focused on immediate gains in a schedule of cumulatively rising industrial improvements, and is deployed before prospective converts with a seemingly boundless enthusiasm which refuses to see any limits in sight.

There is another, grimmer side to the feverish activity of economic developers which only serves further to heighten the pressure. It might be called the universalization of Mill's dilemma. Over a century ago, J. S. Mill undertook to follow up Ricardo's suggestion (abolition of the Corn Laws) for solution of the Malthusian predicament in terms of a further inspection of the impact of rising real wages upon population increase. His initial proposition was that small gains will not have small results; they will rather have no results at all. Small increases in income could only mean more mouths to feed. What was required was a tour de force: something that would within a single generation raise the standard of living of the entire population to the minimum level where the combined effects of the social restraints of education, habitual enjoyment of material and cultural amenities, and an awakened desire to seek further improvements would serve powerfully to slow down the birth rate.

This problem is now world wide. Population pressures in most of the underdeveloped areas of Asia, and in many countries in Africa and Latin America, are already so great that even by the mid-nineteenth-century standards of Mill's time the prospects seem almost hopeless. On the one hand, from the example set by the more developed countries, the sights have meanwhile been greatly raised on what constitutes the minimum level of food, clothing, shelter, health, and cultural welfare; the scale of the gains required has been further multiplied by the massive increase in the numbers of people to be cared for; and the proportions of the task are being still further expanded by the politically inescapable foreshortening of the time span in which tangible improvements must appear on the horizon to the man on the street. On the other hand, as a sort of final turn of the screw, the available natural resources of most of the underdeveloped countries, as will be pointed out in more detail in the following chapters, are—by Western standards at least, and as far as current information about them goes—limited and of relatively poor quality. Such countries will have to learn to run where we have only been required to walk.

It is high time, accordingly, that the facile optimism which has accompanied so much programming for development in these regions be corrected by a more sober and realistic grasp of the essential facts. This effort will yield the conviction that relief can now come only, as with Ricardo's solution in his time, from abroad. But this time it is not cheap food which will turn the trick; it is the massive introduction of Western scientific industrial technology. Those who have advocated a slow, atomistic, "stages" approach have inadequately grasped the essential facts confronting most underdeveloped countries, and have misread their economic history. Since the time of Buckle, historians have ceased to take seriously the notion that countries must pass through successive stages of development, such as is advocated, for example, by Brozen.[31] His counsel to go slowly on account of the difficulties of introducing unskilled workmen to the problems of modern industry is belied by the well-known facts of recent American industrial history and by the experience of, e.g., American firms in areas like Venezuela and the Arabian Near East. His illustration of the "iso-quants," or resource combination,[32] is not, as he indicates, a case for selecting levels of production techniques, but for systems of priorities in introducing the most modern techniques. The fears he expresses over too-rapid industrialization are unfounded; actually the reverse is the case.

No matter how rapid, there is no possible speed of industrialization for which practical plans can now be laid which is fast enough.

At the same time—regardless of how heavily it is supplemented by borrowing abroad, and how much it is helped by advantageous easing of international trade—the huge scale of the resultant demand for the necessary investments to be met out of severely limited domestic savings, especially when also confronted with lean natural resources, makes the public show of strict economy an ironclad political requirement in the underdeveloped economies.

No way has been found out of this dilemma but by resort to comprehensive national planning for accelerated transformation of the economy as a whole. The fact that such plans must be adjusted to deep-rooted economic, social, political, and cultural habits and institutions, and that the latter will call for many changes in detail, even as the plans will stimulate changes in them, serves generally to underscore the emphasis upon advance over a broad front.

These other changes are ignored here not because they are unimportant, but purely because of space limitations. In many cases, internal reorganizations may reveal enormous reserves of manpower or other resources. Various estimates make possible the conclusion that from one-fourth to one-third or more of the population of Asia, Africa, the Middle East, and Latin America could be released from agriculture without decreasing production. No government would dare to make such an adjustment without being prepared to promote industrial development on the widest possible front. However, there has been no such change-over, whether one looks at the experience of Japan, Germany, and the United States before and after the two World Wars, or that of the Soviet Union since the Revolution, which has experienced any serious difficulty in the long-run absorption of such released manpower.

The characteristic habit shown in the past by all newly industrializing countries, that of borrowing whenever possible at the latest levels of technological advance, now involves a new, highly conscious, and concentrated effort to grasp the larger meaning of transplanting a fully matured industrial system, and of adjusting it throughout to the resources, institutions, needs, and wants of its own people.

The underdeveloped countries, in short, have arrived at the point where they must make the effort to "rethink through," industry by industry, and function by function, the structure and organization of the new industrial system which now confronts them in the more highly developed countries.

But the same latter countries are also under compulsions, scarcely less decisive, to proceed in a similar manner. There is the tendency, in short, to begin a type of reëxamination of the processes and interdependencies of industry as a whole which is quite similar to that promoted in the operations of individual plants by such advances as automation.

It is the purpose of the following chapters to show how incisive and far-reaching the rethinking needs to be. The data collected are matters of common knowledge; almost without exception they may be taken as beyond dispute. There is no originality in the facts, nor even in the manner in which most of the data have been put together. But the problems that cry for solution, as the survey proceeds from case to case, face the social-science disciplines—especially economics—with challenges as serious as those confronting physics when the full force of the quantum theory and the closely allied discoveries of the structure of the atom was finally driven home.

Thus from many sides the need for undertaking a reëxamination of the whole of industry is evident. The possible future implications for both theory and practice are quite extraordinary.

II

The Handicap Race with Nature

THE CRITICAL VARIABLES

"Rethinking through" the implications of the scientific revolution in industry must inevitably begin with resource appraisal. Mounting concern over present or prospective shortages of natural resources has become virtually a world-wide phenomenon. Knowledge of what is available in the form of land, minerals, fuels, etc., of varying qualities and locations is clearly inadequate, but, such as it is, presents an alarming picture of grievous inadequacies and rising costs. Availability of alternative and substitute sources is clearly now a matter almost wholly of scientific knowledge of properties of materials, and of engineering methods for turning such knowledge to useful account.

A good deal has already been accomplished. A number of specialists have begun to chart the eventual dates of depletion of nonrenewable or "stock" resources, such as fuels and minerals, and to raise doubts about the ability of "flow" resources,[1] such as lands and forests, to sustain the rising demands made upon them by population increase and advancing standards of living.[2]

The problem is of common interest to older industrial and newly developing countries alike. As pointed out above, for the latter it is now of decisive importance for both short- and long-run expectations. In these areas, where some two-thirds of the world's people are being stirred out of centuries of lethargy to hope for vast increases in national productivity, it appears that their hopes are matched with poorer, leaner, scantier resources than those of the industrial countries. In some areas, such as those of India, China, the Mediterranean littoral, and Southeast Asia, the long-run prospects of any considerable economic advance have been deemed by many experts to be well-nigh hopeless, while the number of voices raised in alarm over deterioration of global-resource–man ratios is itself a cause for a spreading sense of anxiety for the future of the human species.

The reason for pausing to consider the problem of limited resources in this context, however, is not to strike a more balanced or optimistic estimate of the essential facts. The purpose is rather to show how most of the estimates, particularly the more pessimistic, are at some point misconceived because of a failure adequately to grasp the meaning of the way in which technology and science now approach the problem of resource discovery, development, and use as a whole.

While resource scarcity clearly limits productivity possibilities, yet it is in scientific and technological advance that the only possible solutions to resource scarcity are to be found. The advances of science and technology will serve simultaneously to encourage further reorganization of the industrial system at large. To understand this dual effect it will be necessary quickly to survey the more obvious facts about the current state of resources.

VARIABLES WHICH MULTIPLY THE DRAFT ON RESOURCES

1. *The "Gargantuan appetite" of an industrial economy.*—Fifty years ago the suggestion that the United States, believed to be the most richly endowed of all nations in the world, might face a problem of resource scarcity would have seemed fantastic. But the Paley Commission found [3] that while in 1900 American production of materials (other than food and gold) exceeded consumption by 15 per cent, yet by 1950 surplus had turned into a deficit of 9 per cent, and that by 1975 materials imports (estimated in dollars of constant value) would exceed domestic production by 20 per cent. Many strategic materials, both for peace and war, are involved:[4]

Of more than 100 mineral materials we use, about one-third—such things as sulfur, coal, phosphates, but including only two metals—are fully supplied from our resources. Another third of the list we get almost entirely from other lands, and this fraction has assumed greater importance as advances in the technology of high-temperature alloys and electronics have brought into greater prominence such items as columbium, cobalt, high-grade quartz crystals, and others we do not possess. The final third of the list we obtain partly from abroad and partly from domestic output—materials like iron ore, petroleum, copper, lead, zinc, and bauxite. Of 72 "strategic and critical" materials listed by the Munitions Board, the United States imports all of its supplies in more than 40, and part of its supplies in all the rest.

"The United States appetite for materials," the Paley Commission comments, "is Gargantuan—and so far, insatiable." In 1950 the average American consumed 14,400 pounds of fuels; 10,000 pounds of construction materials; 5,700 pounds of agricultural materials; 5,100 pounds of metallic ores; and 800 pounds of miscellaneous nonmetallics. On all the available evidence, the demand for materials in the United States is bound to continue at a rapidly rising rate.

What is true of the United States in this respect holds for other countries, industrialized and underdeveloped alike. The data of the Paley Commission could be duplicated on somewhat lower, but rapidly rising, levels for Britain, Germany, France, the Soviet Union, and other industrial countries. It would hold also for China, India, Africa, South America, and other areas barely beginning industrialization. The problem facing the United States, in short, is not unique; on the contrary, as the huge United Nations reports[5] make abundantly clear, the problem is global in extent, and to some extent it is felt in connection with virtually every major type of resource, whether food, fuel, or mineral.

Furthermore, for a number of reasons which may be mentioned briefly, the problem of adequate resources for developed and underdeveloped countries alike is bound to become increasingly more serious.

2. *The multiplying factor of rising standards of living.*—In the United States, while population was increasing from 76 million in 1900 to 151 million in 1950, per capita national income rose from $325 to $864 expressed in dollars of constant purchasing power. Various estimates anticipate further increases in per capita income ranging from double to fourfold by the year 2000.[6] While the stream of materials required to sustain such advance tends to rise only about half as fast as the national output, multiplying the draft on materials by from 50 to 200 per cent would, clearly, leave few cases where domestic resources would be adequate to meet the demand.

But other peoples are also eager to increase their standards of living, and hence to make increasingly heavier demands upon their own supplies. Merely to bring the rest of the world up to the material standard of living of the United States in 1950, the Paley Commission found, would mean that "world need for materials would increase to six times the present already massive consumption." Furthermore, in the strategic area of energy resources, the supply of which limits and sets the possibilities of all resource utilization, American use on the eve of the Second World War was seventeen times the world per capita average. Since then it has increased until by 1950 it amounted to nearly 100 per cent more. In contrast, annual fuel consumption per capita in Asia (excluding Japan and the U.S.S.R.), with nearly half the world's population, is about the equivalent of that consumed by the average American every two days. If India were, over the next 70 years, to increase her output of steel a hundredfold, her per capita use (assuming meanwhile a doubling of her population) would still be about one-eighth of the rate of use in the United States at the present time.[7] The full meaning of such ratios may be appreciated by glancing at the data on differences in world per capita income given in table 1.

Most of the underdeveloped areas of the world are now operating with plans for rapid economic development. Few of them, it is true, seem to visualize catching up with the American level within foreseeable times, if ever. But all of them have programs for raising their levels to the limits made possible by available domestic resources, or by exchange of such materials supplies as they may possess in surplus for resources available from other areas.

3. *Multiplying factors: population growth.*—Largely as a result of the operation of one advance agent of industrialization, epidemiology, death rates have fallen so rapidly that population has taken a great leap forward over the unindustrialized world. Over half a billion Chinese now inhabit an area but slightly larger than the United States; nearly 400 million Hindus live in an area approximately two-fifths the size of the United States. Some 91 million Japanese live in an area roughly the size of the state of California, with only one-fifth of the total land-surface arable. In all these cases of fantastic overcrowding—not to mention Indonesia, most of Europe, and even sections of Africa and the

TABLE 1

ESTIMATES OF PER CAPITA NET NATIONAL PRODUCT IN CERTAIN COUNTRIES,
ANNUAL AVERAGE 1952-54

| Country | Per capita net product | | Population, mid-year 1953 (thousands) |
	In U. S. dollars	Per cent of U. S. value	
United States............	$1,870	100	159,643
Canada.................	1,310	70	14,781
Switzerland..............	1,010	54	4,877
New Zealand............	1,000	53	2,047
Sweden.................	950	51	7,171
Australia................	950	51	8,815
Belgium.................	800	43	8,778
United Kingdom.........	780	42	50,611
France..................	740	40	42,860
Germany (West).........	510	27	48,994
Netherlands.............	500	27	10,493
Israel...................	470	25	1,650
Chile...................	360	19	6,437
Italy....................	310	17	47,551
Cuba...................	310	17	5,807
Malaya[a]................	310	17	5,706
Union of South Africa.....	300	16	13,153
Lebanon................	260	14	1,353
Turkey.................	210	11	22,461
Japan...................	190	10	86,700
Korea (South)...........	70	4	21,376
Burma.................	50	3	19,045

SOURCE: United Nations, *Per Capita National Product of Fifty-five Countries: 1952-1954*,
Statistical Papers, Series E, No. 4 (New York, 1957), table 2, pp. 8-9.
  [a] 1952 and 1953.

Near East—the annual rates of increase have become extraordinarily high. Further medical advances, particularly those associated with overcoming nutritional deficiencies, promise more
significant reductions in death rates, and hence continuing stimuli
to population growth.

Furthermore, both in the older industrial countries and in the
unindustrialized areas, these rates—a few partial exceptions, such
as France, to the contrary notwithstanding—continue to rise for a
considerable period of time with the mere advance of science and

industrial technology alone. Since the war, the rate of American population growth has actually risen above that of India. According to estimates by Carr-Saunders,[8] while world population rose 33.6 per cent for the hundred-year period between 1650 and 1750, for each subsequent 50-year period it increased as follows: 1750-1800, 24.4 per cent; 1800-1850, 29.2 per cent; 1850-1900, 37.7 per cent; 1900-1950, 49.6 per cent. Willcox's estimates are higher.[9]

While it is generally true that rising standards of living eventually bring pressure toward a declining rate of population increase, largely due to more rapidly falling birth rates, yet it is worth noting that at the present time the net rate of increase in the United States, with the highest standard of living in the world, is slightly above that of India, with one of the lowest standards of living. On present assumptions it seems safe to say that world population probably will have increased by the year 2000 somewhere between 50 and 100 per cent. On this showing alone, merely to hold the per capita materials consumption to present levels would increase the world demand for materials by from 50 to 100 per cent by the turn of this century. If further multiplied by the excess of the American level of consumption in 1950 over the present level of the rest of the world, world consumption of raw materials by the year 2000 would be at least nine to twelve times that of the year 1950.

At the same time, increased longevity of the population—and hence a larger ratio of superannuated persons—and continued extension of the period of schooling and specialized preparatory training of the young tend to reduce the percentage of the population in the work force. To maintain the total population at the same or rising levels of consumption, the productive efficiency of the work force must be increased correspondingly.

4. *Multiplying factors: war and defense demands.*—"With each successive war," the Paley Commission points out,[10]

. . . and now with preparation against the contingency of another, the military has become a greater and greater claimant against the material of the whole economy. There were numerous cases in the last war where the military asked for much more than total available supply could provide, even after civilian uses had been cut to the bone or altogether eliminated.

In World War II, more than 40 per cent of United States productive capacity was devoted to war production. A new war, the Paley Commission believes, would absorb 50 per cent or more.

The Commission gives four reasons for the rising percentage. First, the speed and scale with which an effective striking force could be assembled might be militarily decisive in winning the total war. The only limits to both initial and continuing efforts are imposed by the scale of the productive plant and the materials supplies. Second, high standards of care and supply for fighting forces are essential to mechanized warfare. In the Korean war 35 per cent more cargo per man was landed per day than in World War II. Third, the size and quantity of war equipment required—planes, tanks, aircraft carriers, etc.—are everywhere on the increase. To illustrate, a jet fighter in 1944 used 125 pounds of copper, 1,500 pounds of steel, and 5,500 pounds of aluminum.[11] But in early 1954 it required 513 pounds of copper; 20,129 pounds of steel; and 19,440 pounds of aluminum.[12] At the time of writing, these figures might have to be raised by 30 to 50 per cent.[13] Finally, the logistics of highly mechanized warfare fought at great distances from bases of supply adds multipliers to the scale of demand for industrial capacity, shipping, and materials supplies. In World War II, for something like every 150 to 500 miles added to the distance of the fighting front on land, and for every 1,000 to 3,000 miles at sea, the total productive effort required to maintain the same effective fighting power appears roughly to have doubled.[14]

Since, furthermore, any war might quickly become global, the number of points where massive initial striking power must be located tends to increase, and since there is no theoretical—only a practical—limit to how high this initial striking power might be, it follows that defense preparations tend also to use productive resources in peacetime up to the limits imposed by political considerations. The technical limits then become those of all available plants and militarily strategic materials. Both, accordingly, are expanded to the maximum permitted by nonmilitary considerations, with the result that the ratio of materials absorbed in stand-by industrial plant and stock-piled materials to both (1) the size of the population and (2) the per capita peacetime income tends also to increase. By the mid-1950's materials stock-piling involved an outlay of around $7 billion, while the total of materials supply absorbed by the construction of both stand-by and defense supply plants must be several times as large.

War and defense demand, in short, adds to the demand for materials resources a further set of variables which are not only expanding rapidly, but also are capable of momentarily being further increased by unknown, but always indefinitely large, dimensions.[15]

COMPLICATING FACTORS IN THE RELATIVE INCREASE
IN DEMAND FOR "STRATEGIC MATERIALS"

For both peacetime and war (or defense) purposes, the demands of modern industry tend increasingly to shift from organic materials to minerals and inorganic sources of energy supply. Use of minerals, the Paley Commission found, rose between 1900 and 1950 "twice as fast as [the] total of all other materials." Over these fifty years, on the one hand, "total consumption of agricultural products of all sorts, including food, increased 2¼ times; fishery and wildlife products rose little more, and our total use of forest products actually declined 1 per cent."[16] On the other hand, use of bituminous coal increased 250 per cent; copper, 300 per cent; iron ore, 350 per cent; zinc, 400 per cent; natural gas, 2,600 per cent; and crude oil, 3,000 per cent.[17] "Indeed," the Report goes on to say, "there is scarcely a metal or a mineral fuel of which the quantity used in the United States since the outbreak of the First World War did not exceed the total used throughout the world in all the centuries preceding."[18]

Furthermore, these very materials—increasingly strategic for *both* civilian and military purposes—are both unevenly scattered over the globe and limited in supply. The first requires, even for such a large and generally well-stocked country as the United States, world-wide systems of supply. To illustrate:[19]

The United States' largest current supplier of chrome for steel is Turkey. The Nation draws copper from Africa and the west coast of South America. . . . Tin comes from the Far East as well as from Bolivia; lead from Canada and Mexico; bauxite from South America; iron ore from Venezuela, Liberia, and soon from Labrador. For three key commodities—tin, quartz crystal, and industrial diamonds—the United States is 100 percent dependent on foreign sources. The Nation's position is worsening for 25 other key commodities; in fact in 1952 the United States had become virtually dependent on foreign sources for four of these. The United States produced (1951) only 55 percent of the lead, 38 percent of the bauxite, 26 percent of the antimony, 20 percent of the flake graphite, 10 percent of the cobalt, 9 percent of the mercury, and 8 percent of the manganese it used.

As for energy supplies, which set the real limits to the use of materials and all productive increases, the picture here is also shifting rapidly. World consumption has been increasing at a phenomenal rate. Resources are dwindling for even the most richly endowed countries. As late as 1938, for example, American oil production was 104 per cent of consumption, but by 1952 it was only 82 per cent.[20] The United States, largest producer and consumer of oil products in the world, has already become heavily dependent upon foreign sources of supply. While we have large reserves of oil shale (variously estimated at from 50 to 150 years' supply at current rates of oil consumption),[21] exploitation of all of it will only delay the final accounting a few years. Furthermore,

Coal will not "last for thousands of years." This bubble of hope has disappeared. Because coal will have to be converted to electric power and to liquid and gaseous fuels, less than a century is likely to see the beginning of coal's decline as king of energy sources.[22]

However badly off the United States may be for standard fuel and energy supplies in the long run, most other great industrial nations are infinitely worse off. England, West Germany, and Japan, for example, have virtually no oil or gas of any importance at all. Japan and Italy have very small supplies of low-grade coal, and England, France, and West Germany have supplies which will be used up at current rates of exploitation in from 100 to 300 years, and at accelerated rates in yet fewer.

A further complicating fact with respect to fossil fuels in general is related to the "chemical revolution" referred to in chapter i. The bulk of the new and substitute materials, such as dyes, much pharmacopeia, paints and pigments, rubber, synthetic yarns, and plastics, comes from these fuels. Nonfuel use of fossil fuels, that is to say, while still small, is rising more rapidly than fuel use, and on current evidence will continue rapidly to absorb increasing percentages of oil, gas, and coal.

While, as will be pointed out below, accurate knowledge about total available domestic or foreign supplies of minerals and fuels is woefully lacking, yet such knowledge as we do possess has served to bring home the startling fact that known reserves are severely limited and that they appear to provide exceedingly thin margins of safety in face of the mounting claims being made against them. Table 2, taken from the U.N. Conference on World Resources,[23] is admittedly incomplete and subject to many corrections,[24] yet it will serve to illuminate the point. Accumulation

TABLE 2

WORLD RESERVES OF SELECTED METALS AND MINERALS
(In years of supply, based on various rates of per capita consumption)[a]

Metal or Mineral	Assuming current rates remain unchanged	Assuming world at current United States per capita rate	Assuming United States at current rate and rest of world at current European (excluding U.S.S.R.) rate
Iron ore:			
Actual...............	200	25	66
Potential.............	625	74	200
Manganese ore...........	250	50	140
Chromite...............	47	8	40
Tungsten...............	125	34	...[b]
Copper.................	45	5	20
Lead...................	33	4	11
Zinc...................	39	6	18
Tin....................	38	6	17
Bauxite................	200	31	165
Petroleum:			
Proved and indicated...	22	2.5	20
Ultimate.............	160	18	150
Coal...................	2,200	340	985

SOURCE: *Proceedings* of the United Nations Scientific Conference on the Conservation and Utilization of Resources [UNSCCUR], II, *Mineral Resources*, 4.

[a] Unadjusted for population trends.
[b] Basis for estimate not available.

of secondary supplies (scrap) and more economical use may extend the periods considerably in some cases, moderately in others. But with the best usage, the picture is still alarming.

The mineral and fuel resources listed as most "strategic" for both peace and defense needs are, of course, all of the depletable type. "A ton of ore removed from the earth is a ton gone forever; each barrel of oil used up means one less remaining. This mounting strain upon resources that cannot be replaced has become the most challenging aspect of our present day economy." [25]

It would seem, furthermore, that the "mounting strain" cannot be relieved very far, in the short run at least, by shifting—even when this is made technically possible by the miracles of chemico-physical transmutation—from "exhaustible" or "stock" resources to those of the "renewable" or "flow" type, and this for the simple reason that the latter have also felt the strain.[26]

Ninety percent of our virgin timber stand in the commercial forest area has been cut, and thus far we have done a poor job of growing replacement crops. At present we are using up our inventory of saw-timber at a rate 40 percent faster than its annual growth rate.[27]

VARIABLES DECREASING THE AVAILABILITY OF RESOURCES

1. *Destruction of renewable resources.*—From time immemorial, Ciriacy-Wantrup writes,[28] man has been "one of the most effective geomorphologic agents" who may on occasion and under varying circumstances "destroy important and potentially *renewable* sources of his own livelihood and enjoyment."

Examples are land destruction through agricultural practices unsuited to the climate, slope, and soil; extinction of animal and plant species through hunting, fishing, and disturbance of habitat; prevention of forest regeneration through certain cutting practices and through periodic burning; replacement of valuable plant associations on ranges through inappropriate degree or timing of grazing; spoliation of scenic and other aesthetic values through road construction, roadside development, and placer mining; interference with the utilization of surface and ground water by denudation of watersheds, pollution, excessive pumping, and damage to infiltration areas.[29]

How serious a problem has the destruction of these resources become? Superficially, the facts are alarming. In the United

States, a nationwide reconnaissance survey made by the Soil Erosion Service of the Department of Interior during the summer of 1934 showed that[30]

In addition to the 50 million acres of cropland now virtually useless for further production, because it has been stripped of topsoil or riddled with gullies, another 150 million acres of arable land has declined far enough to make farming difficult or unprofitable. Over an additional area of nearly 680 million acres of all kinds of land, traces of water erosion are now discernible; and on most of this land the damage is constantly increasing in severity. Finally, a large area, located in the Great Plains from Texas to North Dakota and in other parts of the West, is characteristically subject to wind erosion, wherever exposed through the activities of man. The survey indicates that this form of erosion is active in some degree over more than 200 million acres of farm and grazing land.

As late as 1950 it was the opinion of the Soil Conservation Service that "each year the equivalent of half a million acres is permanently lost to production, and in addition, a quarter of our cropland is in critical danger of losing its topsoil, while another quarter is eroding rapidly."[31] Soil losses from these processes are stupendous:[32]

Available measurements indicate that at least 3,000,000,000 tons of solid material is washed out of the fields and pastures of America every year. It is estimated that about 730,000,000 tons of solid matter is discharged annually into the Gulf of Mexico by the Mississippi alone. These materials come largely from the farms of the Mississippi Basin. . . . But the sediment entering the oceans represents merely a fraction of the soil washed out of fields and pastures. The greater part is piled up or temporarily lodged along lower slopes, often damaging the soil beneath; or it is deposited over rich, alluvial stream bottoms or in channelways, harbors, reservoirs, irrigation ditches, and drainage canals.

The net loss of plant foods is even more serious:[33]

. . . erosion removes from the country's fields and pastures every year available and potential plant food amounting to about sixty times the available plant food returned to the soil in various forms of commercial fertilizers. . . . Furthermore, erosion removes not only the plant food itself but actually the entire body of the soil—plant nutrients, humus, beneficial microscopic organisms, and all other constituents. Plant food can be restored to soil worn lean by cropping or leaching; but when the soil itself is washed into the streams and oceans, nature can rebuild its counterpart only after centuries of activity.

Again:[34]

In 1945 a study was made for the Federal Reserve Bank of St. Louis, to determine the loss of plant nutrients and topsoil in the Corn Belt. It indicated that each year 6 billion dollars worth of nitrogen, potash, and phosphoric acid are lost from the soil through the harvesting of crops, of which less than a sixth is replaced. Other authorities believe that less than a tenth is replaced. In addition, according to the 1945 study, 3 times as much nitrogen, 6 times as much phosphorous, and more than 60 times as much potash are annually removed from the soil through erosion and leaching.

There is still a vast supply of good agricultural soil in the United States, but both the total destroyed and the rate of loss are astounding. As Person has said, when the question was first raised some seventy years before as to "whether the United States is a permanent country," it was considered fantastic, but[35]

Recent measurements indicate that it is far from fantastic—[it] is very real and practical—and that one can rationally assert that in another century this great American granary may have become inadequate to support our population if erosion is permitted to continue at the present rate of increase.

Looking at this shocking record, Raymond Swing once estimated that only a fourth of the soil originally present in America would be left in another fifty years, and that "in a hundred years at the same rate of depletion the American continent could turn into the Sahara of the Western Hemisphere." [36] To this, two agricultural experts reply that "even if this staggering statement is only half true, and the American people have two centuries of life on their continent, the prospect is bad enough." [37]

Nor is this picture confined to the United States. According to General J. C. Smuts, in South Africa "erosion is the biggest problem confronting the country, bigger than any politics." [38] Negley Farson found the waters of the Tana River, after traversing the highlands of Kenya, visible seventy miles at sea from silt carried off from one of the potentially richest agricultural districts of the African continent.[39] Variations on this story may be repeated from one end of the continent to the other, and as for Asia, "in much of India the last vestiges of shrub growth already form the ordinary daily ration for the village herd. The amount of erosion caused directly through this state of affairs has to be seen to be believed." [40] And in China,

. . . the Yellow River flowing from the northwestern highlands carries with it each year about 2,500,000,000 tons of silt, a quantity sufficient to increase by 5 feet the elevation of an area 400 square miles, or 256,000 acres, in extent. During the flood of 1933, the north dike of the Yellow River, which had been built to restrain the flood waters, was completely buried by silt.[41]

Much of the balance of China is but little better off by comparison. The FAO study[42] found similar conditions in Szechwan on the tributaries of the Yangtze River, in the province of Kansu, and in all South China—where "nearly all of the cleared hillsides have been stripped of their soil cover."

In Palestine, Turkey, and the Arabian Near East the situation is not much better—soil erosion, flood damage, and wind erosion being related in a cycle of destruction that goes back thousands of years and which has, to some extent, been stabilized over large areas on a desert or semidesert basis. The once fabulously rich "fertile crescent" of Biblical times, which swings in a widening arc between the juncture of the Tigris and Euphrates on the east and narrows down to the tip of the mouth of the Nile to the west, is now almost wholly irreclaimable desert land; the great forests of the cedars of Lebanon are a memory, and only a small portion of the "land flowing with milk and honey" may be reclaimed at all. Throughout most of Asia, with varying degrees of severity, the condition is one of slowly deteriorating environment.

In many parts of the leading cultivated sections of the predominantly arid continent of Australia, soil erosion—particularly damaging to the wheat and grazing lands of New South Wales—has proceeded more rapidly than in the United States. In Canada, the conditions of the American Great Plains country is simply carried northward. Not much is known about erosion in South America, but soil losses caused by deforestation in Brazil and by wind and water erosion in Argentina appear to have reached serious proportions.[43] Annual soil losses in El Salvador's Lempa River valley average 12 million metric tons—enough to cover over

10,000 acres to the depth of one foot.[44] In Mexico, soil losses are swiftly approaching the stage of irremediable catastrophe.[45] Viewing the widespread *milpa* system (burning-off of protective shrub and forest cover for temporary cultivation) and the increasing resort to the cultivation of steeply sloping lands, one author has referred to Latin America as "a continent sliding to ruin." [46]

As for eastern Europe and inner Asia, a survey of Russian literature leaves the impression that erosion as an imminent menace is mainly confined to the intensively cultivated zone, although it is prevalent and increasing, in milder forms, over much larger regions, particularly the "chestnut soil" areas which correspond ecologically with the short-grass country of North America.[47]

Throughout the Mediterranean littoral—particularly in Asia Minor, North Africa, and Italy—erosion has been acute since Roman times. Only in North and Central Europe and in England are there large areas generally free of this problem. In most of the world—notably in the United States, Canada, Australia, the Near East, India, and China—the capacity of the land to produce is steadily deteriorating, and in many cases at a cumulative rate. "Probably more soil was lost from the world between 1914 and 1934," write Jacks and Whyte, "than in the whole of previous history."

Quite as dramatic is the story of the swift depletion of forest and wildlife resources. The United States has been cutting into its original forest resources on a devastating scale. The story of wildlife follows the same pattern.[48]

In summary, it may fairly be said that the destructive effects of man as a "geomorphologic agent" upon renewable resources has up to the present been spreading through most parts of the world, and is generally—in some places catastrophically—on the increase. As demand for these resources is also rapidly on the increase, the destructiveness of man's operations adds to the demand for more resources a further note of urgency and a demand for more effective utilization of what we have.

A similar picture holds for the nonrenewable or "stock" resources. A few of the leading facts should be mentioned.

2. *Destruction of stock resources.*—"In mining minerals," the Paley Commission found,[49]

we still leave an astounding fraction in the ground and in using mined or harvested materials we frequently throw away large quantities. About 50 percent of the commercial grades of coal, and more than 50 percent of the petroleum in an average pool are left behind in the process of production. Roughly one out of every 10 pounds of copper in ores is thrown on the tailings heap; more sulfur is blown from the smokestacks of industry than is consumed; enough natural gas was wasted in 1950 to supply the gas needs of 11 million of the Nation's homes.

A first significant fact about the waste of these resources is that what has been thrown away in the past does not appear to be recoverable in the future, and that as long as such waste remains as a significant component in resource use it adds a further drain upon supplies of stocks which cannot be extended or replaced. Enormous wastage of natural gas occurs by allowing it to escape in the air or be burned in open flares merely to get rid of it.[50] The oil and coal left underground by wasteful mining methods are similarly lost forever.

The United States Coal Commission reported in 1921 that American coal mining, principally by use of the "room and pillar" system, gave an average rate of extraction for the ten coal states of 65.3 per cent.[51] In contrast, Rice reported in 1921 that the British claimed 90 to 95 per cent recovery through their "long wall" system.[52] Again, "In mining hard coal, or anthracite, half of the coal in the mine is wasted. Of soft, or bituminous, coal one ton is lost for every two mined. Of this loss of soft coal, 14 per cent is considered to be unavoidable and 20 per cent avoidable."[53] This American wastage is the equivalent of about half of recent total British output. Nobody believes that much of what is left underground can ever be economically recovered. The same holds for relatively thin seams which have been bypassed on the way down to mining of thicker seams, and for most of the oil left underground by the earlier methods of extraction.

A second leading fact is that coal reserves are no longer believed to be so large as earlier estimates indicated. While the 1938 estimate showed some 3.2 trillion tons of coal remaining in the United States, it did so "only by considering all seams less than 3,000 feet and over 14 inches thick. More than one-half of the total reserve is lignitic and only a small percentage of the remain-

ing coal is of high rank." [54] The figures even on this basis may
be altogether too high. Thus some

. . . state surveys . . . have shown surprisingly large contractions
from Federal estimates of original reserves. The combined contraction for Pennsylvania, West Virginia, and Ohio is six times the total
United States production to date. . . . Between 1907 and 1936 the
geological estimate for Michigan dropped 10 billion tons. . . . A
competent mining engineer believes that the coal economically recoverable in Utah is about 1 percent of the first Federal estimate of
original reserve. [55]

For the United States as a whole, Dr. Fieldner of the Bureau of
Mines believes that further investigations will reduce geologically
inferred reserves by 50 per cent. This would come close to the
estimate of the National Coal Association of 1.6 trillion tons.

Recoverable coal on a national basis has been variously estimated. One mining engineer, Andrew B. Crichton, thinks that
"the present reserves of coal that are economically recoverable
may not exceed 0.224 trillion tons," [56] or less than one-tenth of the
1938 estimate. Whatever the amount remaining that may be
taken out,

What we can be sure of at this time is that coal will soon become both
more costly to produce and more costly to use. In other words, when
it costs more, it will be worth less. It will contain more sulfur and more
ash. It will have fewer btu per ton. It will have to be recovered from
thinner seams, and these seams will be harder to reach. It will come
from areas more remote from major points of use, and transportation
costs will be higher. Even now, almost half the cost of bituminous
coal on the Middle Atlantic coast is for transportation. [57]

A third leading fact, especially important in the case of fossil
fuels, is that many of them have specialized uses and their occurrence is limited:

For example, certain coals are especially suited for coking. Disappear-
ance of the Connellsville seam would seriously embarrass the steel
industry, for nowhere in the United States exists other coal of such
fine quality. Yet, this seam will disappear in 20 or 30 years at the 1929
rate of production. While not as limited as metallurgical coal, the best
steam coals are not as abundant as they once were in the older industrial districts. High-rank coal, without regard to special uses, is
so limited that M. R. Campbell, more than a decade and a half ago,

stated that "before long, perhaps within fifty years, much of the high-rank coal will be exhausted" . . . the famous Pittsburgh seam is estimated to last only 100 years [with] an additional 60 years in the thinner seams. Gas and metallurgical coals are only 11% exhausted in Kentucky, but are 22% exhausted in Virginia and West Virginia. . . . While anthracite is only 0.5% of the total reserve, it is 12.3% of the output and is 29% exhausted. Semi-bituminous constitutes 16.6% of the output from a reserve of only 1.7% of our total coal resources. Coal east of the Mississippi River, of higher quality than that in the west, makes up only 30% of the total reserve, yet from these beds is produced 94% of the total output.[58]

As the thicker seams are exhausted, recourse must be had to the thinner ones:

. . . 70% of Ohio's coal is less than four feet thick; 91% of the Punxsutawney seam of central Pennsylvania is less than four feet thick, and 65% less than three feet thick. Some areas of the United States are already mining under adverse conditions comparable to those in Europe. Kansas' Osage field mines a 21 inch seam at 87 feet with cutting machines and is getting only 1.22 tons per man-day. Michigan is working a 34 inch bed with a yield of 2.51 tons per man-day. While these are isolated cases, they are forerunners of what may well be common practice before many years have passed.[59]

On the average, each new seam is deeper; the hazards of water, gas, faults, sits-and-creeps, slope, and accidents increase; mines are further removed from consumption centers; and coal is of lower quality.

Some British mines are 3,700 feet deep with 14 inch coal being worked at lesser depths. In spite of an exhaustion of only 7% of the coal originally in the ground, a ton of coal in England costs 7.5 man-hours as compared to only 1.7 man-hours in the United States. Increasing difficulties in British mines have long since absorbed the gains of technology, and output per worker has been declining since the eighties.[60]

Britain made strenuous efforts following World War II to reverse this trend; some successes have been recorded,[61] but there is obviously no hope of ever approaching the American level, nor are the chances bright for much improvement in OMS (output-per-man-shift) in the United States.

Much the same holds for most metallic reserves. To cite a single example, that of iron ore:

Reserves [of iron ore] in the Lake Superior District are estimated by the tax commissions of the various states to be 1,460,267,000 tons in 1933. This is a conservative estimate of recoverable ore in sight, and may be considered as the minimum expectancy of iron of present grades and limits. On the basis of the trend of production curve as shown by the past, this reserve should last for 32 years. Future discoveries will considerably add to this life. The Mesabi Range is more fully known than any of the others, but future discoveries are likely to add 15 percent to its reserves. Discoveries on the Michigan and Wisconsin ranges will probably increase the life expectancy as much as 40 percent. In total, a reasonable expectancy for new discoveries, . . . improvements in the technology of ore beneficiation, and possible changes in the art of steel-making, a life of 50 years seems assured.[62]

After fifty years, in short, the huge and still rapidly expanding American steel industry will be compelled to rely upon ores of steadily decreasing quality, such as taconite, or drawn over longer distances and from less accessible locations.

The general problem is common to all industrial countries. England, for example, has largely depleted her tin, the bulk of her higher-grade iron ore, and most of her thicker seams of coal lying near the surface. All of her enormously valuable deposits of china clay will be gone in fifty years. If Germany relied solely upon domestic sources, she would have enough iron ore to last less than a decade. Her lignite will be wholly mined out within another thirty years at the current rate of depletion. The better grades of Swedish and Minette (French) ores are being swiftly skimmed off, and resort must be had to poorer resources.

This is the universal problem, alike for renewable and nonrenewable resources.

THE HANDICAP RACE WITH NATURE

"Because," said Sir Hubert Houldsworth, Chairman of the British National Coal Board, "high extraction in the past means that the coal now left is less in quantity, more difficult of access, and generally lower in quality . . . we have annually to develop a new productive capacity of about 5 million tons"—to maintain the existing position, and to equal the extra costs in tons and money associated with deteriorating conditions of extraction.[63] In the United States, whereas commodities in general advanced an average of 105 per cent in wholesale prices from 1940 to 1950, zinc rose 119 per cent in price; petroleum, 149 per cent; farm products, 152 per cent; lead, 157 per cent; and lumber, 218 per cent.[64] Wherever one looks,

In area after area the same pattern seems discernible: soaring demands, shrinking resources, the consequent pressure toward rising real costs, the risk of wartime shortages, the ultimate threat of an arrest or decline in the standard of living we cherish and hope to help others to attain . . . [because] we have skimmed the cream of our resources as we now understand them. . . . We face . . . the threat of having to devote constantly increasing efforts to win each pound of materials from resources which are dwindling both in quantity and quality. . . . As the best and most accessible resources are used up, it becomes necessary to work harder and harder to produce more supplies from less accessible and lower quality resources [and] the problem becomes one of running faster and faster in order even to stand still.[65]

There is scarcely a raw material which is exempt. Bauxite reserves will run out in another ten to thirty years, and resort must then be to clays and anorthosites, where the costs of aluminum in terms of investment and energy will be far greater. High-quality copper ores will all be gone within a quarter of a century; substitutes will require much greater investments of energy. Since sulphur deposits in the United States are not expected to last more than another twenty-five years, resort must then be had to pyrites, smelter fumes, and eventually calcium sulphate—processes which are fantastically high in energy requirements. The greater the need for phosphates, the greater the need for sulphuric acid used in extraction, and hence for sulphur—already in short supply on other accounts. Even water is becoming scarce. Each person in the United States drinks about 200 gallons a year, and uses about 15,000 gallons for household purposes; but industry consumes 160,000 gallons a year for each person.[66] In many areas the shortage of water is so acute that expensive recycling methods are being instituted; in others, plans are afoot for the even more expensive extraction of fresh water from the sea.

In the attempt to satisfy mounting demands, science, technology, and social organizations are already faced with a handicap race with nature which threatens to take the eventual form of rising costs. The handicap race is faced in most countries, with respect to most of the basic needs and available resources. Thus a continuing advance in over-all economies of production is required merely to meet, step by step, the increasing handicap as rising demand forces the change-over from better to poorer resources, and much more advance to cope with the accelerated speed of depletion and the consequent shortening of the period in which to make the necessary inventions in technology and their correlative improvements in methods of organization; still more is required, in the face of the multiplying handicaps, to effect net gains which are capable of supplying materials at lower costs.[67]

What are the possibilities? There are some who feel, as did the keynote speaker at the 114th annual meeting of the British Association for the Advancement of Science, that "the shortage of natural resources, particularly of food, is bound to cause increasing deprivation and disturbance." [68] A great deal of recent scientific and popular literature on resources and conservation has been dominated by gloomy prognoses—some in terms of impossibilities, others of improbabilities; the first see no way out, and the second discover possible solutions which they believe to be generally unacceptable.

A study at the California Institute of Technology has come up with the problem of a possible future "point of no return":[69]

The present generation, and those just gone or soon to come, has had ample resources of high-grade ores and fuels that can be used through relatively crude technical methods. Tomorrow's generations, with far more people to be supported, must depend on extremely intricate technology. After any breakdown in the energy and processing cycle, the future generations might not be able to put in the tremendous quantity of energy to start the cycle once more.

Whenever, that is to say, the bulk of the world's work is shifted over to an atomic-energy basis, the process of production—beginning with ore extraction and refinement—will require stupendous quantities of energy. To get energy requires enormous supplies of energy. If any breakdown endangers the full minimal scale of subsequent energy required to start once again the cycle of production, then the "point of no return" will have been reached, and from relative plenty, society will immediately plunge into massive scarcity.

In the face of such facts, there exists a dangerous tendency, even among careful and systematic workers in the field of resource conservation, to reach optimistic conclusions, though generally with numerous qualifications. This is the case with the latest edition of Professor Zimmerman's huge volume on *World Resources and Industries*.[70] Ayres and Scarlott, after making what is probably the most complete recent survey of global energy-resources available to the general reader, find that: "This tiny period of earth's life, when we are consuming its stored riches, is nearly over"; yet "man's resourcefulness continues on and becomes more potent with each passing decade. Because of this the future is bright." [71] The Paley Commission is more cautious, but still arrives at the conclusion that technology may meet the rising challenge of materials shortages if fully mobilized.[72]

It will be worth while to glance briefly at the principal lines of emphasis which may be advanced for solution of the problem of limited, or dwindling and higher-cost, resources for the bearing these may have on the subject matter of this study—the economic implications of a "rethinking through" of the lines along which the "new industrial revolution" appears to be developing—for the issue at stake is of the utmost importance.

VARIABLES IN THE SOLUTION OF THE PROBLEMS OF LIMITED NATURAL RESOURCES

1. *The limited knowledge about the total available supply.*—The most striking fact about resources of virtually all types is how little we know about them. A few examples will illustrate the point. Take first the case of highly developed industrial countries. England, for 200 years a heavy user of fuels and minerals, "was also the first country to establish an official Geological Survey which has been conducting systematic geological mapping and investigation since its foundation 114 years ago." By employing more recent methods of exploration,

. . . the carrying out of a properly designed programme of boring and sub-surface exploration [has shown] that even in a country so highly

developed and industrialized as Great Britain, systematic investigation . . . can still lead to successful discovery of important mineral
deposits with results of considerable economic consequence.

For example,

. . . a series of deep borings has been completed and has disclosed
several seams of workable thickness [of coal] at workable depth. . . .
In 1939 a boring for oil in north-west Yorkshire revealed the presence
of the potash minerals, sylvine, carnallite and polyhalite in the permian
evaporite sequence.[73]

Other investigations have turned up new deposits of coal, iron
ore, lead, tin, zinc, fluorite, barylites, and other chemical raw
materials, some in fairly large supplies.

In Sardinia, an island which has been a rich mining center for
a wide range of ferrous and nonferrous metals from early Roman
times and before, recent geological investigations have shown a
series of "concrete possibilities for discovery" of further deposits,
some of which may very well prove both rich in metallic content
and extensive in recoverable tonnage.[74] In Yugoslavia, famous
for centuries for its wealth of metallic, nonmetallic, and com-
bustible ores, and actively mined by and since the Romans, new
methods have lead to the discovery of numerous deposits of the
more familiar ores, and of significant deposits of metals hitherto
not found in Yugoslavia, such as wolfram, beryllium, cerium,
molybdenum, and other raw materials such as asbestos, kaolin,
and dinas-quartzite.[75]

The United States, according to the Paley Commission, is only
about 11 per cent geologically described and mapped.[76] Most of
the data available on mineral resources have come from analysis
and estimates made on the basis of findings of surface outcrop-
pings. Only a bare beginning has been made with depth core
drilling and appropriate analysis of core samples. "At the rate
at which new maps [topographic and geologic alike] are being
prepared, between 150 and 200 years would be needed to complete the job of mapping the United States alone." [77] Even with
respect to a fuel of such critical importance in the national economy as petroleum, the geological data are far from complete.
In 1939 the National Resources Committee found that there were
still some 650 million acres, close to one-third the surface of the

United States, of land which had not been explored for oil.[78] The unexplored area was not appreciably smaller in 1955. The same is true of most of the minor minerals and even some of the major ones.[79]

When we turn from the older mining areas and the highly developed industrial countries to the vast underdeveloped regions of Canada, Latin America, Australia, Africa, and Asia, the only thing we know for certain is that, except for very limited and special areas, relatively little is known about the extent of resources of almost any type. Outside the United States, very little of Canada or Latin America has been systematically explored for either fuels or minerals.[80] Exploration in India has so far "been confined to the use of ordinary geological methods and surface observations. Reliable estimates of reserves are often lacking and detailed prospecting work has been done only in a comparatively small number of cases."[81] The situation in China is even more obscure. Recent discoveries, such as those of iron ore in the Quebec-Labrador region and in Venezuela, and of petroleum in the Leduc field of western Canada, serve to remind us how great some of the probable discoveries in the major unexplored regions may very well be.

A good example of how exploration changes the picture of available resources is provided by the Soviet Union's reported resources of coal. The figure of total coal resources obtained by the Geological Committee in 1913 for all Russia was 230 billion metric tons and constituted 3.2 per cent of the world's total coal resources estimated by the XIIth International Geological Congress, yet

total geological resources of the USSR . . . are now estimated at 1 654 361 mill. tons. . . . At present the coal resources of the USSR make up nearly 21% of the coal resources of the World, instead of the 3.2% they did in 1913, and the reserves of bituminous coals of the USSR [are] 30% of the world reserves of bituminous coals.[82]

Similar data, generally regarded by foreign experts as reasonably accurate, have been given out for other fuels and minerals. "By Soviet estimates its iron ore resources include more than half the world's total, and its petroleum reserves 59% of the world total."[83]

Though foreign experts are inclined to discount such optimistic estimates as the latter, clearly Soviet discoveries of new resources of practically all types have removed some of their problems of scarcity so far into the future that they may no longer have good reason for concern for decades, if not centuries, to come. It does not follow, of course, that this good fortune will be shared by all the unexplored lands of the earth, but on the basis of the available evidence to date there are at least as many good reasons for optimism as for pessimism about the prospects of future discoveries.

There are other and possibly even more important reasons for taking a cautiously optimistic view about several classes of resources.

2. *Science and technology supply the key to resources.*—That a resource is not a "resource" in terms of human use until we learn how to exploit it is a truism so obvious that even experts at times forget how important a role advancing technology plays. Professor Baker offers a good example with respect to the total available supply of foodstuff. In China, when its population (1919) was estimated at 440,000,000 living in a country with a land area somewhat smaller (excluding Mongolia) than the United States (2.5 compared with 3 million square miles), only half as much land was cultivated as in the United States (180 million compared with 354 million acres). Furthermore, while in the United States the cultivated area was 39 per cent of the total adjudged to be "physically cultivable" by currently available agronomical methods and techniques, yet in China this cultivated area, despite a population ratio to total land area which was 3.5 times that of the United States, was 26 per cent of the total.[84]

The reason for this seeming paradox lies in the simple fact that the land not farmed by the Chinese was not "physically cultivable" by them so long as they continued to employ the customary and traditional Chinese peasant cultivation methods. Alternatively, given the methods of modern scientific agronomy, employing the best techniques of drainage and irrigation, machinery, specialized crops, better seed-selection, effective crop-storage, and cheap transportation to markets, this land would become "physically cultivable" as fast as the need for additional acres increased.

Similarly, the possibilities of further expansion of food production, even in the heavily populated and seriously eroded lands of the earth, are in many cases quite astonishing. Baker has also estimated [85] that the replacement of cattle power in India with small tractors would make possible a net increase in the food supply of that country by "50 per cent or more." Bonné made a survey[86] of eight Near and Middle Eastern countries—Turkey, Egypt, Iran, Iraq, Syria, Israel, Lebanon, Jordan—and found 118 million hectares (293 million acres) of cultivable land.

Of this area, less than a third was cultivated, leaving 85 million hectares . . . as land reserve for future cultivation. Now this total does not consider the specific potentialities of irrigation. . . . Of the total irrigable area of 15.8 million hectares in the countries . . . only 7.0 million hectares are at present utilized. . . . [Thus] nearly 9 million hectares are still open for the expansion of irrigated cultivation.

Projecting 1920-1947 population rates of growth into the future to an estimated total of 80 million people in 1967 for this entire area would give an average of four acres of cultivable land per capita, a figure which compares very favorably with the United States, where the amount of land required "to produce adequate diets . . . is from 1.8 to 3.1 acres per capita." [87]

This picture could be duplicated, with some variation, for almost any part of the world. It ignores the possibility of cultivating the vast food-production areas of the seas, and of hydroponics—in itself capable, if the necessary chemicals can be supplied cheaply enough, of multiplying world food-resources manyfold. Further, it may hold for many if not most of the minerals and fuels which provide the strategic resources for industrialization. Before mining techniques were developed, it was literally true that coal, iron, and copper were not resources. Their importance as resources developed along with the growth in the knowledge of how best to use them. This, simply and in summary, is what the Paley Commission had in mind in the volume it devoted to *The Promise of Technology.*

The catalogue of possibilities given by the Paley Commission is so complete, so exhaustive, and so carefully detailed and illustrated that it cannot be summarized in a short space. However, perusal of the data presented makes it possible to draw a few generalizations that are of the utmost importance for world re-source appraisal.

With respect to the total available supply of minerals, including all those used in large volume, and possibly most of those re-garded as "strategic" by the Commission, there is over the world as a whole a relationship between probable qualities and quanti-ties such that (*a*) as quality declines the quantities of the total theoretically recoverable mineral rise, (*b*) the quality generally declines exponentially at a decreasing rate relative to the total quantity to a point where the supply at these lower-quality levels is to all practical intents and purposes indefinitely large, and, (*c*) as the curve of quantity tends to flatten out with declining quality, any further tendency for technological improvements to continue to result in increased efficiency of recovery methods promises to supply these materials at constant or even declining costs.

It should be possible to illustrate these relationships directly with statistical data drawn from the historical records of mining in such extractive industries as copper, coal, and iron ore. In each case the average quality of ores is steadily deteriorating, while costs have been held low as a result of technical advance. Reli-able cost data, however, are very difficult to obtain, and hence the relationships among declining quality, technical advance, and cost cannot be shown with any confidence.

The case of copper, nevertheless, may be more or less typical. In the eighteenth century, ores containing less than 13 per cent of copper were deemed too poor for economical extraction. By 1900, this figure had dropped to 5 per cent. More recent plants are using ores as low as 0.6 per cent in copper content. Mean-while, copper prices—which do not necessarily reflect true costs of extraction—were quoted at the average annual rate of 22.9 cents per pound in 1860, 16.5 cents in 1900, and 21.0 cents in 1947 (an increase, with release of wartime price control, from 11.9 cents in 1944). Making allowance for changes in the price level, "The price of 22.9 cents a pound in 1860, when the general price level stood at 61, corresponds to 37.5 cents a pound at the 1926 price level of 100 and to 57 cents at the 1947 level." [88]

It is doubtful whether many such cases of (inferred) cost decline with markedly falling quality of ores are to be found elsewhere. But, as indicated below, there are also a number of cases where it is possible that the curve of probable falling average quality of ore is flattening out more rapidly than the curve of average costs.

There are several examples of minerals and salts of increasing importance in industry where something like this may be true. In most cases these minerals are mined from a few widely scattered, high-quality ores. But in smaller concentrations, here also, the total quantities available commercially may, at least in many instances, be almost indefinitely large. Three illustrations will suffice.

The first is that of the so-called "complex ores"—ores, that is, which contain two or several minerals, only one, two, or possibly none of which is present in sufficient quantity to justify extraction when taken by themselves, but where several, or even in some cases all, can be taken out by combining ore-dressing methods which successively separate each. For example, certain Philippine ores contain copper, gold, lead, and zinc, each of which is recoverable chemically once the ore has been ground to a fine dust. Nickel is found with copper; zinc with lead and silver; uranium with petroleum, oil shale, and gold.[89] Dozens of other examples might be cited. Some "seven modern ways to dress ores" are now in widespread use.[90] Collectively they hold out the possibility of refining metal mixes and low metal percentages which previously had to be classed as useless "dirt." Upon these and other possible techniques of ore beneficiation lies the possibility of future adequate ore supplies. They appear to be, individually and collectively, just beginning to receive the degree of scientific attention their importance for the future of society merits. "The time must inevitably come," the California Institute of Technology report concludes,[91]

when ores as such no longer exist and machine civilization, if it survives, will feed on the leanest of sources—the rocks which make up the surface of our planet, the waters of the seas, and the gases of the atmosphere. . . . As grades move downward increasing emphasis will be placed upon the isolation of byproducts and coproducts, and eventually we may reach the time when as many as 20 to 30 products are obtained from a single rock-mining operation.

The second illustration of possible large available and hitherto almost entirely untapped resources is that involved in the refining of the ores and salts contained in sea water. Table 3 shows the chemical constitution of average sea water. When it is realized that "a cubic mile of sea water, weighing about 4,000 million tons, contains 166 million tons of dissolved salts," [92] it may be seen how vast the resources of the sea for various metals might conceivably become. Many materials—most notably magnesium, bromine, potassium, sodium, and chlorine—are already being taken on a commercial basis. A British pilot plant is experimenting with the extraction of copper from sea water. Several new methods, of which ion exchange and vapor-compression distillation may be the most promising, may possibly add to this list of commercially extractable chemicals. Supplies would then become, for each separate chemical, virtually unlimited. For example, the Dow Chemical Company has estimated that the extraction of 100 million tons of magnesium per year for 1 million years would use up only about 3 per cent of the magnesium available in the seas.

A third illustration of how and where vast new resources may be opened up by continuing advances of science and technology has to do with the ocean bottom. About half of it

. . . is covered with a thick sediment of red clay, in which are found extensive deposits of iron-bearing minerals, manganese ores, phosphorite, barite, glauconite, cassiterite, and other minerals. At depths greater than about 3,000 feet, manganese and iron oxides are found in red clay in the form of nodules, which are abundant, and some of which weigh several hundred pounds.[93]

Here again, the total potential supply of minerals and chemicals from this one source alone is so great that it provides in each case virtually inexhaustible resources, if ways can be found for economic exploitation.

As with sea water and the air, the lowest common denominator of resources may ultimately include, as the authors of the California Institute of Technology report have suggested, ordinary rock. From 20 to 30 products may be "obtained from a single rock-mining operation." They estimate that "one hundred tons of average igneous rock contain, in addition to other useful elements, 8 tons of aluminum, 5 tons of iron, 1,200 pounds of titanium, 180

TABLE 3

CHEMICAL ELEMENTS IN MARINE WATERS

Element	Symbol	Abundance, in mg./kg.
Oxygen	O	857000.
Hydrogen	H	108000.
Chlorine	Cl	19000.
Sodium	Na	10500.
Magnesium	Mg	1270.
Sulphur	S	900.
Calcium	Ca	400.
Potassium	K	380.
Bromine	Br	65.
Carbon	C	28.
Strontium	Sr	10.
Boron	B	4.5
Fluorine	F	1.3
Nitrogen	N	1.0
Silicon	Si	1.0
Argon	A	.61
Rubidium	Rb	.30
Lithium	Li	.20
Phosphorus	P	.05
Iodine	I	.05
Barium	Ba	.05
Iron	Fe	.01
Aluminum	Al	.005
Copper	Cu	.005
Zinc	Zn	.005
Manganese	Mn	.004
Selenium	Se	.004
Arsenic	As	.003
Tin	Sn	.003
Lead	Pb	.003
Uranium	U	.002
Titanium	Ti	.001
Vanadium	V	.001
Cobalt	Co	.0005
Nickel	Ni	.0005
Gallium	Ga	.0005
Molybdenum	Mo	.0005
Cerium	Ce	.0004
Thorium	Th	.0004
Krypton	Kr	.00031
Yttrium	Y	.0003
Silver	Ag	.0003
Lanthanum	La	.0003

TABLE 3 (Continued)

Element	Symbol	Abundance, in mg./kg.
Neon......................	Ne	.00028
Bismuth..................	Bi	.0002
Xenon....................	Xe	.00011
Chromium................	Cr	.00005
Scandium................	Sc	.00004
Mercury..................	Hg	.00003
Helium...................	He	.0000092
Gold.....................	Au	.000004
Cesium...................	Cs	.000002
Radium..................	Ra	.0000000003

SOURCE: Adapted from data supplied in a letter from Edward D. Goldberg, Assistant Professor of Marine Chemistry, Scripps Institution of Oceanography, April 6, 1955.

pounds of manganese, 70 pounds of chromium, 40 pounds of nickel, 30 pounds of vanadium, 20 pounds of copper, 10 pounds of tungsten and 4 pounds of lead." In addition, the same amount of rock contains approximately 400 grams of uranium, and 1,200 grams of thorium, or sufficient energy to extract all these minerals if and when the appropriate techniques make economical operation successful;[94] supply would then be virtually inexhaustible. So also would it be if heavy water (deuterium) could be used, or, again, if energy from fusion, using hydrogen, is found to be usable.

Here, as elsewhere, *the key is adequate energy resources.* With respect to this "key," the survey by Ayres and Scarlott, previously referred to, indicates many new possibilities: energy from tides, solar heat, wind, atomic power, cosmic rays, industrial photosynthesis, etc. Since fossil fuels are present in various locations in sufficient supply to satisfy anticipated world energy-resource needs for from 200 to 500 years, they provide this amount of time in which to find substitute energy from these possible sources. Still others may turn up with further advances in science. All in all, the theoretical prospects for energy supplies in sufficient amounts to take care of the expanding needs of the future are at this moment very bright. Since Ayres and Scarlott wrote (1951), the total theoretical supply of fissionable materials, for example, has increased several times. A British expert estimates that "the total energy available in accessible uranium ores is about 20 times as great as that in the conventional fuels." [95] This estimate, as shown by various papers submitted at the Geneva Conference and by other data, may already be far too low.

Finally, with respect to all types of resources, careful survey of the relevant lines of scientific, technological, and economic research indicates a number of further reasons for taking a cautiously optimistic view of the future—if and when conservation is taken seriously. For one thing, improved methods of extraction in mines, forests, seas, and land have, as the Paley Commission has pointed out in great detail, enormously improved the ratio of the amounts of deposits which may be recovered, the amount and variety of usable by-products from processing previously thrown away, and the capacity of land, sea, or even the air (e.g., nitrogen, hydrogen) to yield. Such developments as the sawdust-fed gas turbine and the plasticizers have reduced waste in the Douglas fir industry of the Pacific Northwest from about 50 per cent by weight of the tree to virtually zero. Shift in the use of forest resources of Saskatchewan from sawmill to pulpwood increases the average sustained yield of the province from something like $9 million to around $100 million annually.[96] Thousands of similar illustrations might be offered of similar salvage of otherwise waste by-products.

Full realization of such economically available means may add very greatly to the effective resources of the nation and the world. The conditions attached, however, are scientific reorganization of the entire round of extractive processes in mines, seas, and fields in each given case, followed by complete (or as nearly complete as possible) chemical utilization of all chemical-physical components and by-products. Chemical analysis and synthesis offers enormous possibilities for further employment of otherwise neglected, totally wasted, or underutilized raw-materials. For example, around 250 million dry tons of agricultural residues are produced annually in the United States. About one-half is at least theoretically available for industrial uses, and much of this, if not most, is completely lost to industry and at the same time is of relatively little use to agriculture.[97] But possibly of even greater importance than unused agricultural and industrial wastes is the combination of (*a*) vastly expanded reused substitute and alternative materials, and (*b*) the enormously improved qualities of specific materials (as, most notably, in alloy metallurgy) which come from continuous physicochemical transformation of the raw-materials foundation of industry referred to in chapter i above. The necessary condition to the realization of the potentialities inherent in the new advances is the economically valid internal rationalization of the chemical industry as a whole (chap. vii).

But at this point it becomes clearly evident that we are, with respect to resources and conservation, merely at the beginning of the possibilities that lie ahead. There is scarcely a phase of processing or manufacturing which does not offer many, and in some cases very great, possibilities of making better use of materials. When the goods leave the manufacturing plant, as we shall see, there are further possibilities of economy in the way the goods are transported and used, both by producers and consumers. For any desired output of consumers' goods, there are now enormous wastages from mine, field, forest, and sea at very nearly every step of the way—wastages of excess and badly located plants; of materials in the construction of excess streets, highways, railroads, and automotive transportation; of crosshauling; of superfluous sales and distribution facilities; of materials with high and functionally meaningless built-in obsolescence. Resource conservation and resource availability, as the Paley Commission has pointed out, are both global in extent, and are coextensive with the entire pattern of production and human use.

On the purely technical side, however, the quantum of economically available resources is a problem of engineering, and the limiting factor in engineering is the status and potency of natural-science research. Within this frame of reference we are almost at the point where the rule is: as much of natural resources as we have of resources for natural science. If so, the supremely important question is how to render science competent to handle the mounting burdens placed upon it. The burdens are simultaneously those of supplying the resources needed, of supplying the techniques for proper use, and of answering the fundamental questions on how industry can best organize itself along scientifically valid lines.

A preliminary problem is then how to organize scientific research itself. To this we turn in the following chapter.

III

Science as the Key to Resource Innovation

THE STAKE OF ECONOMICS IN THE MORGANATIC ALLIANCE
OF SCIENCE AND PRACTICE

We seem to be entering, the *Bulletin of Atomic Scientists* suggests, a "third phase of the industrial revolution, out of which basic science will emerge as the initiator and the leader of industrial practice." [1]

Without such swift assumption of the leadership role in shaping the technological foundation of society, the triumphant march of industrialism throughout the globe now appears certain to end in a welter of confusion and frustration without parallel in human history. Can science measure up?

This may well be the most momentous issue of the twentieth century. To answer it with positive assurance, science must re-examine—more, must "rethink through"—the entire range of its current organization, its resources, and its approach to the problems of industrial life.

Consider certain implications of the term. "Science," Victor F. Lenzen has written,[2] "denotes a critical activity of discovery as well as the systematic knowledge founded thereon." It is "characterized by the method and form of its knowledge; by the control of data, formulation of generalities, and the achievement of systematic form." Its goal is "unity of knowledge," and its significance "resides in its value for practice and knowledge of reality." Its range, accordingly, is coextensive with both knowledge and reality, and the history of its evolution demonstrates the strength of an underlying, but cumulatively increasing, interdependence of each phase upon the other.

Natural science itself testifies to the extrinsic value of science for the conduct of life. Biology represents man as an organism which maintains itself by interacting with an environment. Man's adaptation to nature is facilitated by his ability to foresee and thereby control events. The discovery of uniformities in phenomena, upon which control is based, is initially prompted by instinctive curiosity. As his knowledge grows, man's sense of wonder concerning the nature of things develops into "the scientific spirit." Although the foundation of science is the impulse to observe and explain, the practical value of knowledge stimulates its acquisition. Among the ancient Babylonians and Egyptians, regularities in the motions of celestial objects served for the direction of agriculture, geometry was useful in surveying, and items of mechanical knowledge were applied in architecture. Coming upon the historical scene after the seeds of science had been sown for several millenniums, the ancient Greeks garnered the harvest prepared for them and molded it into the form of science. Once embarked on the search for rational knowledge, science acquired a life of its own and the perfection of theoretical structure became an end in itself. The creative impulse of Greek science suffered a decline, but its ideals and methods guided the scientific revival during the dawn of the modern era. Copernicus was inspired to revolutionize astronomy by the Pythagorean ideal of a simple mathematical representation of celestial motions, and the theory of conic sections of Apollonius of Perga provided the conceptual tools for the analysis of motion by Kepler and Galileo. However, science was especially stimulated by the technological problems set by the development of new economic, social, and political institutions. The requirements of navigation for voyages of discovery, the demand for machines by industries such as mining, the effort to improve the technique of firing projectiles, and the requirements of transport by water gave impetus to the astronomical observation and development of mechanics characteristic of the sixteenth and seventeenth centuries. The significant contribution of Francis Bacon was his encouragement of experimental philosophy for the purpose of controlling nature.[3]

As we approach more contemporary times, science has been increasingly stimulated by the requirements of practice; this has lead simultaneously to increasing cultivation of pure science, development of which has made possible new achievements in practice. These achievements in agriculture, industry, and communication—in short, in the whole range of modern industrial technology—have transformed our mode of life.

Four strong and mutually reinforcing trends have served to quicken and generalize the transformation. First is the universalization of the "practical interest" itself. Second is the widening acceptance of the value of change per se—as a sort of built-in component in common standards of life—at a time when the bulk of practical changes must of necessity stem from science. Third, science is visibly surrounded on every side with vast areas of the unknown, and has hence gathered to itself more and more of the intelligence and idle curiosity that went in past centuries into exploration and discovery of new lands, seas, and civilizations. And fourth is the well-nigh universal and *conscious* acceptance of the interdependence of science and technology as an ironclad condition for solid achievements in the sphere of the "practical interests" themselves.

Concentrating on the "practical interest," the countries of the Western world have long since become accustomed to dispose existence around the prospects of rising material standards of living. Such has been the product of the inner-value revolution which came about with the decline of world-renouncing medieval Christianity, and with the secularizing influences of the Enlightenment and its subsequent industrial revolution. Through the world-wide political and economic expansion of Europe from the sixteenth to the twentieth century, the new values have slowly, but with cumulative effect, percolated through the lives of peoples, societies, and cultures everywhere. Expressed first in austere humanitarian terms as freedom from poverty and want, and subsequently as mass luxury and social security for the common man, they are now practically universal aspirations. They are asserted in the Russian Five-Year plans. They may be found in detail in the development plans of the Colombo Conference countries of Southeast Asia and those of Ghana and Bolivia. They are spelled out in terms of food, health, clothing, shelter, and recreation for all. As a result, the hold on the popular imagination of the world-denying and world-negating precepts of the great quietist religions such as Buddhism, Hinduism, and Taoism is either being worn away, or the concepts are changing internally so as to accommodate the new material values.

A built-in component of the popular belief in the material possibilities of "change for the better"—though the philosophers may smile—is the acceptance of the value of change itself. Nearly everybody is caught up in the new excitement. To scholars and scientists, science is now the true and only "endless frontier," and it is a frontier where each new voyage of discovery seems to expand rather than to contract the reaches of the imagination. To statesmen, administrators, and businessmen, the extraordinarily dynamic new scientific technology offers the only remaining adventure-land for the Christopher Columbuses and the Henry Morgans of our times. And for the man on the street, the market place is becoming a continuous World's Fair for the exhibition of the new, the strange, the "improved," the perpetually novel and exotic.

The new hopes, as well as the new excitement and its correlative fears of failure, lead by a thousand routes back to the engineer and the laboratory technician, and thence back to the universities and the great centers of pure scientific research. Along most of these lines of contact there is visible a growing, conscious recognition that science holds the keys to all leading expectations in the sphere of the "practical interests." The result has been to provide science with an increasingly more favorable climate for expansion and growth.

One result of this combined private and public apotheosis of science has been the promotion of reconsideration of the conditions and terms under which science can best combine its pursuit of knowledge with its new and enormously strategic role in the realm of practical affairs. The central problem, simply put, is how best to organize scientific facilities and resources so as to promote both objectives at once without detracting from the effectiveness of either at any important point.

A first requirement is recognition of the implications of the essentially interdependent character of most modern scientific research.

THE INTERDEPENDENT CHARACTER OF SCIENTIFIC RESEARCH

While it is of course true that all ideas in science come from the individual scientist, it is also true that his capacity to solve problems is in large part a function of the adequacy of the facilities placed at his disposal. These facilities bring to his aid the speculation and products of fellow scientists working along the same or related lines. The more advanced the work, and the more complicated the problems, the greater is the need for close coöperation.

The most spectacular example is that of atomic research. Speaking of the evolution of scientific knowledge lying behind the production of the first atomic bomb, Niels Bohr has written:

The astounding achievement of producing an enormous display of power on the basis of experience gained by the study of minute effects, perceptible only by the most delicate instruments, has in fact, besides a most intensive research effort, required an immense engineering enterprise, strikingly illuminating the potentialities of modern industrial development.[4]

Since Bohr wrote these words, the work on nuclear fission has spread out rapidly in many directions. More scientists, and scientists from allied fields of research, have been drawn into the widening range of problems. Step by step, the issues, problems, and ramifications of nuclear research have widened until virtually all of natural science and engineering—not to speak of the social sciences—has become involved.

A similar range of scientific problems faces almost any of the great industrial firms of contemporary times. For example, "All the engineering arts and their underlying sciences," an executive writes concerning the telephone industry,

are basic to its progress. All the complex facilities for the transmission of speech and signaling and for the control or switching of channels of communication have had to be devised. New materials, alloys, and compounds have had to be invented or developed. Mathematics, physics and chemistry all underlie this work. Biology and botany enter into the consideration of textiles and timber products used in telephone plant. Physiology and psychology enter into many aspects of the action of the vocal and auditory organs of the human body, so intimately associated with the use of the telephone.[5]

The expanding work of the huge Bell Telephone Laboratories, accordingly, now reaches into practically every one of the great natural-science disciplines. In each case the relevant problems range all the way from issues of "pure" research in physical law and mathematics to the several related engineering fields.

Or, again, take the field of biology:

In turning to good account . . . knowledge of the ecological web . . . we partition up the task among a panel of specialists—soil chemists, entomologists, experts in moulds and fungi, agronomists, foresters, bacteriologists, public health experts, [whose] problems interlock and shift from one field to another [and in turn interlock with] physiology and genetics, embryology and bio-chemistry and other sister sciences.[6]

Similar illustrations might be multiplied, and might be drawn freely from almost any field of contemporary science, industry, or technology. The implications are obvious. The problems of science as a whole make up a "seamless web." Progress in the natural sciences increasingly depends upon advances in engineering, while the solution of engineering problems becomes increasingly a function of close, exacting scientific research. In the case of atomic energy, the "radiation lab" at the University of California, the Argonne Laboratories at the University of Chicago, and the various laboratories set up at Los Alamos, Oak Ridge, and Hanford—themselves only nodal points or nuclei of a vastly greater web of research agencies coöperating in the work—are jointly related centers of a more or less closely unified system of organized and internally coördinated scientific and engineering research. But the same is also true in varying degrees of the laboratories of Bell Telephone, of General Electric and Westinghouse; of Standard Oil and Shell; of Du Pont and Dow Chemicals; of General Motors and Ford. In varying degrees the pattern is duplicated in laboratories of large and small concerns here and in Europe. It is characteristic, too, of the great government laboratories such as, in the United States, those maintained at the Bureau of Standards and in the Department of Agriculture.

From considerations such as these it appears, as J. D. Bernal[7] has written, that:

Quite apart from the size of science, the increasing complexity and interdependence of its different parts . . . show that the whole system needs to be linked together so that every section can profit as soon as possible from the results of any of the others. We can no longer, as we could in past ages, leave the organization of science to chance or to the personal relations of individual scientists.

To this end, Bernal continues, "five principles must guide the organization of science" in the future. They are worth quoting at length (italics added):

The first principle is that science must have a strategy: objectives must be considered and the available forces distributed between them. That does not mean a dragooning of science. It only means that it is the responsibility of scientists themselves to consider collectively where they are going and to act accordingly. The Royal Society did in fact do this towards the end of the war in reporting in detail on the needs of fundamental science. Neither does it mean, if our objective is human welfare, that no science that does not immediately conduce to it should be undertaken. To have a strategy for research means precisely the opposite. Every immediate practical application of science depends on the past and present activity of scientific workers concerned with completely different aspects of natural phenomena— what used to be called the pure and are now called the fundamental sciences, such as physics and biology. Indeed, in considering the over-all balance of science, it is becoming clear that more and not less support, absolutely and relatively, must be given to fundamental science.

The second principle of organization is teamwork, each member of the team contributing both his own special knowledge and his own individual intelligence to a collective work. Science grows continually in range and complexity. What any individual can learn is absolutely limited. Close personal association is therefore a growing necessity in science.

The third principle is flexibility. In science it is impossible to lay down lines of progress in advance. Therefore, the organization of science has to be adjusted to rapid change of emphasis: to the revaluation of previous knowledge in the light of new discovery and to the working out of its implications in all related fields.

The fourth principle is freedom of communication. This means more than the absence of the restrictions of military industrial secrecy which are already threatening to choke the progress of science. The increasing scale and complexity of science require a rapid and extensive positive communication service which will keep every worker informed with the least delay of everything that should be of interest to him, while not overburdening him, as at present, with irrelevant material.

The fifth principle is respect for individuality; the actual process of discovery is always achieved in an individual mind, though it often happens that many individual minds reach the same answer at about the same time. The conditions of organization must be such as to protect and cherish individual activity, however wayward it may be. This is in no contradiction with the idea of teamwork. Experience shows that individuals become greater as people as well as scientists when working together; that the solitary worker may become a hindrance even to himself.

How far, and along what lines, the organization of science has proceeded may be illustrated with a few cases.

THE HISTORICAL EVOLUTION OF NATIONAL ORGANIZATIONS FOR SCIENCE IN EUROPE: THE CASES OF BRITAIN AND GERMANY

The first great impetus to systematic promotion of science along the lines traced out by Francis Bacon in his *New Atlantis* came not in the universities—which were everywhere regarded as the "Cinderellas of the Church" [8]—but with the founding of the national scientific academies in the seventeenth century, which enlisted the support of most of the great scientific figures of the times.

First in order of time was the Academy of Experiments, founded in Florence in 1657, mainly on the initiative of two of Galileo's most distinguished students, Viviani and Torricelli. The society was disbanded in 1667, largely under clerical pressure. More successful was the founding of the Royal Society for Improving Natural Knowledge (commonly abbreviated as the Royal Society) in 1662 by a group of men who had been meeting informally at each other's homes or at Gresham College since the early 1640's chiefly to discuss the ideas in Bacon's *Novum Organum* and *New Atlantis*. The original members included Sir Robert Boyle, the chemist; Sir Christopher Wren, the architect and mathematician; Sir William Petty, the political economist; the poets Dryden and Cowley; and, later, Newton, who was president from 1703 to 1727. In the early years many nonscientists and laymen were members, but after 1820 control passed to the scientists and the Society became an institution devoted solely to advancement of science.

According to Robert Hooke, writing in 1663, the business and design of the Society was

> . . . to improve the knowledge of naturall things, and all useful Arts, Manufactures, Mechanick practises, Engines and Inventions by Experiments,—(not meddling with Divinity, Metaphysics, Moralls, Politicks, Grammar, Rhetoric, or Logick). . . . To examine all systems, theories, principles . . . in order to the compiling of a complete system of solid philosophy for explicating all phenomena produced by nature or art, and recording a rationall account of the causes of things. . . . In the meantime this Society will not own any hypothesis, system or doctrine of the principles of natural philosophy . . . nor the explication of any phenomena whose recourse must be had to originall causes (as not being explicable by heat, cold, weight, figure and the like as effects produced thereby); nor dogmatically define nor fix axioms of scientificall things, but will question and canvass all opinions, adopting nor adhering to none, till by mature debate and clear arguments, chiefly such as are deduced from legitimate experiments, the truth of such experiments be demonstrated invincibly.[9]

On the continent, the French Académie des Sciences held its first meeting in 1666. It grew out of a series of "informal gatherings of a group of philosophers and mathematicians in Paris," including Descartes, Pascal, Gassendi, and Fermat, and was very similar to the Royal Society.[10]

In Germany, after experimentation with a number of local scientific academies, the national Berlin Academy was founded in 1700, largely on the initiative of Leibnitz:

> The interests of the society were to be very extensive, and were to include history, commerce, records, art, education, etc., besides science and technology. Extensive research was to be carried on in anatomy and physiology, and new methods in social science were to be tested in connection with the treatment of the sick poor, the technical education of orphans, the supervision of prisons, etc. The society was to send out travelling teachers, and to publish a journal through which useful inventions, by whomsoever made, could be widely circulated.[11]

In various memoranda Leibnitz complained that "in Germany important inventions are not applied to practical life for the good of mankind, as they might be." It was his hope that the Academy should become "the center of a network of related societies extending all over Germany and eventually all over the civilized world." [12]

In the course of time similar academies were established in many other countries scattered over the world. Most were modeled directly or indirectly on either the Royal Society or the Berlin Academy.

With the rise, expansion, and secularization of the great universities—particularly after the middle of the nineteenth century—a good deal of the work previously centered in the academies was shifted to the universities. Nevertheless, close liaison work continued between them and the academies.

The history of the Royal Society is typical. From 1850 the Society received, in addition to private funds, special grants from Parliament. In 1900, members of the Society participated in the establishment of its counterpart in the social sciences, the British Academy for the Promotion of Historical, Philosophical and Philological Studies. In the same year the Society helped found the International Association of Scientific Academies, and remained a member until the latter was dissolved in 1914. After World War I, the Society represented Great Britain on the International Research Council (the postwar successor to the International Association of Scientific Academies), and remained as the British representative when the Council was renamed the International Council of Scientific Unions (ICSU). The ICSU is now an international scientific body working in close coöperation with, and occasionally receiving funds from, the United Nations Educational, Scientific, and Cultural Organization.

As a going concern, the Royal Society is a fellowship of Britain's leading scientists, and through such membership serves to some degree as a central clearinghouse for scientific work in all fields of natural science and for the various great specialized scientific professional associations of the country. Its relation to the government is semiofficial, but fairly close, the Society serving in effect as the supreme authority for the government on matters involving science. For many years the Society managed the National Physical Laboratory—the British equivalent of the American National Bureau of Standards—until it was transferred in 1918 to the Department of Scientific and Industrial Research.

Thereafter its scientific work has been supervised by an Executive Committee appointed by the Royal Society with the agreement of the Lord President of the Council. In the same fashion the Meteorology Office of the Royal Society was transferred to the Air Ministry. At virtually every important point the Society gave advice and participated in the founding and operation of the subsequent British machinery for promoting scientific research described briefly below.

With some differences in emphasis, the work of the other great national academies has been conducted along lines similar to those of the Royal Society. Meanwhile in all the European countries, but particularly in Britain and Germany, several new lines of development began to show the need for further organization of scientific resources. Private industry began to interest itself in scientific research, mainly in such new lines as electricity, heavy chemicals, synthetic dyestuffs, alloy metallurgy, and the new synthetic fibers. Large concerns such as Imperial Chemicals and I.G. Farben in Germany had by the middle 1920's come to depend on huge laboratory resources for their capacity to maintain and expand markets. Numerous research associations came into existence to serve entire industries. Established almost entirely after World War I, there were 40 such research associations in Britain in 1954 covering almost every one of Britain's main industrial branches.[13] Germany, in the same year, had some 25 industrial research associations.

Simultaneously governments began to concern themselves with the promotion of scientific resources, partly out of interest in the enhancement of national productivity, and partly as a stimulus to defense and the conduct of war. Germany led the way with the founding in 1911 of the Kaiser Wilhelm Gesellschaft, designed to coördinate the work of a huge chain of special national laboratories, each of which would serve as a clearinghouse for the scientific work, pure and applied, of universities, public institutions, private industrial corporations, and research associations. Britain followed in 1916 with the Department of Scientific and Industrial Research (D.S.I.R.), under the authority of the Lord President of the Council.

The course of World War I served to bring out in sharp focus the advantages of the new forms of organization for the advancement of science and technology for the purposes of both war and peace. The summary made in 1919 by Henry S. Pritchett, President of the Carnegie Foundation for the Advancement of Teaching, is so compact and complete that it requires no comment. Contrasting the time when the scientific investigator was able, like "the old time prospectors for the precious metals," to delve here or there as chance or inclination might lead, he went on to summarize the then current posture of affairs in the scientific world:[14]

The prosecution of research today is upon an entirely different basis. Not only do those in the same science coördinate their work, if they are to attain the highest results, but all branches of science are regarded not as separate and unrelated agencies, but as parts of a common effort. A research started in a purely physical field may find its solution in a chemical reaction or a physiological process.[15] The research men of a nation are not isolated individuals but an organized and coöperating army.

A striking illustration of the outcome of this conception is afforded by the history of the great industrial research establishment at Grosslichterfelde outside Berlin [one of the chain of laboratories included in the research system of the Kaiser Wilhelm Gesellschaft]. In this vast establishment covering many acres, are brought together research men from every field of science working together in the solution of problems arising in the industries. A problem in textiles, or metals, or sanitation may require the coöperative efforts of men in the fields of science that we ordinarily consider as foreign to each other. In the field of industrial research, chemistry, biology, mechanics, physics, are not separated and unrelated sciences, but parts of one universal science.

As a result of this coöperation the German manufacturer may take to this great research laboratory any problem of scientific industry. Manufacturers of steel, brass, stone, textiles, dyes, bring their difficult problems here to be solved. The first act of the administration is to put the enquirer abreast of the literature of the whole world. In many cases it will be found that the problem has already been solved somewhere, oftentimes for a purpose widely different from that of the particular enquiry that has called for the solution.

This same basic conception has governed the subsequent expansion of national research facilities in both Germany and Britain down to the present time, and in each case current organization may properly be regarded as a more or less straight-line development therefrom.

In Germany, by far the most important organization is the Max Planck-Gesellschaft, successor in 1948 to the Kaiser Wilhelm Gesellschaft referred to above. In 1954 it consisted of a chain of 37 research institutes, covering among them virtually every branch of science, fundamental and applied alike. Most of the separate institutes and their leading subdivisions are directed by professors associated with the German university system. Included on the staffs in 1952 were six Nobel prize winners; twelve other Nobel prize winners had been associated with the predecessor Kaiser Wilhelm Gesellschaft, including the famous names of Einstein, Planck, Fischer, and Haber. As such names suggest, the emphasis throughout has been heavily upon fundamental scientific research. Research work is carried on independently of both government and industry. The central direction of the Max Planck-Gesellschaft is in the hands of

. . . a Senate consisting of representatives of science, business and Government which appoints from its members an Executive Committee for administration and finance. There is also a Scientific Board to advise on scientific matters, divided into three subsections: physical and chemical sciences; biology and medicine; philosophy, psychology and education.[16]

The machinery for relating the work of the Max Planck-Gesellschaft to all other types of research conducted in Germany and to the practical problems of industry, commerce, and the state is comprehensive and closely knit. At the top is the German Research Association, which concentrates primarily on grants to individual research workers. Research grants are given after examination by special Expert Committees: "There are 131 of these, each consisting of two university professors, and covering the whole gamut from theology through natural and applied sciences to forestry."[17]

To provide closer liaison with practical problems, and a direct link between science and industry, the Fraunhofer Society for the Advancement of Applied Research was founded in Munich in 1949. On the financial side, its work was supplemented by the League of Benefactors for German Science, with the object of raising money from industry to supplement grants from the German Federal Government and the various states (Länder), and to promote coördination between the research of private corporations and various industrial research associations with government laboratories and the Max Planck-Gesellschaft. In 1953 an interdepartmental committee on research administration was set up in the Federal Chancellor's office.

German pooling of research and practice is actually more thoroughgoing than this discussion indicates. For example, the Federation of German Engineers (*Verein Deutscher Ingenieure*) was originally organized in 1856 and has served since that time to coördinate research conducted by the various engineering societies in the country. It assisted in the founding of the Kaiser Wilhelm Gesellschaft in 1911, and is closely associated today with the Max Planck-Gesellschaft and similar organizations. In 1921 it helped found the National Board for Economy and Efficiency (*Reichskuratorium für Wirtschaftlichkeit*), reconstituted since the War as the *Rationalisieurungskuratorium der Deutschen Wirtschaft*), a central clearinghouse for all types of technical research and training in every phase and aspect of national production which had not hitherto been formally included in the work of the great national laboratories, public and private, or the major engineering societies.[18]

German organization of research appears to be both far more inclusive and much better streamlined than that of the British. It is also more closely tied to the universities and is in the main more heavily concentrated on basic research. But appearances are at least partly belied by the facts. The rough British equivalent of the Max Planck-Gesellschaft is divided among three governmentally operated research organizations: the Agricultural Research Council, the Medical Research Council, and the D.S.I.R. Of these, the last is the most important. The Department has established or assumed responsibility for more than a dozen research organizations, and through these laboratories, stations, etc., with the exception of medicine and agriculture, "embraces in its scope all branches of natural science and their application to industrial processes including the storage and processing of foodstuffs and the utilization of timber."[19] The Medical Research

Council has a central research establishment, the National Institute for Medical Research, at Mill Hill, London, and "maintains some 50 research units, departments or groups attached to university or hospital institutions; some of these are concerned with clinical research and others with laboratory studies." [20] It also administers the Public Health Laboratory Service, consisting of a chain of public-health laboratories throughout England and Wales. The Agricultural Research Council has 14 research stations and units under its direct control in Great Britain.[21]

Close liaison is maintained by these laboratories with other government research institutions on the one hand, and with private industrial and university research on the other; both categories involve extensive and rapidly mushrooming research facilities. Of the three defense agencies—War, Air, and Admiralty—each has at its disposal special research establishments. In addition, under the same authority as the D.S.I.R., the Lord President of the Council, there appears the huge chain of laboratories administered by the Atomic Energy Authority. Most of the newly nationalized industries, such as the National Coal Board, the British Electricity Authority, and the Gas Council, maintain special research facilities. The Post Office has a Research Branch of the Engineering Department for research relating to telephone, telegraph, and radio systems. Additional supplementary and special-purpose research establishments are found in other government offices, such as the Ministries of Agriculture and Fisheries, Food, Transport, Housing and Local Government, the Department of the Government Chemist, and the Colonial Research Office.

As for private industry, a comprehensive survey conducted by the Federation of British Industries[22] in 1947 revealed around 1,000 British firms conducting research, of which 420 spend £1,000 (then around $4,000) or more per year, with the estimated national total for all firms estimated at around £30 million (around $120 million). Total staff was estimated at 45,000, with 10,000 of these having a university degree or its equivalent. About 100 firms had extensive research facilities embracing both pure and applied research, and approximately 300 had established close working relationships with universities and technical colleges. A subsequent survey made in 1952 for the year 1950-51[23] showed total expenditure on research and development increasing by from 50 to 100 per cent since 1945-46, and the number of qualified staff by about 50 per cent. In addition some 40 industrial research associations spent (in 1953) some £4 million ($11.2 million) on problems of special importance to specific industries. About one-third of this total was contributed by the government through D.S.I.R.

During the war the United States and the Commonwealth countries established Scientific Missions in London, and Britain and the Commonwealth countries established Scientific Missions in Washington. After the war these were consolidated in a British Scientific Office in London and the British Commonwealth Scientific Office in Washington. Further overseas liaison work is conducted by the Overseas Liaison Division of D.S.I.R., the Commonwealth Agricultural Bureau, and the British Council. The aim of the last is to foster closer coöperation between British and overseas scientists; it has representatives abroad in some 60 countries.

The British government first experimented with direct sponsorship of scientific research when it established the National Physical Laboratory in 1900. With the founding of the D.S.I.R. in 1916 it accepted, for the first time, the responsibility for the general stimulation and direction of research facilities for the nation as a whole. At the end of the Second World War, the government established an Advisory Council on Scientific Policy "to advise the Lord President of the Council in the exercise of his responsibility for the formulation and execution of Government scientific policy." The first Council had fifteen members, "12 eminent scientists from the universities, industry and Government service, and 3 senior Government administrators." [24] This scientific policy involved a budgeted central-government expenditure of over £248 million (nearly $700 million) for scientific research and development for the year 1954-55.

This partial and incomplete outline of the research facilities of Great Britain—it has not, e.g., included the enormously important work of the universities, the learned societies, and the great natural-science museums—indicates how extraordinarily rapid has been the expansion of laboratories, of expenditure on research, of efforts at national coördination and international liaison, and of the central role of the government. Research is now literally Britain's leading resource for the future.

FURTHER EXPERIMENTATION WITH NATIONAL ORGANIZATION FOR SCIENCE: THE SPECIAL CASE OF THE SOVIET UNION

National mobilization and long-range planning of both fundamental and applied scientific research have become general since the First World War. Thus, to cite a few examples, in 1923 the Italian government set up its National Research Council; in 1932 the Netherlands established its Central National Organization for Applied Scientific Research; in 1937 Denmark founded its Academy of Technical Sciences; in 1939 France merged two institutions into a National Center for Scientific Research; in 1946 Ireland established its Institute for Industrial Research and Standards; in 1951 India elevated an older organization into a Ministry of National Resources and Scientific Research. In all cases the pattern is more or less the same: promotion of close liaison between pure and applied research; coördination of private and industrial research and that of a steadily widening chain of government research institutions; coöperation and exchange of information between all these and the major universities at home, and with other national and international scientific institutions abroad.

Special interest attaches, however, to the most extraordinary efforts made along these lines by the Soviet Union. Alan T. Waterman, Director of the National Science Foundation (United States), has observed that "in general, the size and structure of the Russian scientific and technical manpower pool is substantially similar to ours," while "the indications are that we are already unable to match Russia in our output of engineers." [25] In 1955 the United States expected to graduate about 23,000 engineers, the Soviet Union about 40,000. Between 1928 and 1954 the Soviet Union graduated 682,000 professionals in the engineering field—as against 480,000 in the United States.[26] Russian research facilities are being expanded to keep pace. Between 1940 and 1952 research establishments increased from 1,560 to 2,900, and in these institutions at least "certain of their basic research, notably in the fields of psychology, solid state physics, low temperature physics, nuclear physics and aerodynamics is of excellent quality." [27]

Furthermore, Russian fundamental and applied research of all types is tightly coördinated on a national basis, most of it under the highly centralized administration of the Academy of Sciences. The Academy stems from the days of Peter the Great, having received that monarch's approval in 1724 following a series of discussions with Leibnitz and other founders of the great seventeenth-century European national academies referred to above.[28] Writing in 1947, the Australian scientist, Eric Ashby, found that the Academy

. . . combines, among others, the functions of the Royal Society and the Department of Scientific and Industrial Research. It covers not only science, but literature and language, philosophy, history, economics, and law. It consists of a very select body of 139 Academicians whose mean age is about 65, and a scarcely less select body of 198 corresponding members, whose mean age is scarcely less than 65. Most (though not quite all) of these men were appointed for their distinction as scientists, and it is no exaggeration to say that the Academy is a more difficult body to enter even than the Royal Society of London.[29]

This highly select Russian aristocracy of science now manages a vast chain of scientific institutions and serves as scientific advisor to the government. According to Ashby, as of the middle 1940's,

The Academy finances and controls 57 institutes, 16 laboratories, 15 museums, 31 commissions and committees, 73 libraries, 35 research stations and 7 societies. In January 1945 its scientific staff alone consisted of 4,213 workers and 600 research students (aspirants) in addition to large numbers of technical assistants, laboratory workers, librarians, secretaries and accountants. The libraries under the Academy are said to contain over ten million volumes. . . . The 57 institutes of the Academy are organised under eight divisions as follows: (i) physicomathematical science, (ii) chemical science, (iii) geological and geographical science, (iv) biological science, (v) technical science, (vi) history and philosophy, (vii) economics and law, (viii) literature and language. Each division is divided into institutes, laboratories, libraries, museums, commissions and the like.[30]

The Academy at that time published 43 regular journals, 71 nonperiodic publications made up mostly of monographs too long for inclusion in the regular journals, and some 19 series of monumental publications. It operated with a budget of 200 million roubles.[31] In addition to facilities placed under its several divisions, it operated a number of regional "filials," and apparently worked in close coöperation with the entirely independent and separately financed Union Republic academies. Between 1946 and 1954 the latter had increased from seven to twelve in number.

Though the Academy serves as central planner and governmental adviser on scientific problems, there is also a considerable supplementary system, or systems, of research institutes and laboratories under the direct supervision of several ministries. In 1946 there were "some 965 scientific research institutes, stations, and experiment farms (known as 'points') under the Ministry of Agriculture." [32] There is also a large chain of research institutes under the Ministry of Health; of these, some 25 each had scientific staffs of over 800 in 1946. In addition,

The Ministry for Food Industry has scientific institutes for sugar, canning, and starch products. . . . The Ministry for Meat and Milk has scientific institutes for meat, dairy products, and refrigeration. The Ministry for Foreign Trade has scientific institutes for food production, refrigeration, and fur production. . . . The Ministry for Coal has scientific institutes for peat, coal, chemistry, and synthetic rubber. The Ministry for Chemical Industry has scientific institutes for synthetic rubber, nitrogen, and the applications of physical chemistry to industry. The Ministry for Posts and Telegraphs has scientific institutes for radio propagation. The Ministry for Fish Industry has scientific institutes for lake and river fish, pond fish, marine biology, oceanography, deep sea fisheries, and refrigeration.[33]

Not a great deal is known about the conduct of Russian scientific work in detail, but expert opinion abroad seems generally to accept two conclusions: first, that the bulk of the purely scientific work—at least over the range of most of the natural-science fields —is generally and consistently of a very high quality, and, second, that it seems throughout to be linked up very closely with engineering and practice at all levels. The engineering emphasis of necessity means interlinkage with the vast Soviet planning apparatus. From the early days of the Five-Year Plan system, the intention, it seems, has clearly been to place the burden of technical innovation squarely on the shoulders of organized research. Thus in the 1930's the Webbs reported a Five-Year Plan for the Academy which organized special studies relating to the over-all planning program into the following "complexes":[34]

(1) The complex of problems relating to the study of the structure of matter, and based on the latest achievements in astronomy, physics, chemical physics, and chemistry; (2) the group of problems relating to the study of utilisation of the natural resources of the Soviet Union; (3) the problems connected with the systematic investigation of the power resources of the Soviet Union, with the opening up of new sources of power, with questions of distant power transmissions and electrification of industry, transport and agriculture; (4) the group of problems relating to the new construction developing throughout the Soviet Union, with questions of distribution of the productive forces, seismic investigations, investigation of building materials, questions of health protection, etc.; (5) the group of problems connected with the chemification of the country; (6) the complex of problems relating to the study of the evolution of the organic world, the solution of which should stimulate greater harvests, assist in combating drought, in cultivating new crops, in the intensification of cattle-raising, in the creation of raw material basis for light industry; (7) the complex of socio-historical problems connected with the task of overcoming capitalism and the survivals of earlier social formations in the mentality of the people.

Science, in short, is expected literally to provide the "salvation" of mankind in all particulars and with respect to all problems. The net result seems to have been a staggering rate of increase in Soviet expenditures on scientific research, and a mounting popular enthusiasm for both pure and applied sciences.

EXPERIMENTATION WITH LARGE-SCALE ORGANIZATION OF SCIENTIFIC
RESOURCES IN THE UNITED STATES

In the United States, as Hodgins has put it, "Between 1940 and 1955 the rush into research has been so pell-mell that there has been little opportunity for administrators to take thought." [35] By 1955 the total national expenditures under this general head were estimated around $4 billion to $5 billion, and trends pointed to a further rapid increase over the years ahead. The problem of the best use of the enormous resources was becoming acute. What Hodgins has called the "strange state of American research" at this point, is characterized by certain outstanding features: (1) the great and increasing importance of the government; (2) within government, overwhelming concentration on defense needs; (3) relatively close liaison between the federal government and both industrial and university laboratories; (4) extraordinarily heavy emphasis upon "applied research" with corresponding general neglect of fundamental or basic research; and (5) general lack of adequate organization.

Between 1941 and 1952 the share of the federal government in total national expenditures on research and development increased from 30 per cent to 56 per cent.[36] Of this, roughly 80 per cent was spent by the Department of Defense and the Atomic Energy Commission.[37] With respect to federal expenditures for both defense and civilian purposes, roughly half is used "to support investigators located in universities, research foundations, and industrial laboratories."[38] One result is a very close working relationship between the federal government and the private research facilities. In 1950, for example, some 194 colleges and universities had contracts with the government to the amount of around $90 million. In 1954 there were some 3,300 industrial research laboratories in the United States employing about 165,000 persons. Of these, a fair number likewise had research contracts with the government.[39]

At all levels, the emphasis appears to be overwhelmingly on "application" and "development." While estimates vary and the relevant data are quite unsatisfactory, *Fortune* believes that about 93 per cent of all federal government and about 99 per cent of all private research falls into this class.[40] Alan T. Waterman has estimated that even where the government gives money to colleges and universities, four-fifths is "provided for the applications of science rather than to basic research."[41]

As such data suggest, the need for better organization of these rapidly growing facilities, and for some redirection toward research of a more fundamental and basic character, has been widely recognized. The range of research supported by the federal government has become extraordinarily widespread.[42]

Concentration is overwhelmingly in favor of the physical sciences.[43]

As indicated above, at most levels there is fairly close liaison between governmental and nongovernmental research organizations. Coöperation, however, appears mostly to be on specific and detailed projects. Efforts at general over-all coördination between government departments, or between governmental and nongovernmental agencies are just beginning under the auspices of the National Science Foundation; it will require a great deal of further effort to bring this work to the level of the German Max Planck-Gesellschaft, the British D.S.I.R., or the Russian Academy of Sciences.

The need has long been recognized. Three major steps have been taken in this direction in the past. The first dates back to the Civil War, when in 1863 President Lincoln signed an Act of Congress setting up the National Academy of Sciences. Its Charter stated that "the Academy shall, whenever called upon by any department of the Government, investigate, examine, experiment, and report upon any subject of science or art." [44] In effect, it was, and remains to this day, a select assembly of the nation's leading scientific figures serving in an advisory capacity to the government at their own discretion. The Academy as such conducts no research whatsoever, and has no laboratory or library facilities.

In 1916 the Academy offered to "organize the scientific research of the country" in preparation for entry into World War I. The result was the establishment of the National Research Council, first on an emergency basis, and then by Executive Order (May 11, 1918) as a permanent peacetime agency. The Council was placed under the direction of the Academy of Sciences, and became in effect its research division. Its duties were broad: to stimulate research in the mathematical, physical, and biological sciences, and in the application of these sciences to engineering, agriculture, medicine, and other useful arts, with the object of increasing knowledge, of strengthening the national defense, and of contributing in other ways to the public welfare.[45]

Important as the National Research Council became, a number of developments subsequently called for more extensive efforts.

Among these developments, three were of decisive importance. First was the extraordinarily rapid expansion in both government and private research activities during and following World War II. Second was the growing realization that the vast bulk of this research was directly or indirectly related to both the war and postwar defense programs on the one hand, and to the possibilities of peacetime prosperity on the other. And third was the evident, and cumulatively more serious, general neglect of basic or fundamental scientific research.

As for the first, the more recent research activities of the federal government have already been indicated. An admittedly incomplete study conducted by the National Academy of Sciences and the National Research Council yielded data of a roughly comparable sort for industry. It seems safe to say that the total of financial and personnel resources in private industrial research must at least have doubled in the decade of the 1940's, and that it may have doubled again by the middle 1950's. At this point it must be around twenty times greater, or more, than it was in 1920.[46] As a further comparison, programmed industrial research in America at the turn of the century could be said scarcely to have existed at all—the first industrial laboratory set up on a continuing basis was that which the General Electric Company founded in 1900.

The Second World War forced a second major effort at nationwide mobilization of all scientific resources. The subsequent events centering in the atomic bomb and the "cold war" demonstrated the general, and in some respects quite alarming, American neglect of basic research. Both needs were met during the war by the Office of Scientific Research and Development. Continuation of this work in peacetime was proposed by Dr. Vannevar Bush in the now famous report to President Roosevelt called "Science—The Endless Frontier." Shortly after the war a special President's Scientific Research Board was established for bringing in a report on the status of American science and making recommendations concerning federal research programs.[47] Its report, commonly referred to as the "Steelman Report" (from its chairman, John Steelman), finally resulted in the establishment, in 1950, under federal charter and with federal funds, of the National Science Foundation.

The purpose of the Foundation was to promote basic research on a national scale, but it suffered initially from several weaknesses. These weaknesses have in part been overcome. First, by law it was stated that the Foundation should not, itself, operate any laboratories or pilot plants. A departure from the rigid interpretation of this rule, possibly of some future importance, seems to have been made in 1956 when the Foundation acquired title, from the Federal Facilities Corporation, to the government laboratories for rubber research located in Akron. This transfer was pursuant to an evaluation of the program for rubber research contained in the report of the Foundation's Special Commission for Rubber Research (December, 1955), and was apparently considered as a preliminary step to the disposal of the laboratories to private industrial interests.

Second, the Foundation acquired by law the duty to evaluate scientific research programs undertaken by the federal government. In addition to the Special Commission on Rubber Research, it has set up a Special Committee for Medical Research (at the request of the Secretary of Health, Education, and Welfare), and the Committee on Minerals Research. The Foundation possesses, of course, no more than advisory means for taking steps in the direction of effecting better relationships between government and private and university laboratories.

Third, the initial grant of funds, limited by law to $15 million, seemed ridiculously small. In 1955, this sum was raised to $20 million, and in 1956 to $40 million, plus an additional $26 million for support of the research programs for the International Geophysical Year.[48] The Foundation, in short, has considerably expanded its functions and resources. In 1954 it established an "Advisory Committee on Government-University Relationships" for the purpose of discussing "problems and mechanisms for insuring liaison and cooperation" between research staffs of government and university laboratories.[49] Through a wide series of special Divisional and Advisory Committees and Advisory Panels,[50] the Foundation greatly broadened its range of contacts.

A system of grants to special research institutes, and to scholars working on special research projects—in the fiscal year ending June 30, 1955, totaling 588 grants at a cost of $7,847,395—also enhances its capacity both to encourage research and to promote better organization of scientific work.

The Foundation will probably continue to yield first place to the National Research Council as the most important research coördinative agency in the country. But the latter "cannot be expected to ensure coordination of the Federal research and development program since it has no organic connection with the executive branch of the Federal Government." [51] Furthermore, neither it nor the Foundation possesses means for actually directing coöperation between government and private research institutions. The net result is that while the national resources being poured into scientific research in the United States are probably the largest in the world (although they may be second to those of the Soviet Union), we possess only the beginnings of effective national coöperation and pooling, and relatively little has been accomplished in correcting the major weakness, i.e., the overwhelming emphasis upon practical applications with a consequent general neglect of basic research.

To summarize the American story, scientific research has become a major national resource, here as elsewhere. But it is a resource which is, in some respects, as wastefully utilized as our lands, forests, and mines. Throughout, American research badly needs improved national organization and administrative reorganization with a view to greater emphasis upon fundamental research and better facilities for scientific coöperation. Something of experimentation in national organization along the lines followed by foreign countries seems clearly in the offing. Both government and business enterprise show signs of awakening to the urgency of the problem. [52]

Among other reasons for this expectation is the enormously enhanced international importance of the United States in a world economy where nine-tenths of the world is seeking types of rapid economic development realizable in large part only through new developments in research and their newer engineering applications. The growing international importance of science has been paralleled by efforts at international organization for improved pooling and coöperation in all branches of science.

International coöperation in science has a long history. From the time of the establishment of the great post-medieval universities —particularly the first national scientific academies in the seventeenth century—and roughly down to the outbreak of the First World War, scientists more or less uniformly regarded themselves as members of an international fraternity. Interchanges of personnel, visiting staff-members, scientific publications and congresses, etc. have generally proceeded on this oecumenical assumption. Thereafter, and precisely at the time when the advantages of these activities were becoming everywhere evident, the nationalistic extremism of the First World War and its aftermath began to make them difficult, and in many cases impossible.

One consequence of this crisis for science was the setting in motion of counteractive steps toward better international organization—simultaneously complicated by some considerable accentuation of the creeping paralysis of secrecy.

As for the first, historically,[53]

The grand international congresses of different disciplines in the natural sciences began after 1850. . . . Paralleling this development, was the growth of two kinds of permanent agencies for international cooperation—inter-governmental and non-governmental. An example of the inter-governmental form of cooperation is the *Bureau International des Poids et Mesures*. In 1872, the International Meteorological Office was organized; it recently became the World Meteorological Organization, a new specialized agency of the U.N. International non-governmental organizations were often established by the international congresses, for example, the international commission on the map of the heavens established by astronomers in 1887, and the International Commission on Zoological Nomenclature, in 1895.

At the end of World War I, several plans were under way for widening and systematizing international coöperation on the most comprehensive basis possible. In 1919 an International Research Council was established in Brussels with the aim of providing for continuous coöperation between the various national scientific academies. In 1931, the name of the Council was changed to the

International Council of Scientific Unions. In 1945, with the establishment of UNESCO (United Nations Economic, Social, and Cultural Organization) the basis for international scientific cooperation was broadened to include practically all forms of special and general research, and this was done with a view also to bringing research in all fields—however abstract or theoretical—into the closest possible contact with practical problems and with issues having a bearing upon general international policies.

It would be impossible, in a short space, to attempt a summary of the scope and variety of the scientific work involved, and of the methods employed to effectuate this comprehensive international pooling and interchange of scientific work. The coverage ranges all the way from agencies concerned with promotion of the most abstract types of research to international bodies concerned primarily with issues of policy. Of the former sort, the bulk of the international organizations are brought together under the auspices of the International Council of Scientific Unions (ICSU).[54] The thirteen Member Unions are as follows:[55]

General Unions:
    International Astronomical Union (IAU)
    International Union of Biological Sciences (IUBS)
    International Union of Pure and Applied Chemistry (IUPAC)
    International Union of Geodesy and Geophysics (IUGG)
    International Mathematical Union (IMU)
    International Union of Pure and Applied Physics (IUPAP)
Specialized Unions:
    International Union of Crystallography (IUC)
    International Geographical Union (IGU)
    International Union of History and Philosophy of Sciences
      (IUHPS)
    International Union of Theoretical and Applied Mechanics
      (IUTAM)
    International Union of Physiological Sciences (IUPS)
    International Union of Biochemistry (IUB)
    International Scientific Radio Union (URSI)

Delegates from each of these Unions and from countries that support these Unions meet every three years as the General Assembly of the

International Council of Scientific Unions. The last meeting of the Assembly was in Oslo in 1955 and it is expected that the next General Assembly will be in Washington, D.C. At the Oslo General Assembly [1955] two new Unions were added to the membership—the International Union of Biochemistry and the International Union of Physiological Sciences. The International Union of Logic, Philosophy and Methodology of Science was combined with the International Union of History and Science to form a Union of History and Philosophy of Science. The proposed admission of the International Union of Scientific Psychology was postponed to the next General Assembly. The application of the Union of Soviet Socialist Republics with the Soviet Academy of Sciences as the adhering body was approved by the Assembly as a national member.

The organization and operation of the individual Scientific Unions are similar to that of the Council of Unions. The adhering organizations in most countries consist of the principal academy of science. For Great Britain it is the Royal Society, for France, the Académie des Sciences, and for the United States, the National Academy of Sciences. Most of these organizations have established National Committees that cooperate with the International officers of the Union in carrying out the program of the Scientific Union. The principal part of this program is involved in establishing conferences in special fields, arranging for suitable delegates and participants, and in securing financial support for the expenses of these international conferences.

For example, in the last year and this year the International Union of Pure and Applied Physics has sponsored conferences on:

Frontiers on Optical Physics	Boston
Electron Physics	Maryland
Acoustical Physics and Physiology	Cambridge, Mass.
Nuclear Reactions	Amsterdam
Semi-conductors and Phosphors	Munich
Transport Phenomena and Statistical Mechanics	Bruxelles
Electron Transport in Metals and Solids	Ottawa
X-Ray Microscopy	Cambridge, England
Systems, Unit, and Nomenclature	Paris
Electromagnetic Phenomena in Cosmical Physics	Stockholm
Fundamental Physics Constants	Turin
Theoretical Physics	Seattle
Magnetism of Rocks	London
Magnetism	New Delhi
Radiation Pressure in Ultra-sonics	Marseilles
Theory of Relativity	Berne

Very Low Temperatures   Paris
Commission on Publications   Varenna
Cosmic Rays   Guanajuato, Mexico
Elementary Particles   Pisa

In addition to these general conferences [of] the Union of Pure and Applied Physics there are special commissions on Symbols, Units, and Nomenclature, publications of Abstracts and of Tables of Constants, Spectroscopy, Cosmic Rays, Acoustics, Optics, Thermodynamics and Mechanics, Low Temperature, which have been established to work on special problems.[56]

In addition to these unions there is a host of other international organizations concerned largely, or primarily, with scientific problems. Examples are the International Statistical Institute (established, London, 1885) and the Inter-American Institute of Agricultural Sciences (established, Washington D.C., 1942). Other organizations exist for the special purpose of fixing standard terms and nomenclature, and for promoting any necessary research prior to making further changes in these. Examples are the International Commission on Illumination, the International Electrotechnical Commission, the International Bureau of Weights and Measures, and the International Standards Association. Practically all of the organizations concerned with problems of regulation or coöperation on political, social, and economic activities have research staffs engaged in continuing studies. Among such are the International Labor Organization, the Inter-American Conference on Social Security, the International Bank for Reconstruction and Development, the International Monetary Fund, and the various international committees for regulating commodity production and trade in tin, cotton, sugar, wheat, wool, and rubber.

Several international congresses are set up in such a way that a great deal of continuous research work is conducted by special committees during intervals between congresses. Such, for example, is the case with the International Power Congress, the International Scientific Management Conferences, and the various bureaus, committees, conferences, and unions associated with the International Telecommunications Union. In addition there is the research financed by various foundations such as the Rockefeller, Carnegie, Ford, and Nobel foundations. Finally, there are added the special liaison relationships between various national research institutes, universities, and private (corporate) and government research departments and divisions operating in different countries.

Aside from the International Council of Scientific Unions (ICSU), whose major emphasis is upon pure and theoretical science, and such agencies as the International Telecommunications Union, whose major emphasis is upon international unification of practices in operation and regulation, the first attempt to effect general coöperation among all national and international organizations regardless of interest—that is, whether pure or applied science, whether natural or social science, whether concerned primarily with technical problems or with general problems of regulation and policy formation—came with the establishment of the Intellectual Cooperation Organization of the League of Nations. This organization was one of four "technical" organizations established in 1921 under general League auspices (the other three were on Health, Communications and Transit, and Economic and Financial Organization). It was made up of five bodies or groups of bodies: (1) the International Committee on Intellectual Cooperation, an official advisory organ of the Council and Assembly; (2) the Special Committees of Experts, some of the more important of which were the permanent Committee on Arts and Letters, the Advisory Committee on the Teaching of the Principles and Facts of Intellectual Cooperation, and the Committee of Scientific Advisors; (4) the International Institute of Intellectual Cooperation, with headquarters in Paris, which was the chief functional organization in all these arrangements; and (5) the forty-four national committees of the member nations, serving as liaison bodies between the International Committee and intellectual circles in various nations.[57]

After World War II, the United Nations, in effect, picked up where the ICSU and the Intellectual Cooperation Organization left off. Among the several U.N. agencies engaged in this work, the dominating role is played by UNESCO.

According to its constitution, UNESCO aims to "maintain, increase, and diffuse knowledge" by (1) conserving the world's inheritance of books, works of art, and historical monuments, (2) encouraging cooperation among the nations in all branches of intellectual activity, and (3) "by initiating methods of international cooperation calculated to give the people of all countries access to the printed and published materials produced by any one of them."[58]

It is, accordingly, not a research organization in itself, but rather an organization for promoting, assisting, and encouraging international scientific coöperation, cultural interchange, and mass education.[59]

In 1956 a total budget of almost twelve million dollars was approved for UNESCO, of which about 15 per cent was spent on promotion of the natural and social sciences. This promotion consists, broadly speaking, of two types of activities. One is to assist in the organization of new scientific associations. Thus, among its early activities it helped establish the International Union for the Protection of Nature, the Council for the Co-ordination of International Congresses of Medical Sciences (1949), and the Union of International Engineering Organizations (1950).[60] Several other such international organizations and congresses have been set up since. Particularly noteworthy is the European Nuclear Research Establishment (CERN), initially under the auspices of UNESCO. International coöperation in this field was vastly accelerated as a result of the 1955 Congress on Atoms for Peace, in Geneva. The International Geophysical Year (1957-1958) has further extended such international scientific work.

The other main emphasis is found in the promotion of international scientific congresses of learned societies and in financial aid to various international and regional scientific organizations. Financial aid consists principally of supplying travel grants to scientists attending meetings, assistance in the publication of scientific journals and memoranda, and special subventions to maintain administrative offices.

While UNESCO is unquestionably the most important of the U.N. agencies engaged in promoting better international organization and coöperation in science, such work is by no means confined to it; all the "specialized agencies" are involved in the promotion or actual conduct of some research work; the research, however, whether basic or applied, is generally promoted, as will be indicated below, for the most intensely practical purposes.[61]

SUMMARY AND CONCLUSIONS

Any additional detailing of organization and expenditure for scientific research should serve further to impress the reader with the importance now generally conceded to these activities in solving the crucial problems of contemporary times. In the varied fields of resource utilization and production technology, scientific advance now holds the main, and sometimes the only, key to the future: to new materials, methods, processes; to efficiency and economy of production; to plenty or scarcity; to high or low levels of consumption; to the manner in which the industrial system as a whole is put together and managed.

But also, science contains, as it is organized at present, certain basic weaknesses which seriously inhibit its effectiveness and weaken its internal viability. In many cases, particularly in so far as the industrial laboratories are concerned, it is virtually impossible to find out the extent to which the sums spent are actually devoted to direct advance of scientific research and not absorbed in administrative overhead, laboratory construction, pilot-plant development, and such other expenses as promotion and travel allowances for delegates to conferences. Looking over the recent literature for the United States and abroad, and comparing estimates made at different times by persons approaching the question from many different points of view, it would seem safe to say that not more than 50 per cent of the average industrial-research dollar finds its way into the laboratory or the scientist's study. A more proper figure might be half again this size. In contrast, projects sponsored or financed by the National Science Foundation show very little money diverted away from direct scientific research.[62]

This is not to argue, of course, that some, or on occasion all, overhead expenditures may not be necessary. But it does raise questions—first as to the scale of expenditure for real scientific research, and second as to the scope, quality, and nature of the organization necessary for making the research most effective. These questions apply both to the advance of science itself, and to its practical uses.

A closely related question concerns the division of resources between basic or fundamental research and practical applications. At one extreme may be the United States and the Soviet Union, and at the other Great Britain and Germany. The emphasis in the former two is heavily, and in many instances solely, upon practical applications; the latter two appear to have paid more attention to basic research. The first emphasis tends to "mine out" scientific resources, the second to deepen and widen the potential resources for the future. In the United States around 80 to 90 per cent of all research funds come within the first category. There is increasing interest in a reversal of this arrangement but no evidence that the percentages available for basic research are significantly on the increase. Very careful estimates by the National Science Foundation show that, of federal research expenditures, those for basic research were about 7 per cent of the total in 1954, 6.8 per cent in 1955, and 7.7 per cent in 1956.[63] For all industries, in 1953 (the only year for which estimates have been made), the comparable figure was 4 per cent.[64] It is generally believed that the Soviet emphasis may be even more heavily "practical" than the American.

With respect to both types of research, and despite the emphasis upon organization briefly outlined above, there are wide areas where interchange of information is difficult, and a few where the difficulties seem actually to be increasing. Internationally, as the UNESCO study made clear in 1951,[65] since the outbreak of World War I increasingly nationalistic policies have caught up scientific interchange in the vast and complex expansion of restrictionist practices.[66]

Among the restrictions have been the prohibitions on the free flow of information between the Soviet bloc and the outside world. There is, to be sure, a great deal of leakage both ways; numerous Russian scientific journals are received abroad, and the Russians buy copies of most foreign scientific publications. But the Russians are still generally suspicious of "bourgeois" science, while the remainder of the world is equally suspicious of possible quackery in "Marxist-Leninist" science. Suspicions are accompanied on both sides by many actual restrictions, whose rules and regulations make international scientific intercourse difficult and at times impossible. The Russians, for example, do not belong to many of the U.N. "Special Agencies," [67] and they do not participate in most of the special international scientific and engineering conferences and congresses which are sponsored or subsidized in part by UNESCO.

After Stalin's death, there was evidence of a change in Soviet policies in this field. Russian scientists participated actively in the Geneva Conference on Atoms For Peace. At the Oslo Conference in 1955, the Soviet Academy was admitted as an "adhering body" to the International Conference of Scientific Unions. In 1955, Russian physicists attended the Rochester Nuclear Physics Conference, while fourteen American physicists attended the Nuclear Physics Conference held in Moscow. The International Astronomical Union was invited to hold its 1958 General Assembly in Moscow.

Still, since comparatively little is known about the massive resources devoted to scientific research in the Soviet Union, it may well be true that obstacles remaining in the path of free flow across the Iron Curtain are one of the major weaknesses of the present world organization of science. But there is a further complicating factor which affects all national groups alike, and that is the enormous percentage of scientific research which is devoted to war and security purposes. All, or very nearly all, of this scientific work is in general walled off from the remainder of the scientific world.

The situation in the United States on this point may be more or less typical of an overshadowing malady affecting science everywhere. Currently, and at a time when "the expenditures of the Federal Government for research and development represent approximately half the total expenditures of the Nation for this purpose" [68] more than 80 per cent of such outlays were devoted to "major national security." [69] This is equal to 32 per cent of all American money devoted to scientific research; the whole 32 per cent is research whose results may at any time be given security classification and hence may not be available directly to the scientific community at all.

A fair percentage of this "security research," and nearly all the work done on atomic energy, involves problems of fundamental research. This means that a very large part of fundamental research in such fields as mathematics, physics, astronomy, chemistry, biology, and medicine may at any time be placed behind an "iron curtain" of its own. Worse still for the advance of science, generally speaking, the more basic the research, the more apt it is to be conducted in university laboratories and under university auspices. And this means, in turn, that there is a large and possibly increasing segment of research in the leading centers of learning which may momentarily become wholly or partially unavailable to students and the scientific fraternity as a whole, for reasons of security.

Outside government circles, especially in the United States, the principal support for science comes from the great private industrial laboratories. Here again the information, the discoveries, the theories, and even the speculative results are technically "private property," and much of it is held—at least in the short run—incommunicado to the remainder of the scientific world. While scientific personnel are permitted generally to publish papers and attend meetings for discussing fundamental research problems, the position is reversed the instant corporate interests are at stake. To cite a simple illustration, not even the Federal Bureau of Mines is able to find out from private mining companies the precise extent and quality of their ores. A large percentage, accordingly, of basic resource data is not available to geologists, the general public, or even the government. The veil of secrecy also holds generally for any product or process that is patentable, and wherever "know-how" is of decisive importance.

Thus it comes about that in the United States at any given time somewhere between 75 and 80 per cent of research may in reality be subject to classification as secret. While the percentages may not be quite so large in other countries, certainly in most it is of considerable importance, and in the Soviet Union it may be larger than here. The ideal, in short, of a universally free and open fraternity of scientists who coöperate with each other on both a disciplinary and an oecumenical basis after the model of Solomon's House is far from being achieved. In fact, and despite the magnificent efforts made in recent years to effect better national and international machinery for improving coöperation, on balance the blight of secrecy still appears as a significant handicap to much scientific research.

To this is added a further handicap, that of the vast and increasing complexity in both the problems of the scientific world and the machinery for bringing scientific results to the attention of its researchers. In the more highly specialized fields, the cases are rare where it is possible for a scientist to begin to read even the leading articles in the leading journals. Personal interviews by the writer with representatives of a wide range of the sciences have elicited an almost uniform complaint: sheer inability to sift through the accumulating literature and separate the important grains of wheat from the mounting piles of straw.[70]

Nevertheless, and despite these—possibly mounting—handicaps, the goal of a universally free and coöperative science remains as a fixed objective within the scientific fraternities. Since the end of World War I, and particularly with the dawning realization of the more spectacular implications of the scientific revolution in industry, the objective has been heavily reëmphasized. Among the results are the National Science Foundation, the reestablishment of the Kaiser Wilhelm Gesellschaft as the Max Planck-Gesellschaft, the growing influence of UNESCO and its success in freeing many national barriers to scientific interchange, and the reëmphasis upon basic and fundamental research to be found not only in the scientific journals of the Western world but also in the Soviet Union.

Yet it remains true that in improved organization of scientific resources, both national and international, lies one of the major possibilities of better planning for the future. The achievements to date are impressive; what is needed is for the most part entirely obvious. The ground has been thinly surveyed; the needed "rethinking through" has enormous tasks lying directly ahead.

IV

The Delicate Moving Balance
between Order and Innovation

THE STRATEGIC ROLE OF STANDARDS

Almost every main aspect of the scientific revolution in industry reveals the importance and the implications of a rational system of standards. It may readily be shown that the extent to which any economy is enabled to make the fullest and most effective use of the newer mass-output methods depends, more clearly than upon any other single technical factor, upon the nature, comprehensiveness, and general viability of its system of standards.

This is to say—at each level and in all stages of production from the raw materials and extractive industries on through to the range of ultimate end-products and services—the advance of standardization quickly becomes a precondition to unlocking the full effectiveness of research, of basic lines of technological innovation, of efficiency in the production processes and in supplying low-cost, high-quality goods to ultimate consumers. Properly speaking, a system of standards may do even more than this; in addition to supplying goods at minimal cost it may make possible the provision of a widening variety of high-utility goods which are capable of meeting almost every conceivable want, taste, or even aesthetic quality required in the bulk of workaday consumption goods.

Because of the absolutely strategic role of standards as the "priceless ingredient" of mass production, because their impact on current practice becomes potentially more revolutionary as one moves through the process of production toward the distribution and consumption of goods, and partly also because the meaning of standards is so rarely understood and so frequently misunderstood, the subject merits careful preliminary consideration.

THE TECHNICAL PRECONDITIONS TO MASS OUTPUT

Historically, the technical prerequisites to the full realization of the latent potentialities of a mass-production system may be stated simply. Excluding for purposes of this study all nontechnological factors (such as investment, markets, social organization, etc.), the extension and general permeation of a system of mass output is possible only when certain specific technical conditions are met. With respect to these conditions, leaving aside the long and painful processes of technical evolution that lie behind each, it may be said that without *every one* of the following developments the fullest potential of mass-output methods cannot be achieved.

First, there must be low-cost metal. The decisive step here was the Bessemer process, perfected during the 1850's, which within a decade reduced the price of steel to approximately one-tenth of its former level. Subsequent developments in metallurgy—open-hearth methods, electrometallurgy, alloying technology, use of lighter metals such as aluminum and magnesium—primarily represent refinements. For mass production, requiring heavy loads, high speeds, and precision, metal machinery was necessary. With the Bessemer process and subsequent metallurgical refinements, the basic ingredient—steel—was made economically accessible for the first time in human history.

Second, low-cost machinery made out of metals is possible only when machines are themselves machine-made, or, that is to say, when machine tools have been invented and perfected. The key steps here, such as the slide rest and cross-feed, the turret lathe, the screw machine, and the development of high-speed cutting tools, were taken between 1840 and 1885. By the latter date it was possible, at least theoretically, to produce virtually all types, sizes, and varieties of machines by machine methods, though the operation of these was largely manual.

Third, low-cost machinery requires mass supplies of raw materials to turn out mass quantities of finished goods. This requires low-cost bulk overland-freight facilities to supplement less expensive water-transport, which becomes possible only with the development of the railroad and the practice of universal railway interlinkage. This was a development of the 1840's and 1850's. From then on, facilities of highway and heavy-truck haulage and air freight represent primarily refinements and supplementary improvements of rail and water haulage.

Fourth, the capacity of machinery to move at high speeds and to carry heavy loads depends upon the ability to reduce friction and thereby prevent high temperatures and the resultant heavy wear of moving parts. This solution came with the development of oil refining and the general usage of mineral-oil lubricants in the decade of the 1860's. Roller bearings, and even the latter development of oilless bearings, again primarily represent refinements of the basic change, i.e., of mineral in the place of animal or vegetable lubricants.

Fifth, machinery of any given type operates most efficiently, and may be synchronized with other machines most easily and flexibly, when it is powered by an indefinitely flexible motive force. Great and important as was the introduction of steam-powered line shafting and belt operations, the more significant change here was the introduction of individual prime movers—reciprocating engines, or electric motors. It is everywhere clear that in mass-output industries precision control rests upon electric motive power. This comes first with electric power and electric drive, introduced during the 1880's and 1890's.

Sixth, the capacity to specialize plants on production of individual components of assembled products, every part of which must fit and function coördinately with every other part, and to repair machinery and equipment economically and expeditiously, comes with the development of systems of interchangeable parts. Lack of recognition of the problem retarded for decades the development of the steam engine itself.[1] Eli Whitney, largely as a result of his spectacular methods in the assembly of firearms in 1793—though he was anticipated in the use of these methods by Venetian shipbuilders in the fourteenth and Dutch shipbuilders in the sixteenth century—is known as the "Father of Standardization" as far as interchangeable parts are concerned.[2] But limitation on an extensive scale became general only in the last quarter of the nineteenth century.

Seventh, thoroughgoing mechanization at the semi- or fully

automatic levels depends upon the ability at once to regulate volume and control quality at all levels of each stage of productive operations, and to synchronize both (*a*) preceding and following operations and (*b*) all mutually converging operations (as in belt-line assembly operations) one with another by synchronizing automatic-control devices through the instrumentality of master sequential-control panels.

Eighth and finally, when each and every control device, both on the spot of duty and at the central control panel, is automatically adjusted by the use of "feed-back" control, the plant operations as a whole have then introduced the ultimate in mass production, the automatic plant.

Underlying the seventh and eighth points is the development of master systems of gauges, control instruments, and electronic devices. These are, almost in their entirety, developments since the turn of this century. Most of the control instruments now in use in the United States have been introduced since the First World War, and the electronic and feed-back mechanisms are just beginning to spread rapidly throughout the industrial plants of the country as a whole.

Where all of these are to be found together, rationally and consistently worked through in keeping with scientific and engineering advances and with the structure of user and consumer preferences, the end results contain some astonishing potentialities. On the one hand, they culminate in the generalization of the conditions favorable to automatic plant operation (automation). But this very generalization itself, on the other hand, makes interplant coördination, and hence automation (perhaps in a *looser* sense, but not necessarily), possible after the pattern of intraplant operations.

A basic precondition to plant automation is the planning of standards on a plant-wide basis. A basic precondition to interplant and component integration is the evolution of coördinated systems of standards between all plants and supplementary carrier, intelligence, communication, and other supplementary services whose materials or processes are to any significant degree related to each other, either in the narrow technological sense, as on an assembly line, or in the broader marketing sense. The

second level may under most circumstances mean alternatively
the establishment of industry-wide standards, or national standards, or even international standards. At both general levels, an
additional problem concerns structuring the system of standards
so that it may, while at all points catering directly to permeation
of mass production, still be flexible enough to permit and promote
adjustments to technological changes and ready adaptation to
the vagaries of consumer choice.

THE STRUCTURE OF A SYSTEM OF STANDARDS

Using the classification of the American Standards Association
(ASA), the most appropriate system of standards might be structured as is shown in the following outline.[3]

STRUCTURE OF A SYSTEM OF STANDARDS

Types of standards	*Functions of standards*	*Coöperating sciences and expertise*

1. Nomenclature
    a. Definitions of technical terms used in specifications and in contracts and technical literature
    b. Abbreviations
    c. Letter symbols for quantities used in equations and formulas
    d. Graphical symbols (ideographs or pictographs) used on drawings, schematic diagrams, and the like
	Appropriate classification, definition, and specialization of the language, classifications, abbreviations, signs, symbols, methods of representation, etc. for all natural sciences, all technology, and all technical aspects of trade and marketing of goods and services	Natural sciences; social sciences; engineering societies; accountants; actuaries drawn from private enterprise, trade associations, engineering trades, government departments, etc.— ranging from those interested in standard coinage, weights, measures, language, statistics, etc., including all great systems of scientific classification, to specific detailed nomenclature for describing all processing and all procurement specifications

2. Uniformity in dimensions necessary	Supply conditions to (1) assembly from	Mostly those firms, trade associations, and

Types of standards	*Functions of standards*	*Coöperating sciences and expertise*
to secure interchangeability of parts and supplies, and the interworking of apparatus	mixed lots of prefabricated parts, (2) repair of worn-out parts by simple replacement from stock, and (3) minimize inventoried stocks for both (1) and (2)	engineering societies, and procurement and repair interests involved in the assembly of complex machinery such as automobiles, generators, durable household goods, army ordnance, etc.
3. Specifications for quality of materials and products	Definition in precise terms of the dimensions and properties which each part and assembled product must possess, and functions it must be able to perform	Mostly private, institutional, and government procurement agencies; purchasing agents; all specifications testing agencies; all marketing interests selling by quoted prices, as in the case of the grain, rubber, and cotton exchanges
4. Methods of test for materials and products	Precise and comparable methods for testing comparability of results of testing, and for testing for compliance with specifications for goods supplied on order	Mostly industrial and government (such as the General Services Administration of the United States Government) scientific and engineering staffs; purchasing agents; engineering societies such as the American Society for Testing Materials
5. Ratings of machinery and apparatus	Establish test limits under specified conditions as a basis of purchase specifications, or which establish requirements as to performance, durability, etc. under operation	Same as for §3 and §4, but with special attention to machinery and apparatus both as purchased and as used for testing purchases

Types of standards	*Functions of standards*	*Coöperating sciences and expertise*
6. Safety provisions	Standards for safety of all workmen—scientific, manual, office, etc.—engaged in production or use of machinery and equipment, or exposed to other hazards of employment or use (e.g., traffic lights)	Employers; public or private trade unions; casualty insurance companies; government safety-inspection services; public-health, welfare, and accident - prevention agencies
7. Standard processes and operations for industrial establishments	Precise definitions of functions, jobs, and methods of handling, repairing, etc. all machinery and equipment used in production	All employers and trade unions; engineering and safety councils and societies, etc., as in §6; also time-and-motion experts, electronics and quality-control specialists
8. Standards providing for concentration upon the optimum number of types, sizes, and grades of manufactured products	Eliminate all or most rarely used nonfunctional (i.e., not used or inferior in use) types, sizes, and grades of commodities manufactured or entering markets	All the interested groups listed above, plus consumer testing and rating services; farmers; the Department of Agriculture, the Department of Commerce, home economists, etc.

A cursory survey will reveal how comprehensive the coverage of standardization has become in a modern industrial society. The outline stands literally for a systematic and orderly carrying through of what Werner Sombart in his monumental study, *Der Moderne Kapitalismus,* has characterized as the "inner rationalization" of the enterprise,[4] but, as he also indicated, it goes far beyond the limits of the individual factory. For clarification, a little more detail is added regarding the range of activities involved at each of the more important levels of application.

STANDARDS IN THE MICROCOSM: PLANT STANDARDS

According to Dickson Reck, an outstanding authority on standardization, whenever repetitive situations are the subject matter in business enterprise, standards are interrelated with administration in the following ways:[5]

1. Decision making, which in turn involves:
   a. (in cases where conscious analysis is made) searching and researching to find the alternative solutions which hold forth the prospect of being the most desirable ones for achieving the objective sought;
   b. (in all cases) deciding on one solution which is estimated to be the most efficient one economically available for reaching the objective;
   c. (in all cases) crystallization of the decision in the form of a standard appropriate for communication;
2. The use of the standard as a model to be followed in directing operations;
3. The use of the standard as a model to be followed in training personnel;
4. The use of the standard as the basis for comparison in controlling operations;
5. The use of the standard as a part of the company's system of standards in coordinating operations; and
6. Periodic repetition of the processes, that is, continuing research to find better combinations, decisions to adopt them, and consequent revisions and application of standards, whenever advances in the state of knowledge make such action economical.

To illustrate, Professor Reck lists[6]

. . . in rough order of their generality, some of the important decisions and their corresponding standards which guide the performance of the research, engineering, and production functions required to manufacture a single item of the company's product line, in this case an electric switch. Eleven standards, or types of standards, are shown in the hierarchy [ranging from the most general and substantive to the most operational and detailed], but these include many thousands of detailed standards. . . .

As this hypothetical example indicates, virtually every important decision, and hence virtually every important operation

SOME IMPORTANT DECISIONS AND STANDARDS IN THE SYSTEM OF CO-
ORDINATING THE PRODUCTION OF AN ELECTRICAL SWITCH IN A HYPO-
THETICAL ELECTRICAL MANUFACTURING COMPANY

Decisions	*Standards*
1. To form a corporation with the objective of maximizing profit from the investment of capital in a manufacturing enterprise	1. Oral or written agreement of the promoters
2. To engage in the manufacture and sale of electrical equipment	2. Purpose clause of the corporate charter
3. To manufacture a particular line of low voltage electrical equipment	3. The company's catalog and sales data sheets defining the product line
4. To manufacture a particular type of switch included in the product line, to be called catalog number 38,372, which will perform as well or better than competitive switches	4. Prototype model of proposed catalog number 38,372, developed by the research department
5. To manufacture 38,372 following a particular detailed design involving a multitude of decisions covering design details for the final assembly, each sub-assembly, each manufactured part, and each purchased material and part	5. Complete detailed engineering design drawings, bills of material, and supplementary written specifications for the final assembly, each sub-assembly, each manufactured part, and each purchased material and part
6. To invest in tools to manufacture catalog number 38,372	6. Standards for equipment, tools, dies, and fixtures for the final assembly, each sub-assembly, and each manufactured part
7. To produce certain quantities of 38,372 to meet forecasted demands	7. Standard order quantities for the final assembly, each sub-assembly, each manufactured part, and each purchased material and part

Decisions	*Standards*
8. To use certain production methods for the final assembly, and each manufactured part of 38,372	8. Standard operation sheets showing the tools and routing to be used for producing the final assembly, each sub-assembly, and each manufactured part of 38,372
9. To install certain inspection procedures to control the production of 38,372	9. Standard methods of sampling and inspection
10. To produce the final assembly, each sub-assembly, and each part within certain times	10. Standard times for each operation for producing the final assembly, each sub-assembly, and each part
	11. Standard costs for the final assembly, each sub-assembly, and each part

and policy, within a well-conducted enterprise involves construction, reference to, and constant use of company systems of standards. "Using the analogy of language," Earle Buckingham, Technical Director of the Geartronics Corporation, writes,[7]

the design of the assembled mechanism may be considered as the complete essay or text on a particular subject. This mechanism may include several complete subassemblies that perform certain duties. They, in turn, may be considered as chapters or sections of the complete text. The mechanism with its subassemblies is built up from a large number of individual parts or components, which may be considered as paragraphs or phrases. Each component may have many features. A feature is a distinctive and essential characteristic of the component. For example, a machine screw carries the following features: the head which may be of cylindrical or conical form; the slot for the screw driver; the body or stem which is of cylindrical form; and the threaded section of the stem. Each feature may be considered as a word of the phrase. These features must be definitely specified or spelled out, often by notes, dimensions, and tolerances, which may be considered as the alphabet used to spell out the particular word.

The differences between companies are not in the use of standards, but in the thoroughness with which the subject has been gone into, the adequacy of the system evolved, and the use to which it is put. Many large companies have evolved special standards bodies or divisions for this purpose. Standards are, of course, not limited to manufactures alone. They are of basic importance in all extractive, chemical, agricultural, transport, communication, and consumers' goods industries alike.

It is very difficult to illustrate the importance of good standards systems in precise economic terms, for they exist as indispensable components of processes which also involve closely related research, mechanization of power-systems automation, and all the other allied changes which go to make up what we have referred to as the "scientific revolution in industry." The miscellaneous data brought together below,[8] however, will serve to illustrate a

EXAMPLE OF SAVINGS EFFECTED THROUGH STANDARDS

Manufacturing process or company	Place where savings were made	Direct annual savings	Indirect savings
Photographic supplies	Standard shipping containers	$9,000	Savings of "several million dollars annually" to manufacturers, distributors, and consumers from dimensional standards for films, papers, cameras, and accessories
Chemical products	Company use of 2,740 standards —7 types	$4,000,000	. . .
Chemical products	Savings in purchasing	$100,000	$50,000–$85,000
Baltimore & Ohio R.R.	"Recent company standards"	$861,615	. . .
Western Union Telegraph Company	Standard component parts for desk-fax	20%	Engineering—eliminating design, testing of new parts. Procurement— larger quantities, use of existing manufacturing tools. Warehousing— fewer items. Reduction in field maintenance stocks; reduced training of maintenance personnel
General Electric Company	Over-all gains from standards	15%	In virtually all departments—in floor space, increased labor productivity, decrease in inventory, etc.

Manufacturing process or company	Place where savings were made	Direct annual savings	Indirect savings
Joy Manufacturing Company (mining conveying-machinery)	Engineering records, procedures in Franklin Plant	$194,631 (est. "next year")	In virtually all departments—in floor space, increased labor productivity, decrease in inventory, etc.
Cooking utensils	Reducing storage warehousing costs	$184,716	. . .
Freight-handling installation	Payroll savings	$1,000,000	. . .
Architectural firm	Decrease of draftsmen's dimensional increase from modular measures	Reduction of draftsmen's time by 20%	. . .
General contracting firm	Modular construction reducing bulk waste, labor-time	8% materials-labor saving	. . .
Building firm	Houses of 1,000 sq. ft.—use of storage walls as room dividers	$300-$400 per house	. . .

few types and the range of economies involved. Since, in any precise sense, no cost accounting is sharp enough to separate out clearly and unambiguously the percentage of any realized economies due singly and solely to standards—or for that matter to any other type or line of economy—from the other components with which it is associated, it may be that in most cases claimed economies are smaller than those that might otherwise be allowed. The larger economies are those of mass production, where each and every advance in mass production as a whole will be found necessarily to require further extension of the web of company standards.

STANDARDS DRAWN ON AN INDUSTRY-WIDE BASIS

Where the technical or commercial issues relating to standards are clearly of industry-wide concern, standards may be and frequently are drawn up by trade associations and engineering societies for general acceptance throughout the industry. Before

World War II the National Bureau of Standards published annual lists of organizations engaged in such work. They ran into the hundreds. In 1956 some 74 trade associations, technical societies, professional groups, and consumer organizations were members of the American Standards Association and nearly all of the associate members, some 48 at that time, were of this type.[9] Most of these organizations were engaged in carrying through standardization work independently and outside of the ASA as well as through the services of that organization.

Examples are to be found in the work of the Society of Automotive Engineers (SAE) which has evolved partly on its own initiative, partly in coöperation with the automobile-manufacturing industry, quite complete systems of industry-wide standards which are generally used by all companies making parts for assembling or repairing automobiles. Somewhat the same situation exists as among the American Society of Electrical Engineers, the Society of Refrigerating Engineers, and the American Society of Mechanical Engineers on the one hand—mostly through the ASA—and the producer trade-association for electrical goods of all sorts, the National Electric Manufacturers' Association, and the power group, the Edison Electrical Institute, on the other. In many cases the work is carried along almost entirely by engineers on their own professional initiative, as is the case with the American Society for Testing Materials; in other cases it is carried out more or less exclusively by the trade association, as with the American Institute of Laundering, or the Copper and Brass Research Association.

The line separating company from association standards in a nontechnical sense is at no place clear, and is frequently of more or less accidental historical origin. In general it may be said that the instant the technical or commercial issues involved appear to transcend the internal problems of a single company schematically, they should then be given over to industry-wide standards bodies. Many, if not most, of these issues will, however, involve nonindustrial buyer or user industries, and will, accordingly, be properly referable to the ASA in its capacity as a clearinghouse for all national standards.

THE ORGANIZATION AND FUNCTION OF THE AMERICAN
STANDARDS ASSOCIATION

How industry standards lead directly to national standards may be illustrated by the photographic industry, where various American interests,

. . . working through the facilities of the American Standards Association, have developed nearly 300 national standards since 1931. This was the accomplishment of a united effort by producers, large and small, of photographic materials and equipment, along with consumers, distributors, and associated organizations of many types. Photography, in scarcely a hundred years time, had developed from an interesting experiment to an industry of eminence in the American economy, with other industries either wholly or substantially dependent on photography for their existence. This development had come about without the benefit of industry-wide or national standards, for the photographic industry, prior to 1950, had no trade association. The organization and growth of one large company and several smaller ones had taken place in an atmosphere of intense competition with no tradition of mutuality and no cooperative attempts to solve industry problems on an industry-wide basis.[10]

The American Standards Association was originally established in 1918 (as the American Engineering Standards Committee) for the purpose of providing central clearing machinery for handling standards problems of great urgency in connection with the war. Three such national standards-correlating bodies preceded it: the British Engineering Standards Association (now known as the British Institute of Standards) in 1901; the Dutch Centrall Normalisatie Bureau in 1916; and the Deutscher Normenausschuss in 1918. Many others have been established since. By 1956 some 39 national standards bodies, covering all the major and, directly or indirectly (e.g., through British Commonwealth contacts), most of the minor producing areas of the globe, were in existence. Since 1926 the national standards bodies have been united in an international standards organization—of which more later.

In 1956 the American Standards Association membership was made up of 122 trade associations, technical societies, and consumer organizations, and 2,341 companies, state and city governments, colleges and universities, and a total of some 7,500 technical persons. In addition, federal government departments, bureaus, and administrations working closely with the Association covered virtually the entirety of federal government work in this field.[11] It serves essentially as

. . . a service organization—a federation of [scientific, technical, and engineering] associations and societies. It functions as the machinery through the use of which standards or ideas for standards may be coordinated. ASA does not make standards; it makes standards possible.[12]

At the end of 1953, there were 1,309 ASA-promulgated American Standards in effect, as shown below.[13] (By July, 1956, the number had increased to 1,630.)

Field	Number of Standards
Civil engineering and construction	182
Mechanical engineering	138
Electrical engineering	242
Metallurgy	62
Rubber	11
Chemicals	65
Textiles	80
Mining	18
Photography	150
Drawings	30
Petroleum	69
Gas-burning appliances	28
Motion pictures	75
Specifications for protective clothing	43
Dusts and gases	32
Miscellaneous	84
Total	1,309

The machinery for carrying forward this work can be summarized as follows:

The Standards Council, made up of representatives from each of the Member-Bodies, has jurisdiction over procedures in the development of standards and their approval. Serving in an advisory capacity to the Standards Council are the correlating committees, which make recommendations as to the initiation of projects and their scope, and supervise the work of the various sectional committees. It is in these sectional committees, where all groups interested are represented, that most of the technical work of the Association is handled. A Board of Examination [later changed to Board of Review] performs a similar advisory function for miscellaneous projects.[14]

The section committees of the ASA are, not infrequently, the standards agencies for the industry as a whole. Such, for example, is the case with the American Gas Association. Standards for the industry are "developed by a subcommittee [and,] after publication and distribution for criticism, are completed . . . and submitted to the Executive Board and to the American Standards Association." Up to this point, manufacture in compliance with the American Gas Association standards means the right to use the AGA emblem; after acceptance by the ASA, industry use of the AGA emblem indicates compliance with the particular American Standard. But acceptance as an American Standard comes only after employment of ASA procedure which requires opportunity for full and free participation by all interested parties in the discussion and formulation of the standard.

The coverage of these activities, both on the industrial and the national level, is in many cases extraordinary. For example, the approval, listing, and installation requirements "developed by the American Gas Association and approved as American Standards by the ASA" covered "practically all types of domestic gas appliances, many commercial appliances and appliance accessories" of all types, including all parts, processes, uses, controls, and methods of testing, etc.[15]

According to the ASA, it operates with three major principles:[16]

Every group substantially concerned with a standard—whether designer, manufacturer, distributor, seller, consumer, the government, or any other—has the right to participate in deciding what standards are developed, how they are developed, and the provisions contained in each standard.

The issues are broken down into parts small enough so that each part can be handled by a committee made up of representatives of the groups concerned. Having decided to participate, each group is given its say and its vote at committee meetings.

Decisions are not made by simple majority vote, but rather by the consensus principle. Every effort is made to thresh matters out so thoroughly around the circle that a decision is reached which is unanimous or nearly so.

To illustrate better the practical nature of its work the ASA cites a few examples:[17]

As late as 1927 American traffic signals varied from state to state according to the wishes and peculiarities of 48 legislatures. Acceptance by most states of the American Standard for traffic signals brought about a consequent reduced toll of accidents. Today, it is practically a world standard.

American Standards developed by the cooperative effort of many groups have brought about on a national scale the interchangeability of machine elements such as bolts, nuts, screws, and bearings.

ASA correlating functions have brought about a unified set of national standards for motors, wires and cables, and other electrical equipment and supplies. They have done the same with specifications for iron and steel products and nonferrous metals. They have made possible similar standards for many other industries, including mining and building.

Manufacturers once produced 1400 different types of steel poles for trolley wires. The American Standard reduced this number to 16.

The American Standard for screw threads and the Whitworth Standard of the British differed very little in their dimensions, but the lack of interchangeability that resulted cost us time in two World Wars, hundreds of millions of dollars, and precious cargo space filled with extra screws, nuts, and bolts,[18] shipped as spare parts. But in November, 1948, a unified screw thread agreement, . . . now in full operation, was the result of five years of work through ASA, the British Standards Institution, and the Canadian Standards Association. The American Society of Mechanical Engineers and the Society of Automotive Engineers acted as sponsors for the American part of the effort.

Despite these notable instances of complete and wide-ranging ASA Standards, it is still accurate to say that the Association has barely scratched the surface of what needs to be done on the national scene. Nor is this deficit overcome by the activities of other more or less independent national agencies whose work precedes and leads up to the establishing of standards under the ASA procedure. The work of the other agencies, however, is very important, and, for the reader unfamiliar with the essential facts regarding the extraordinary role of standards in the scientific revolution in industry, will be given brief attention here.

OTHER NATIONAL STANDARDIZATION AGENCIES

The most important of the other agencies working in this field are several branches of the federal government. Their range of coverage is very great. For example:

. . . federal control in some important fields has been delegated to regulatory agencies which issue standards of many kinds. The Interstate Commerce Commission makes regulations affecting equipment and operating procedures in transportation by land and water; standards for air transportation are established by the Civil Aeronautics Board [and the Civil Aeronautics Administration], those applying to communications by the Federal Communications Commission. The Food and Drug Administration promulgates standards which set minimums of quality permissible for food and drugs. The Department of Agriculture has established standards for grading of a great many of the more important agricultural commodities produced in this country. Some of these standards are mandatory for futures trading in certain staple products, such as cotton, grain, potatoes, butter, and wool tops. Others are applied in specific markets or on request of producers of other products, including meats, poultry, eggs, butter, tobacco, and fresh or processed fruits and vegetables. An interesting exception to the general rule of Federal control in agriculture is fertilizer; the marketing of this commodity is controlled by state laws in which a high degree of uniformity has been attained by cooperation between manufacturers and state officials through the Association of Official Agricultural Chemists.[19]

The grades, quality regulations, and weight and volume standards of the Department of Agriculture govern to some extent the bulk of the foodstuffs sold across state lines at the wholesale level. Those of the Food and Drug Administration regulate virtually the entirety of retail commerce in foods and drugs, maintain the standard drug reference, the United States Pharmacopoeia, and divide with the Federal Trade Commission responsibility for labeling and advertising of food and drug products. The Federal Trade Commission, in addition, enforces the Wool Labeling Act, and has general charge of certain trade abuses or unfair trade practices in the form of false and misleading advertisements regarding the vending of goods in general.

A second major contribution by the federal government to the establishment and maintenance of standards is found in the work of the National Bureau of Standards as caretaker of all national standards of measurement. The Bureau of Standards is concerned with establishing and maintaining standards for virtually every conceivable problem, aspect, or phase of measurement, and with the setting up of meaningful nomenclature and other standards for use in science, industry, or commerce. Its work influences the production of practically every conceivable variety of the raw materials and finished goods entering into trade channels.

Special attention is paid through the Commodity Standards Divisions, Office of Technical Services, of the Department of Commerce to the problem of reduction of meaningless varieties of sizes, shapes, and dimensions in a vast range of products traded throughout the American system. This Division is responsible for developing Commercial Standards which establish the standard quality-requirements, testing methods, rating, certification, and labeling of commodities, and provide uniform bases for fair competition. They are developed by voluntary coöperation among manufacturers, distributors, consumers, and other interests, upon the initiative of any of these groups, through a regular procedure.[20]

The Simplified Practice Recommendations—lists of stock items retained after superfluous variety has been eliminated—effect reduction of excessive variety of manufactured products, or of methods. They also are developed by the voluntary coöperation of industry groups, under a regular procedure of the Commodity Standards Division.[21]

Federal Specifications and Federal Standards for governmental procurement use are developed by the Standardization Division, Federal Supply Service, General Services Administration. In the course of their development, Federal Specifications and Standards, which are mandatory for all federal agencies, are widely coördinated among federal agencies, industry, technical societies and associations, and other industry groups. Interim Federal Specifications, which are developed generally to solve an immediate procurement problem, are not as widely coördinated but represent the best technical data and knowledge available at the time of their issuance. After experience and use of these specifications, the majority of them are fully coördinated and converted into mandatory Federal Specifications.[22] As of October 31, 1956, there were some 3,887 standards and specifications out of an estimated requirement of a total of 6,000 needed to cover the overwhelming bulk of government purchases of common-use items.

The standardization program of the General Services Administration is closely coördinated with that of the Department of Defense. That Department has a series of specifications known as MIL's, which cover strictly military items and which are fully coördinated within the Department of Defense; these are mandatory for the various defense activities. However, with respect to common-use items, the Department supports Federal Standards and Specifications, so that military specifications dealing with such items can be developed ultimately within the Federal Specifications and Standards area.

When the Federal Catalog System, which will provide a uniform name, number, and description for all supply items of the government, is completed, greater standardization will become possible of accomplishment.

Direct savings to the government from reorganizing its purchases on the basis of such specifications and standards have been estimated at very high figures. But their significance reaches beyond such random data as accounting may turn up. What they call for in detail and at large is a careful and continuous revamping of technical, physical, and instrumental requirements for the goods the government purchases, to the end of making optimum use of materials supplied to it, and to obtaining them at minimum cost. In addition, many state, county, and municipal buyers use government specifications in making their own purchases, with the result that the weight exercised throughout the economy by government-standards procurement methods is already very heavy, and is steadily growing in importance.

Close liaison work brings together representatives of industry —companies, trade associations, engineering societies, consumer groups, and trade unions—and of government on a great deal of this work. Much of it is handled through the facilities of the ASA.

Also coöperating, but entirely independent of both ASA and the federal government, are a number of other special-purpose agencies interested in the promotion of issuance of standards. Among these are the National Association of Purchasing Agents, the Consumers Union of the United States, the American Society for Testing Materials, the American Hospital Association, the American Medical Association, the American Dental Association, and a growing number of scientific societies including most meteorologists, mathematicians, physicists, chemists, and biologists.

Where the issues are of *supranational* importance, the work is carried out increasingly on an international basis. The International Organization for Standardization is the central coördinating body for this work.

INTERNATIONAL STANDARDS: ISO AND OTHERS

"The International Organization for Standardization (ISO)," a brochure states,[23] "is the place where nations meet in a cooperative effort to develop this common technical, commercial and legal language. It is the world's clearinghouse for the development and promotion of international standards." Originating in 1926 as the International Federation of National Standardizing Associations (ISA) in New York City, it ceased functioning during the war only to be revised in 1946 as an outgrowth of the work of a United Nations standards-coördinating committee, wherein twenty-five nations participated. In 1947 the hitherto independent International Electrotechnical Commission, formed in 1906,[24] merged with ISO to become one of its leading technical divisions.

The ISO has a consultative status with the Economic and Social Council of the United Nations, and is, accordingly, an agency working in close coöperation with the United Nations. Some thirty-seven national standards bodies, including that of the Soviet Union, take part in this work. It has a General Assembly meeting every three years, and is governed by a council chosen by and representing the member bodies. The technical work of the ISO is carried on by committees made up of a delegation from each of the member bodies wishing to take part in the work of the committee. There are now more than eighty technical committees and forty technical subcommittees at work on ISO standardizing projects.[25] Some idea of the range and variety of the work may be had by glancing at the following list of ISO Technical Committees and Subcommittees.[26]

ISO TECHNICAL COMMITTEES

Screw threads
Bolts, nuts, and accessories
Limits and fits
Ball and roller bearings
Pipes and fittings
Paper
Rivets
Shipbuilding details for sea navigation
Shipbuilding details for inland navigation
Drawings (general principles)
Unification of boiler codes
Quantities, units, symbols, conversion factors, and conversion tables
Shaft heights of machinery
Shaft ends
Couplings
Keys
Steel
Commercial zinc
Preferred numbers
Aircraft
Fire-fighting equipment
Automobiles
Agricultural machines
Sieves
Cast iron
Copper and copper alloys
Solid mineral fuels
Petroleum products
Small tools
Measurement of fluid flow
Tires, rims, and valves
Splines and serrations
Refractories
Agricultural products
Raw material for paints, varnishes, and similar products
Cinematography
Terminology (principles and co-ordination)

Textiles
Machine tools
Pulleys and belts (including vee-belts)
Photography
Acoustics
Welding
Rubber
Documentation
Chemistry
Laboratory glassware and related apparatus
Lac
Pallets for unit-load materials handling
Hermetically sealed metal food-containers
Packages for frozen foods
Essential oils
Resinous lumber (sizing, defects)
Mica
Surface finish
Gas cylinders
Building construction
Gears
Plastics
Sheet and wire gauges (designation of diameters and thicknesses)
Screw threads for glass containers
Method of testing for performance and efficiency of fuel-using equipment, excluding internal-combustion engines
Manganese ores
Determination of viscosity
Material for pipelines and other fixed installations in the petroleum industry
Standardization in the sphere of banking
Statistical treatment of series of observations

ISO Technical Committees

Definitions of engines and machines
Concrete and reinforced concrete
Textile machinery and accessories
Marks indicating conformity with standards
Hydraulic binders
Stretchers and stretcher carriers
Transfusion equipment for medical use

Products in asbestos cement
Aromatic hydrocarbons
Light metals and their alloys
Safety colors
Common names for pest-control chemicals
Mining
Gymnastics and sports equipment
Syringes for medical use and needles for injections

Subcommittees Set Up by the ISO Technical Committees

Title	Secretariat
Preliminary work	France
Taper roller-bearings	U.S.A.
Gas list tubes and other steel pipes	Switzerland
Cast-iron pipes, fittings and their joints	France
Nonferrous metal pipes	France
Flanges and their joints	Switzerland
Fittings (other than cast iron)	Switzerland
Pipes and fittings of plastic material for the transport of fluids	Netherlands
Identification colors and symbols for pipelines for land installations	Belgium
Design formulas and stresses for tubes and pipelines at all pressures and temperatures	Switzerland
Nomenclature-Terminology, Substances	France
Test methods and quality specifications	United Kingdom
Dimensions	France
Paper and cardboard packages	(not allocated)
Materials for boilers	Germany
Strength of pressure parts	France
Welding construction	Netherlands
Coal preparation	United Kingdom
Measurement of liquid flow in open channels	India
Terminology	United Kingdom
Test methods and sampling	United Kingdom
Linseed stand-oil and lithographic varnishes	Netherlands
Titanium dioxide	United Kingdom

SUBCOMMITTEES SET UP BY THE ISO TECHNICAL COMMITTEES

Title	*Secretariat*
White spirit	United Kingdom
Ultramarine	France
Ochres	France
Lithopone	Netherlands
Color-fastness tests	United Kingdom & U.S.A.
Shrinkage of fabrics in washing	U.S.A.
Systematic reduction of the number of cloth widths	Czechoslovakia
Systematic restriction of the number of yarn counts	Netherlands
Yarn testing	U.S.A.
Fiber testing (with special reference to man-made fibers)	France
Ropes and cordages	France
Definitions of weld positions	United Kingdom
Calculation of welded connections	Belgium
Filler materials and electrodes	France
Arc welding equipment	United Kingdom
Tests and inspection of welds	Italy
Resistance welding equipment	United Kingdom
Graphical welding symbols	France
Gas welding equipment	Switzerland
Documentary reproduction	France
Color identification of gas cylinders	U.S.A.
Valve outlets	France
Cylinder design	Netherlands
Modular coördination	Belgium
Elements of building construction and equipment	(not allocated)
Spinning preparatory, spinning and doubling (twisting) machinery	Switzerland
Winding and weaving-preparatory machinery	United Kingdom
Weaving machinery	United Kingdom
Dyeing and finishing machinery	France
Definition of safety colors	Netherlands

As with the national standards bodies, the ISO does not include all the agencies working in the international standards field—although most of the other bodies do, in fact, work fairly closely with it in most cases. Other bodies setting up internationally valid standards include: The International Postal Union; the International Commission on Illumination; the International Telecommunications Union, and the International Bureau of Weights and Measures (for securing agreements on international standards). There are many other international bodies of a scientific, engineering, or business character which participate in, or in some cases even initiate, the establishment of internationally valid standards.

STANDARDIZATION AND THE ADVANCE OF SCIENTIFIC RESEARCH

Viewing the problem of research primarily from the industrial angle, Maurice Holland asked: What factors are responsible for the "time lag" between discovery in pure science research and use in mass-production industry? How are the milestones in progress marked? To which he answered:

They are marked definitely. The successive stages in the development may be designated thus: First, discovery in pure science research; second, applied science; third, invention; fourth, industrial research; fifth, industrial application; sixth, standardization; and seventh, mass production. This is the "cycle of research." [27]

This appears to be a very neat and orderly way of outlining the process, but it involves both oversimplification and an unnecessarily complicated, mechanical, and rigid summary of the essential facts. The oversimplification consists of the assumption of a series of direct steps. As was brought out in the previous chapter, it is a well-known fact in most contemporary scientific research that its problems stretch all along the route—from general intuition of a mathematical or logical character, on through to the most ordinary matters of day-by-day consumption of consumer goods and services. No sharp divisions such as those implied by Holland can any longer be clearly marked even in the narrower fields of industrial research.

The unnecessary complication derives in part from the attempt to oversimplify. In plain point of fact, standardization, properly carried out, is enmeshed in the "cycle of research" from beginning to end. To be sure, conventionally, and in point of strict logic, organized research provides the "Open sesame!" to change and industrial vitality, and standards are properly regarded as keepers of the seals of mass production. But the implication is that the one frees thought, expands experimentation, and widens horizons, while the other freezes, narrows, compresses, limits, confines. This opposition of "progress" and "standardization" involves a misconception which is not only very dangerous but also misses the vital interconnection between the two.

To cite a few familiar examples, until the introduction of the Linnaean system of classification in biology, that of Berzelius in chemistry, and that long familiar to every schoolchild—the dictionary, scientific research, and scientific writing were retarded by faulty and inadequate means of stating propositions, summarizing data, communicating ideas. The mere introduction of an orderly, definite, uniform, and constant meaning of words, classes, types, genera—comparable with the previous, time-honored division of languages into nouns, pronouns, verbs, adjectives, etc.—enormously facilitated the simplest processes of learning, and in so doing paved the way for that detailed, painstaking, and objective method of study of phenomena commonly called "scientific research."

Albert W. Whitney, a distinguished American engineer and one of the early leaders among the pioneers of the standards movement in this country, long ago expressed the matter so well that his statement is worth quoting at length:[28]

. . . nature, uncontrolled, would fill the world with endless variety. There would not only be the myriad types that we now have but innumerable modifications of those types. Natural selection, however, acting upon this variety, has had the effect not only of choosing certain types as worthy to survive but of endowing those types with a certain degree of permanence and stability and isolation. It is as though nature had not only given each type a chance to survive but had gone further and cleared out the weeds near by so as to give it the best possible opportunity to get light and air.

The effect is that nature, instead of filling the world with a continuum of plants and animals, has filled it with a discrete and actually enumerable assemblage of types, and furthermore, an ordered assemblage, each of which has a considerable degree of stability and among which certain type-conserving forces operate, such as those that inhibit miscegenation.

Now this establishment of a system of discrete and enumerable types in nature [clear among the higher form of life, blurred among the lower] is the exact analogue of standardization as a purposeful, human activity, and the two are subject to the same abuses.

Not only has nature developed types which can be enumerated and classified, but she has standardized for each a multitude of organs and functions. Individuals of the same species resemble each other in the minutest details of structure and function. If this were not so, organized life would be practically impossible. Everything would be an individual problem with no possibility of generalizations. Institutions and customs would be impossible, for institutions and customs and laws depend upon an underlying sameness of reaction. There could be no medicine for there would be no uniformity of physical organization or response; there could be no surgery, for the surgeon would not know whether he were cutting into a heart or a liver; there could be no organized education, because each mind would be an educational problem in itself. An underlying sameness is the basis for every civilization.

It is precisely this process of "clearing out the weeds near by" —i.e., eliminating the useless, low-quality, and unnecessary (in terms of specified functions)—which constitutes the central concern of the standards movement. Until the clearing-out is carried through, scientific research itself is handicapped. It is handicapped with respect to its technical language; to its means of stating propositions and conclusions so that they may be universally understood and subject to criticism and correction; to its knowledge of and control over the physical and chemical properties of the materials in the laboratory; to its capacity to weigh, measure, and evaluate the results of experimentation. In short, lack of standards in science makes science difficult, when not indeed practically impossible. Contrariwise, the existence of standards opens up the possibilities of precise statement, precise control over experimentation, precise analysis of interrelations of cause, effect, interdependence; in a word, standards make possible control over variation, or *controlled variation*. It is, in the language of Whitney, the conscious, scientific equivalent of the process in nature known as natural selection.

Nevertheless, the notion of "underlying sameness" referred to in Whitney's statement seems to carry with it overtones which continue to bother people with visions of a regimented culture, where all action patterns as well as all beliefs, ideas, and artifacts of living are cut to uniform and indistinguishable designs. In the popular mind, standardization bears the ugly stamp of dull, boring, wearying sameness—same hats, clothes, houses, cars, furniture, books, music, ideas, attitudes, and responses: the one dead-level of Huxley's terrible *Brave New World,* or the nightmare of Orwell's *1984.*

The advocates of more standardization in industry must not only cope with this widely held belief; they must also admit that failure properly to set up and use standards can lead to the very things their bitterest critics condemn. There are two extremes to the position: in the natural sciences, thus far it is extremely difficult to see many instances in which standards have done anything but facilitate, promote, accelerate, and generalize the methods of scientific research; but in consumers' goods and services there is a great deal of evidence of the very things the critics fear.

Since the ultimate value of any productive system depends upon the nature and quality of consumers' goods and services, it will be worth-while to glance at the criteria which can be applied to see that the promotion of standards shall bring what might be called the "scientific research effect," not the "Brave New World effect."

STANDARDS APPLIED TO CONSUMERS' GOODS AND SERVICES

As in any other application, standards with respect to consumers' goods should be drawn *functional to use.* The goods, that is, should perform well. To illustrate, standards should grade the Jonathan apple to the effect that, as delivered to the consumer, it should be of the right species and free of rot, germs, worms, dangerous spray residues, etc. The washing machine should be properly designed to wash clothes, should be as low in initial cost and operating expense as possible, and should be easy and safe to operate and maintain. And so on throughout the range of goods and services. About this much, there is no general dispute. But much more needs to be said.

In the first place, a line can be drawn between that portion of the world of goods where uniformity does not matter and that where taste factors enter. *Below the threshold of taste or discrimination*—where the eye, or the ear, or the sensibilities in general either do not encounter the particular object at all outside workaday hours, or where it clearly does not matter to them—functional design can be purely utilitarian in the ordinary crass meaning of the term. Thus throughout the producers'-goods industries, and in a wide range of consumers'-goods industries, taste plays a relatively small role. The community, to be sure, may well have an interest in external appearance of the factory, in standards which promote smoke abatement, in plant safety, and in many other aspects of industrial production, but, given efficiency and effectiveness in these operations, little else counts. For all these problems, the standards drawn may run simply and purely in terms of efficiency, cost, and over-all economies.

So also may be the case with a large range of consumers' goods themselves. For example, whatever goes into the walls, foundations, floors (below the finish) of houses, and into the unseen parts of automobiles and other durable goods, is a matter of complete indifference to the consumer as far as aesthetic and similar interests are concerned. Here in the *sub-threshold* area, utility in its technical meaning is what counts.

In the second place, the area *above the threshold of discrimination* where style, fashion, likes and dislikes, aesthetic criteria, and creative interests weigh heavily in the balance, standards may be applied in one large segment without raising any questions whatsoever. This is in the area *below the threshold of discrimination*. A good example is provided in the standardization of housing materials to permit prefabrication of all parts while admitting the widest range of choices in individual design in terms of sizes and arrangements of rooms, placement of doors, windows, fireplaces, alcoves, etc., and of details of both external and internal designs and finishes. This is precisely what modular construction, for example, is designed to make possible. It will serve as a good illustration of the issue at stake.

According to Professor Kinne (of the Architecture Department, the University of Illinois), the whole idea of modular construction can be contained in the following:[29]

Definition. This is a simple system for establishing standard dimensions for building materials and components, paying especial attention to the way they may be fitted together in a final building assembly.

The idea is new; it is based on sound principles; it is enough in its infancy that it does not work 100 per cent in practice, nor has it been accepted uniformly. You will hear pro and con statements from wise and seasoned building-industry men on this subject, and you will get the distinct impression that the principle is yet to be proven and accepted to the satisfaction of all. This is true.

But—In your professional lifetime, modular design and construction will be the norm.

Explanation. In the United States, all appropriate materials are or can be fabricated or manufactured to dimensions that fit into four-inch increments (or multiples) when in place in a building assembly or subassembly. Contract documents (plans, details, specifications) are prepared so that standardized material sizes are most easily figured, laid out, produced, and assembled, on the drawing board, in the shop, and in the field.

Theory. This system encourages cooperation on the part of the many producers of countless different building materials, so that designing architects and engineers can regularly produce contract drawings that will lead to better materials utilization (less waste); and better labor utilization (easier assembly or erection).

Modular construction, in effect, makes possible mass production of parts and at least partial preassembly on a factory basis, and reduces on-site construction to the fitting together of such parts. The cost savings in residential construction may be very high. One estimator has placed the possible economies as high as one-third of the ordinary cost of construction of the typical residence. The same expert finds that it leaves the designer—the architect and his confederates—as much freedom as ever, and may give him more:[30]

I maintain that the designer's palette is still the same, only purer in values. He still has mass, he still has fenestration, he still has voids, he still has color, and he still has the textured differences of exterior materials with which to work. In addition to this he has the usual appendages to the basic house: porches, entrances, garages, and, finally, landscaping and planting. If from this array he finds it impossible to design, then I would say that he is essentially not a designer; and I add that standardization has simplified, rather than complicated, his problem.

In the case of modular construction, that is to say, standard dimensions for all housing components involve differences in heights, widths, proportions, etc., which are below the threshold of taste. The eye cannot catch or note the differences below a certain point, and a house made out of module materials to any given design would be indistinguishable to all except the most expert eye from one made in the usual fashion. But the modular house would be governed by standards from beginning to end, and thus subject in its production to the economies of mass output.

In the third place, *above the threshold of discrimination,* we are faced with several possibilities for the wide application of standards without giving offense to aesthetic criteria. (*a*) When standards relate directly to the feature of goods selection and use most directly in the "line of vision" (that is to say, where taste and creative expression are most active, variable, and unpredictable) they may exist if woven into a pattern of *controlled variation.* The colors of fashion goods, if standardized to the pure colors of the chromatic scale, can be modulated and matched by formula. Modulations to achieve almost any conceivable color tone are possible, but the variation is everywhere subject to artistic control. Such fidelity in artists' paints and pigments is the prerequisite to good painting, whether the paintings be of the classical, surrealist, or any other school of expression.[31] A standard chromatic scale for use in industry makes possible matching and combining colors in clothing or interior decoration.[32] Here standardization makes for more rigorous, exacting, and sensitive control by the artist, designer, or architect over his medium of creative expression, and thus becomes an indispensable ally to creative work. (*b*) A more mundane area in which the ultimate consumer welcomes standards is that where they relate to pure convenience-factors—health, safety, efficiency, etc. Standards of workmanship in cutting and putting together women's clothes improve the quality in a manner to enhance the style values. The same holds for standards relating to inflammability of sweaters, blankets, draperies, and similar goods. Standards are also important for long life and wearability where they relate the thread-count and type of weave of fabrics, modes of washing or cleaning garments, dye fastness, resistance to perspiration, size comparability, etc. Factors of this order are to be found in connection with all types of style or artistic goods. (*c*) Standardization is acceptable to the most discriminating buyer when the range of desired variation is narrow and may be, so to speak, supplied from stock. The possibility of varying, by small dimensions, or colors, or various constant qualities, many different types of consumer goods in keeping with a rigorous system of standards is so great in most of these lines—e.g., pencils, pens, socks, stockings, and virtually the entire range of pharmaceuticals and raw foodstuffs—that virtually any desired quality can be supplied to the consumer by completely standard output. (*d*) Finally, there is the area where standards promote purely functional beauty in its own right. As Lewis Mumford pointed out at great length in his book on *Technics and Civilization*, and as may be seen in the work of numerous architects, artists, and designers—e.g., Le Corbusier, the Bauhaus group, Frank Lloyd Wright, Brancusi—in many lines of goods the "purely functional" has aesthetic appeal in its own right. The point once made is so obvious that it requires no elaboration. We find it on every side—in housing, furniture, bridges, trains, automobiles, airplanes, jewelry—and in most cases it is rapidly on the increase.

These four areas above the threshold of discrimination must encompass the bulk of the goods and services sought by consumers where taste, fashion, and artistic considerations play an important role. When combined with the sub-threshold area, standards may be seen to apply to the bulk, probably more than nine-tenths, of consumers' goods. The possible implications for the reorganization of the entire system of distribution are enormous. Among other things it would render almost all trade and brand names and identifications meaningless or wholly unnecessary except in so far as they might be reformulated to inform or guarantee standard or above-standard performance. On the assumption—implied in all organized standards work—that the very drawing-up of the standard and its use in the drafting of procurement specifications calls for the closest approximation to the "one best way" currently permitted by over-all engineering and scientific know-how, standards would open the way for the massive application of mass-output methods long familiar in manu-

facturing processes. We are beginning in a few instances to witness the possibilities of such a line of development. They forecast
nothing less than a "new industrial revolution" in wholesale and
retail distribution (chap. xi).

SUMMARY

Standards, instrumenting and promoting the components of order,
selectivity, and functional performance, are part of the equivalent
in industry and production to Darwinian natural selection in
plant and animal life. Science, ingenuity, art, and taste introduce
an ever richer variety. Standards represent the choice among
widening alternatives. The criteria of choice run in terms of better
use of basic raw materials; higher levels of mechanization and
use of labor-saving devices; increased efficiency in the processes
of production; better, cheaper, more versatile, and more clearly
functional products; meaningful product-differentiation; further
facilitation of the necessary conditions for both scientific advance
and intelligent consumer choice.

In this general sense, standards represent not more or less variety but ever more meaningful variety among ever more numerous alternatives. At the factory level, steady expansion of the
network of interrelated standards is the indispensable prerequisite, step by step, to each and every move in the direction of
complete automation. At this last level, each and every process
must be "geared" together; every process and every machine must
"mesh" with every other process and machine. Materials must be
of standard properties, and must be fed through the concatenated
processes in smooth and even flow. Volume and timing must be
ever more precise, control over successive steps ever more exacting.

What becomes true of the individual plant thus moving toward,
or already arrived at, complete automation is then of necessity
true of antecedent processes which deliver equipment and work
materials to the plant, and it holds with increasing rigor for both
subsequent processing and end products. Pressure for better and
more rigorous standards moves backward to supply-plants and
forward to industrial or ultimate consumers. The conditions to
plant automation, in short, promote in each instance the spread

of standards on an industry-wide basis and the still further expansion of standards of mutual interest on an interindustry basis.

As a consequence, scarcely have standards been developed for corporate use when the need for conferences arises for the development of standards of mutual interest to entire industries or congeries of industries. Sale of products on widening and more distant markets adds further pressure for expansion of standards. Historically some standards, such as those concerned with basic weights, measures and systems of measurement, and nomenclature, have originated largely on a national basis. But many have also begun at the local factory or company level. But at whichever level they originate, they tend quickly to become of national importance, and increasingly of international significance.

The need for standards begins in, and permeates, scientific research. It ends in criteria of meaningful product-differentiation for the ultimate consumer. But selection of the best, most useful, or most meaningful at any or all levels requires reference to some set of principles. The drafting of individual standards quickly raises the question of their place in a system of standards. This system must be so devised that each standard supports, reinforces, and enhances the potentialities of the other standards, and yet is sufficiently flexible throughout so that it may adjust, in detail and at large, to further innovations from the laboratory, from "Yankee ingenuity," and from changing consumer interests, desires, and moods.

The critical importance of this problem is evidenced by the rapid expansion of plant, industrial, national, and international standards groups over the past century. But review of the work of the organizations set up for this purpose quickly shows that a "rethinking through" of the whole problem is badly needed.

Relatively little by way of a *system of standards* exists beyond basic weights and measures and systems of nomenclature. Outside this same area—although there are numerous exceptions even within it—there is even less by way of *principles for the guidance of standards systems*. In some industrial areas, the need for reworking of process and product standards is rapidly assuming critical proportions. Good examples are the entire electronics industries, most chemical industries, almost the entire range of consumers' goods and services, and very much of the equipment and goods entering into international trade.

At the international level, valid systems of comparison exist only at the top scientific level. At the national level, standards still do not exist for almost the entirety of consumers' goods and services. In many branches of the chemical industries, standards of performance either do not exist or lack adequate methods for testing performance. For mechanical equipment, complete standards for national and international interchangeable parts exist only for military goods (and are not complete even here).

Untold quantities of raw materials are wasted in the production of equipment and goods of unnecessarily low quality. Meaningless product-differentiation adds enormously to manufacturers', wholesalers', and retailers' inventories and the complexities and frustrations of buying (chap. xi). Lack of standards of performance increases frequency of breakdown, swells repair and maintenance costs, and multiplies the difficulties of quality control. Nonfunctional product-mix robs production of the economies of plant specialization. Cases may be cited where this tendency not only inhibits steps toward complete automation, but actually appears to be reversing the process—favoring moves toward less of large-scale methods and more of semi-handicraft techniques.

In summary, it would be difficult to cite a single instance in the whole history of the rise of modern industrial methods where the need for complete, exhaustive, and painstaking reëxamination is more badly needed than here. Scientists have given standards the most support. Engineers have shown increasing interest. Economists are almost wholly unaware of its problems. Aside from a narrow range of industries, industrialists have paid it relatively little attention. Trade and distribution have almost entirely bypassed its issues or taken a hostile position toward it. Ultimate consumers scarcely know the meaning of the word.

Yet, to repeat, as far as the processes of production are concerned, standards systems are an indispensable key to the scientific revolution in industry, and a key which becomes ever more important as that revolution widens out over the productive processes of society as a whole.

PART II

The Sweep and Inner Logic
of the New Industrial Order

V

The Principles of Unitization in Mining

Perhaps more rethinking in keeping with the scientific revolution in industry has been done in the field of mining than in any other sector. The compulsions to do so have been enormously powerful. When face to face with the facts of limited, depletable resources, the geometrically rising demand for fossil fuels and minerals has forced mining to become conservation-minded. This conservation-mindedness has stimulated attempts to combine economical operations with the facts of location, size, and richness of ores, in such a way as to give rise to new methods of mining. These methods extend from initial exploration on through to the processing of the ores mined, and they favor operations which are coextensive with the structure of the deposits.

THE CONSERVATION ANGLE

A petroleum engineer once confessed that, like the Frenchman who admitted that "everything" reminded him of a beautiful woman, so everything in mining reminded him of conservation.[1] The reasons are simple. High-quality reserves are severely limited, and attention to problems of conservation has served in surprising ways both to increase the recoverable ratio and as a stimulant to more economical production.

As for the first,

A review of the discoveries made within the last two decades, particularly in the base metals, reveals only a few of major importance. With minor exceptions the metals are today coming from areas that were discovered many years ago.[2]

For all practical purposes,

. . . there is reason to believe that whatever developments may take place in mining exploration, no deposit will be found of sufficient size to change the present order of magnitude of production. . . . 80 per cent of existing Australian production comes from deposits detected before 1900. . . . Even in the Union of Soviet Socialist Republics, where sensational discoveries are frequently vaunted . . . [in the main they] derive from deposits already described in the classical treatises dating back to before the 1914 war.[3]

This statement should be taken to mean not so much absolute scarcity as relative scarcity of *high-quality* deposits. The amounts of material available in the earth's crust are quite definitely known.[4] What is not known in all cases is the precise manner in which the deposits are scattered throughout the earth. The supposition is that the principal deposits of most of the more widely used metals have already been located, and that from here on mining technology will have to cope, in the main, with smaller deposits, less rich ores, or ores located in less favorable locations. The search for ores has resulted in a veritable revolution in the methods of exploration.

THE METHOD OF SYSTEMATIC SURVEY

Systematic surveying conducted by mixed teams of highly qualified specialists is gradually being substituted for the "treasure hunts" of the past:

. . . the method of surveying for the appraisal of resources is that of inventory, and not "treasure hunting." Whether the purpose of the survey is to discover and to study lands appropriate for agricultural development, or to determine the existence and extent of mineral deposits, or whatever purpose, the economical as well as the scientific method is to proceed by making first *a systematic general coverage of the total area under consideration,* making the general surveys, of course, only to specifications of such detail and accuracy as are necessary for inventory purposes. The next step is that of more intensive surveys and investigations of the smaller areas in which resources of whatever category have been located in the inventory process. In such of these areas as appear to be potentially profitable, an exhaustive study and appraisal should then be made. This is the pattern of proper resource surveying. The "treasure hunt" method, whether looking for new areas for settlement or for deposits of precious metals, is, because of its accidental character, always less desirable than systematic inventory procedure.[5]

Surprisingly enough, despite the general recognition of the supreme importance of the first step, not a great deal has been accomplished along these lines—even in such a highly developed country as the United States. Speaking of "only four elements of what we might agree is a proper schedule of resource surveys, namely topographic mapping, geological surveys, soil surveys, and hydrologic surveys," Randall found that one American area "comprising about one-half million square miles" had development under way "for construction amounting to more than five billion dollars" in various projects; yet, "it is a fact that only about 10 per cent of the required information in these categories now exists in this area." [6] This is typical of the situation for most sections of the United States, and does not seem to differ much from the situation in most European countries.

As for the more intensive investigation following the general survey, very complex and costly methods are needed to supply the type of accurate information required for beginning mining operations. For example, with respect to petroleum, "The need to elucidate geological structures with greater accuracy and to deal with the areas of inadequate geological exposure has led to the adoption of various methods of geophysical exploration" of which the "more successful . . . in oilfield practice are the Gravimetric and Seismic Surveys." [7] A wide range of special scientific and engineering skills are required at this stage, and the logic of the operation calls for attempts at appraisal of the size, perimeters, depths, richness, and geological conditions of each major deposit as a whole.

In most countries of the world, the first step, that of mapping geologic, geographic, hydrologic, soil, and similar data, has become a generally recognized governmental function. In most American and European mining ventures, the second step requires both close coöperation with government surveying crews and a pooling of resources of all interested parties in the coöperative effort at adequate appraisal of the deposit.

This is then prefatory to "unitization" of exploitation.

UNITIZATION OF EXPLOITATION: THE CASE OF OIL

Properly speaking, the term "unitization" has in actual practice been confined to the exploitation of petroleum deposits, and can best be explained in that context. The principles behind it, however, are capable of wide application to many, if not most, mining ventures wherever (*a*) deposits are large scale, and (*b*) the ores are complex, so that the operation can extract simultaneously several or all of the various ores present in significant quantities.

In the case of petroleum deposits, unitization has two aspects. One relates to the means of sharing the proceeds among owners of segments of property or property rights in a pool, and the other to the unitized operation of the pool as a whole. The first, involving primarily legal matters of coöperation and adjudication of disputes among separate property holders, will be ignored here except to point out that it has been forced upon most owners of such properties by the obvious facts of petroleum pool formation, and has then been heavily reinforced by subsequent technological adjustments thereto.

The case for unitized operation of the pool as a whole rests upon the facts of petroleum geology, where the term "pool" is not to be understood as though it were an underground fluid reservoir or lake, but as masses of oil and gas permeating porous rock—usually sandstone or limestone—which in turn underlies nonporous rock. Since the gas and oil are lighter than either rock or water they tend to move upwards through porous stone until stopped by nonporous rock formations, where they may then be entrapped by the buckling and folding of the earth. "These traps are of three major kinds. All of them consist of layers of porous rock covered by layers of nonporous rock." [8] The three types of traps are known as the anticline, fault, and stratigraphic.

With respect to each type of trap, and on the principle that it is necessary that the crude oil be displaced and forced upwards by an energy source that moves it from the reservoir rock to the well bore, there are three methods which may be applied, separately or in some combination. The first is the dissolved-gas drive, where "gas escapes from solution within the oil upon reduction of pressure and drives the oil from the reservoir into the well." The second is the gas-cap drive, where the gas, exceeding in amount what may be dissolved in the oil, has moved above the oil zone, and where it may provide a pressure "to expand and move downward, forcing the oil ahead [in an action] similar to the expulsion of water from a siphon type of soda water bottle." The third is the water drive, where the hydrostatic head of the under-ground water found below the oil in the trap is able to force the oil upwards as the well pierced through the cap lowers the pressure above.[9]

Quite obviously these methods require simultaneous control over oil, gas, and water conditions throughout the whole "pool." They may be used separately or in combination, depending upon circumstances, and with widely varying results in contrast to non-unitized field production. Four examples described by the Engineering Committee of the Interstate Oil Compact illustrate reservoir conditions under varying types of production control:[10]

A stratigraphic-type reservoir in its initial or discovery condition [has a trap which] is fairly persistent and is connected to a source of water energy. The reservoir rock has considerable dip and good permeability. The oil in the reservoir is saturated with gas and a gas-cap is present.

[1.] If each well in this reservoir were produced wide open, much oil otherwise recoverable would be left in the reservoir. Uncontrolled production of wells completed in the gas-cap would develop a low pressure therein, so that oil would move into the gas-cap. A significant amount of oil would be made unrecoverable by wetting the gas-cap rock and wasting the energy of the gas-cap. The water-drive would be ineffective since production by the down-structure wells would make it impossible for the encroaching water to keep up with the rate of oil production. The reservoir would not be controlled by water-drive, but by solution-gas expansion, because the method of operation would compel it to be so. A reasonable estimate of ultimate recovery by such a method of operation is 15 to 25 per cent of the initial oil-in-place. . . .

[2.] The reservoir could produce as a solution-gas expansion type under certain restrictions and recover greater oil volume. If all wells in the field were restricted to rates of production that voided equal volumes of reservoir space, there would be less tendency for oil to move up structure and be left in the originally dry gas-cap. Approximately 20 to 30 per cent of the original oil-in-place could be recovered. . . .

[3.] The same reservoir could be produced under solution-gas expansion and gas-cap expansion and recover 30 to 45 per cent of the oil if (1) all gas wells were shut in and (2) oil wells completed below the gas-oil contact and those at the water-oil contact produced only enough water to prevent water encroachment on the oil zone.

[4.] A greater recovery could be realized from a reservoir of this type if oil production and gas production were both strictly controlled.

The reservoir would be a combination water-drive and gas-cap expansion reservoir if gas wells were shut in, high gas-oil ratio wells were restricted, and the combined rate of oil and gas production from wells in all parts of the reservoir limited to the rate at which water entered the reservoir. In this operation 45 to 75 per cent of the oil-in-place could be recovered. . . . Such efficient operations are feasible only where the owners of wells on individual tracts agree that production shall be taken from those wells which are located most advantageously on the structure.

In other words, unitization has here tripled recovery over the old individualistic methods. If there be many property owners of surface rights, each on the average obtains in this case triple the amount of oil through such unitization, and the effectively recoverable oil resources may be multipled threefold (although, on the average, doubling may be more realistic). Unitization can be applied to old as well as new fields. An example is offered by the Shuler Field in Arkansas:

Prior to unitization the field produced a total of approximately sixteen and a half million barrels of oil with a drop in reservoir pressure of from an original pressure of 3548 to 1625, or a drop of 1923 pounds. The oil so produced was an estimated 11% of the original oil in place. In other words, in that short four-year period 55% of the vital reservoir pressure was expended in the production of 11% of the total oil. Contrast this with the eight years subsequent to unitization during which time thirty million barrels of additional oil had been produced with a reservoir pressure drop of only 185 pounds as of today.

Probably not pertinent to our particular inquiry but of interest is the fact that based on the rate of pressure and production decline prior to unitization the Shuler Field would have long since been exhausted so far as primary competitive operations were concerned, with an ultimate recovery of not to exceed thirty-five million barrels of oil. With unitization and gas injection, however, that decline was almost immediately arrested and ever since 1944 the field has continued to consistently and regularly produce on the average 8700 to 9000 barrels of oil a day until [in February, 1949] it was cut back, as were most fields, because of market conditions. In February it produced an average of 8350 barrels per day. . . . Waterflood operations have since been adopted to supplement gas injection. The estimated recovery as a result of unit operations is approximately seventy-five million barrels of oil, being 65% of the original oil in place and a 100% increase over and above competitive operations. Incidentally, the lifting cost as of now [1949] is approximately 13¢ per barrel, which compares favorably with the cost of producing flush production. This operation should convert the most ardent skeptic.[11]

The key to maximum as well as to economical extraction depends upon conservation of dome pressure (i.e., reservoir pressure), maintenance of level gas-oil and oil-water contacts, and close attention to gas-oil ratios. An initial requirement is the making of a careful, accurate, systematic, and coördinated collection of physical, chemical, and mechanical data throughout the field as a whole.[12] With such data in hand, and ability freely to manipulate oil recovery by gas or water pressures, it is then possible to regularize flow so that reservoir pressure remains constant, or drops but slowly, throughout the life history of the field. In Iran, such unified management made possible the extraction of 170 millions of barrels of crude oil with a reservoir pressure drop over three years of only 5 pounds.[13] Control over the rate of production is thus of critical importance,[14] both to conservation and to reduction of cost.

Control may best be effected, once the appropriate geological and other technical data are in hand, by proper spacing of the minimum number of wells. This prevents the drilling of superfluous and unnecessary wells. Correlative advantages are the avoidance of multiplication of surface facilities and of auxiliary services such as roads, water, power, and housing; the reduction of hazards; and the improvement of the possibilities offered for research work.

As for the number of wells, "the total production required from the east Texas field could have been provided by many less wells than the 20,000 or so already drilled." But,

The most striking illustrations are probably to be found in the Kirkuk field of the Iraq Petroleum Company, where a total of some 45 wells has been sufficient for effective delimitation of the field and to meet the production requirements of their 1,170 miles of pipe line to the Mediterranean coast. The line is of 30 millions of barrels per annum capacity and production in 1935 approximated to 27 millions of barrels. In the Haft Kel field of the Anglo-Iranian Oil Company, from which approximately 27 million barrels were produced in 1935, a total of some 40 wells has been sufficient for delimitation and production purposes. Both these figures include early exploratory wells which, as is to be expected, contain a number now redundant to requirements.[15]

Avoiding further detail, the over-all picture of fully unitized oil-gas operations may be summarized as follows: (1) Each pool is prospected, drilled, and managed in a coördinated enterprise. (2) This enterprise has simultaneous control over the flow of gas, oil, and water in the subsurface formations throughout the pool as a whole. (3) Gas and water taken out are reinjected (recycled) as need be to maintain required reservoir pressures, and to effect the resultant regularized flows. (4) Storage at the oil field is reduced to a minimum, gas and oil either going directly or, after first processing, into long-distance oil or gas transport lines. (5) Pipelines and the oil field as a whole are then managed, in effect, as coördinate parts of a single continuous-flow operation.

Beyond the limits of the pool and at the end of the oil and gas lines, or at appropriately placed points along the lines of flow, are then located processing plants or (for gas) communities of ulti-mate-consumer users. In effect, this means that where the transport distances are great, the supplies large-scale, and the pipeline capacity high, the line may serve at once as a common carrier to several petroleum fields and to a wide variety of industrial, commercial, and ultimate-consumer users—the supply managed throughout (at least in effect) on a unified basis.

In these circumstances, the principles of unitization are to all intents and purposes extended beyond the individual pool (a) to all pools feeding into common carrier pipelines, (b) to include pipeline operation itself, and (c) to embrace the supply to user plants and (for gas) consumer distribution-systems. Supplementing and paralleling the steps leading to this end result, another series of steps has introduced—at each point of separate handling or processing and in such ways as to synchronize all such points and volumes—automatically functioning, feed-back controls. Pool operation, pipeline networks, processing plants, and public-utility supplies then become unified segments of a single automatically operating system.

In some cases, such as those associated with the more recent development of the Texas and Oklahoma oil and gas fields, the scale and regional coverage of synchronized operations are enormous. Even where the flow of fuels proceeds not by pipelines, but by water, rail, or truck, close examination will show that it is so managed as to approximate—in capacity, scheduling, and timing of flows—the conditions obtaining with pipelines. From the oil-gas fields outwards, the several great producing, transport, processing, and consumer-supply industries of one of the leading oilfields of the world are increasingly being handled as technically synchronized, industrial complexes under unified management, and regardless of whether the properties and property rights are held by single owners or companies, or by a series of coöperating corporations.

Needless to say, law, custom, and practice are not always in keeping with the technological trends. First official recognition of unitized field operations came in the United States in 1924. State laws permitting it came but slowly, and of the five great oil-producing states, California, is still without such an enabling law. In most of the great oilfields abroad—particularly those in Venezuela and in the Near East (Iran, Saudi Arabia, Kuwait, Iraq) unitization of pools, and in most cases of pipeline or water transport, has been taken for granted from the very beginning.

UNITIZATION OF COAL EXTRACTION AND THE MINING
OF OTHER TYPES OF ORES

While there is a certain poetic license in speaking of "unitization" in other fields of mining,[16] still many of the newer lines of development in the mining of coal and other minerals are so similar to those outlined above for oil and gas production that the term, when used with due caution, may nevertheless be applied. In the case of coal mining, the whole shift—particularly noteworthy in England following the nationalization of coal in 1947—has been away from the small, local mine which is confined in scale of operations to a given piece of surface property, and over to the development of huge, unified operations which are either coextensive with the geographic extent of underground deposits, or which divide up larger fields into two or more such operations.

The famous Reid Committee report, upon the basis of which the subsequent nationalization measures were carried through, commented that

During the last 25 years or so, there has been a marked trend towards the construction of much larger mines than have been contemplated in the past, and in Holland, Poland and the Ruhr, mines have been sunk which were producing before the War over 2,000,000 tons annually (8/10,000 tons daily) and were laid out for double-shift coal-getting. . . . With such large outputs the importance of long-term planning is greatly enhanced.[17]

In keeping at once with the imperative of conservation and with the most widely accepted mining techniques, such long-term planning possesses the following general characteristics:

(1) Comprehensive geological exploration determines first the exact physical outlines, depths, and physical-chemical characteristics of the deposit as a whole. The results yield a picture which, for coal, would show the thickness, slope, depth at which found, presence of water, etc., and the quality of successive minable seams down to a depth of 3,000 to 5,000 feet.

(2) Exploitation would be coextensive with the deposit, unified operations being laid out with a view to moving through the total deposit continuously until the whole is exhausted. This is the "geological plan," and will be found today in the development plans for virtually every major ore deposit and most minor ones.

(3) Where (a) property holdings divide the coal or ore bodies under competing ownership groups, the "interests" tend typically to combine holdings in such a way as to be consistent with unified mining operations, and *as though* they were held by a single mining concessionaire. A simple device is a jointly owned mining company. Such, for example, are the Hollinger North Shore Exploration Company, in the newly developed northern Quebec fields (combining the interests of the Hollinger and the Hanna groups), and Kennec Exploration, Limited, in northern Labrador (combining the Kennecott Copper Company and the N. J. Zinc Company interests). Where (b), as with many coal deposits, there are several superincumbent layers, and where the ore field is much larger than may adequately be handled by a single optimum-sized mining operation, efficient exploitation may call for cutting the total field into two or more separate, unified, and nowhere overlapping operations. The effect is *as though* the whole deposit were mined as a single operation. Thus upon the basis of the Reid report for England, referred to above, plans were dis-

cussed for eventually substituting for over 1,700 mines, most of which produced under 100,000 tons per annum, some fifty to a hundred producing from 1 to 3 million or more tons per annum, each of which would mine either an entire deposit or some aliquot part of a major deposit. Where (c) the ores are complex, mining operations tend to extract every mineral—as a representative of the Anaconda Copper Mining Company put it in commenting upon plans for the huge new Kelley mine in Butte, Montana—which emits a payable "squeal." [18]

(4) *De facto* "unitization" of deposit exploitation is frequently combined—particularly when mining operations are located, as is typically the case with copper, in isolated spots—with refining at the same or a nearby location. In this case operations are planned with a view to providing continuous and evenly spaced movements ("flows") of ore directly from the face of the ore deposit, on through beneficiation and subsequent refining processes, to final transport and shipping facilities. Where mining is a long distance from refining, as is the case with the Mesabi, Ungava Bay (Labrador), and Cerro Bolívar (Venezuela) ores, the transport and ore handling capacities, as well as the mining operations and refining plants at the further ends of the lines, are proportioned in such a way as to approximate the conditions that hold for interprocess coördination where they are not so separated.

(5) In either case, such "unitized" mining always—or nearly always—involves the development of series of coördinate services such as water supply, power, and transport. If water is scarce, as with the Chuquicamata copper mines in northern Chile, supply may require extensive planning of multiple-purpose watershed, stream flow, and other miscellaneous-use controls. If location does not make power supply from grid sources possible in adequate amounts, a power system must be developed. Typically, existing transport facilities are used, or new transport media are developed to unite mines and process plants *as though* in a continuous-flow mechanism. The transport system of the United States Steel Corporation in the Cerro Bolívar project, for example, combines mining at the one end with rail haulage from the mines to the Orinoco River, and from thence water haulage to Atlantic and Gulf sea-

port plants—some of them, as with the Birmingham and eastern Pennsylvania plants, requiring additional haulage from seaboard points—in a single, continuously functioning flow system.

(6) As the last point implies, in many—perhaps most—cases "unitization" of mining operations has been combined with and is a coördinate part of other cost-reducing programs which call on the one hand for regional placing of plants in terms of varying structures of market demand, and on the other for such a scheduling and synchronization of plants involved in successive steps of refining and finishing that each succeeding stage absorbs in its entirety the output of each preceding stage within the system. In between stages the mineral does not, so to speak, "go on the open market." Mining then becomes a phase of nationally or internationally extensive operations turning out widely diversified lines of goods, each step in the production of which has been technically integrated with all other steps, and this holds whether plants are regionally agglomerated or widely scattered.

No doubt, nothing quite so completely rounded out as this statement implies is to be found in actual practice, although the systems evolved by the United States Steel Corporation, Anaconda Copper, or the Alcoa, Reynolds, and Kaiser aluminum concerns, to mention a few of the better-known examples, leave very little untried along these lines.[19]

(7) As one moves closer to the mining operations themselves, while mechanization is advancing on every side by leaps and bounds, yet relatively little of it is as yet completely automated. In a few cases beneficiation of ores has been put on a nearly automatic level.[20] Nevertheless, the underlying pattern of organization is typically one which is being laid out *as though* automation were only a final step in a series logically leading to such an eventual consummation.

SUMMARY

Clearly, the trend in the major fields of ores mining is generally toward some approximation of "unitized" development on the pattern of the idea and practice evolved in the oil and gas industries. Conservation plays an important role in all cases, though it is not always officially recognized as such. Just as the newer oil and gas pools tend on the average to be smaller, poorer, deeper, and more difficult to exploit, so with respect to coal, iron, copper, bauxite, tin, zinc, etc., depletion of high-quality ores is everywhere in sight. The movement is toward more distant, or smaller, or leaner, or badly located ores.

The struggle against rising real costs is found in nearly every case. The industrial reaction has been a cumulatively progressing internal technical rationalization. Very nearly every phase of this technical rationalization has tended to promote further "unitization" of mining operations, and to make of this unitization merely a first and logical step in the direction of comprehensive, long-term industrial planning of mining operations on a national or international basis.

VI

Determinants and Prospects of Industrialized Agriculture

In agriculture, practice generally lags far behind theory. Much of the "rethinking through" required to place production on a scientific footing has been done. In contrast with mining, however, all the separate pieces have rarely been put together. Yet, if anything, the stakes in further reëxamination are of more critical importance for the future prospects of mankind.

"Civilization," said Lowdermilk, "is running a race with famine, and the issue is still in doubt. . . . For 7,000 years, mankind has sought a more abundant life on this planet, but with more of failure than of success." [1] The evidence of past failures is found in recurrent famines over vast areas; in a legacy of spreading deserts and barren, eroded hills where once the land was fertile and well watered; in "stark ruins of stone buildings, of villages and market towns" standing "lifeless as ghosts" where once great civilizations flourished—reminding us that "when food fails, all else fails—civilization falls apart" and that "when the soil is gone, all is gone."

The evidence of current failure is no less impressive. At a time when world population is growing at an unprecedented rate, when the underdeveloped areas, two-thirds of the world, are seeking rapid and large-scale industrialization with its concomitant increase in demands on the land, and when some "70 per cent of the world's population are farmers," we still find large areas of recurrent famine; "more than half the world undernourished"; "no more continents," as in the past, "to discover, to explore or to exploit" when the old soil is worn out or gone; and a high and mounting scale of destruction of soil and land resources which is without precedent in human history, and which is common alike to most regions of the earth. [2]

Whether destruction of "man's natural habitat" in the past was avoidable or not may be debated at length. But it is now true that virtually all the important means are known for not only putting a halt to this process, but also of vastly expanding food production. Thus it comes about that all proposals for significant and long-run improvement in agricultural production must first root their premises in two sets of superficially contradictory facts. On the one hand there stands readily available a well-demonstrated knowledge of how to expand considerably the actual acreage and the further capacity of the land to produce. And on the other there is found on all sides a generally deteriorating supply of natural land-resources. The first calls for engineering and economic reconsideration of the whole farm-operation system. The second requires the emergency coöperation of all interested parties and agencies on a heroic scale. The stakes center in the hope that success in a handicap race with nature for higher standards of living may not be turned into a "rat race" for survival. And this success turns on the ability to plan scientifically far beyond current practices.

To put the matter differently, land, above all other resources and everywhere throughout the world,

. . . is vested with a social or public interest; . . . the long reign of individualism created widespread social and economic maladjustments in the use of land, which could be corrected only by governmental policies based on social planning; . . . each acre of land has a socially best use, which must be discovered through the process of land planning.[3]

The "individualism" of which Gray thus speaks affects the livelihood of two-thirds of the world's population, and the most important item in the standard of living of all.[4]

The central features of land planning are provided by the nature of the "web of life" itself. "It is important," J. Arthur Thomson writes,

to acquire as a habit of mind the vision of the web of life. It is distinctively the scientific way of looking at things, to appreciate their interrelations, to see Nature (and human life as well) as a vibrating system most surely and subtly interconnected. But in addition to the influence on our theoretical outlook, there is the practical importance of the idea of interrelations. If we are to persist and advance in civilization, we must pay more heed to the web of life, to all the strange junctions in our lines of communications. We cannot play the game without observing the rules, and these include recognition of the web of life. We are part of a system, in which it is not the first or the second consequence of a move that counts, but the sum of consequences.[5]

THE "SUM OF CONSEQUENCES": THE POSSIBILITIES

A consequence of *partial* application of science to agriculture has been a vast increase in the capacity to produce. Most of the more important applications are of recent years. The American data are to some extent typical. Agricultural output was 27 per cent higher in 1929 than in 1909, and required 7.5 per cent fewer persons to produce it. Farm labor productivity increased 150 per cent between 1870 and 1929, and 40 per cent between 1909 and 1929.

In all farm production, each farm worker in wartime in 1945 produced enough agricultural products to support himself and more than 13 others, whereas in 1920 one farm worker had supported himself and 9 other persons and in 1820, himself and only a little more than 3 other persons.[6]

By 1950, another estimate has shown, one farm worker supported eighteen other persons.[7] Changes such as these are not confined to any one crop or area. To some extent the story is the same for all fields of agriculture. The swift mechanization of corn, wheat, sugar-beet, cotton, and similar large-scale crops, improved seed selection, new crop species, and a host of related changes have set the pace. The result is a speeding-up of output until it does not seem absurd to speak of a "new agricultural revolution." Nor is there an immediate prospect of a slowing down of the process. One estimate has it that twice as many people were "tractored out" of the corn, wheat, hog, cotton, and sugar-beet belts in the first ten years after World War II as met with this fate in the corresponding decade prior to the war. Former Secretary of Agriculture Wallace once estimated that under certain circumstances it might be possible

. . . within 20 years [to produce] the present supply of pork and lard with half as much man-labor as at present, with 35 million instead of the present 50 million acres in corn, and with probably half as many farms and half as many people living on farms.[8]

By 1950 that prophecy had practically been fulfilled.

This situation is not, of course, unique to the United States. Between 1870 and 1939 the proportion of the German rural and agricultural population to the urban shifted from a ratio of 70 per cent of the total population to 30 per cent, thus exactly reversing the proportions between the two in a period of sixty years. Growth in domestic agricultural productivity may account for about half of this increased capacity to feed a larger population at higher levels of food consumption. In England, improved agricultural techniques have made it possible for 7 per cent of the gainfully employed population to supply from domestic sources about half of the nation's food supply,[9] and for the gross food production of her small island to equal that of the vast expanses of Canada. Some experts believe that England might even raise all the foodstuffs she needs and at lower over-all costs.[10] Similar figures might be cited from other European countries and many of the leading overseas areas of specialized agricultural crop production.

Even in the more densely populated areas of the Far East the possibilities of future agricultural production are very great.

In India it is estimated that improvements in agricultural practices and technique alone, through the use of better seeds and fertilisers and through irrigation works, could by 1956-7 secure increases over the current estimated levels of production of 8 per cent (3,000,000 tons) in foodgrains, 30 per cent (195,000 tons) in cotton, 50 per cent (375,000 tons) in jute and 30 per cent (1,500,000 tons) in oil-seeds. In Ceylon it would be possible in the long run to bring another 3 million acres of land under the plough, thus doubling the cultivated area. In Pakistan two irrigation projects at present in hand, at Thal and Kotri, will make an additional 4,800,000 acres available for cultivation, and a further 2,300,000 acres at present lying waterlogged in West Pakistan could be recovered by the construction of tube-wells to lower the water-table in the area.[11]

Similar prospects are in view in many other parts of the world. In general, they will continue to widen as mechanical and other improvements in labor productivity are accompanied by means for finding the "best use" for all types of land, and as techniques are devised for bringing more land under cultivation. On the surface, all such data present an exceedingly hopeful picture. Agriculture, while it shares with other forms of industrial activity the rule that "nature's gifts are the basis of all economic life," differs in one fundamental respect from all the rest. While industries based upon given stocks of minerals such as coal, oil, and the chemical and metallurgical raw materials face the problem of final and complete depletion,[12] the resources of agriculture are capable of being managed so that they become perpetually renewable. But the capacity to renew with high and rising yields depends upon the ability to adjust and to manipulate all forms of life involved in the natural cycles of climate, water, life-essential chemicals, and ecology (botanical and zoölogical life interdependencies). As Person has put the matter:

Through countless centuries there has been built up a balanced, fruitful relationship among waters, soils, grasses, and forests. Each dependent on and helpful to the others, they have learned to work together, through physical, chemical, and biological processes, to create and maintain a continent of abundant, useful resources for the habitation and sustenance of Man.[13]

The basic natural patterns to which all land utilization must be adapted, if agriculture is to be placed on a stable footing, require planned adaptation on a thoroughgoing basis. The more important of these patterns are the following:

Meteorological, or the diurnal, seasonal, annual, and long-run "cycles" [14] of sunshine, heat, and precipitation.

Hydrological, or the cycle of precipitation, soil absorption and runoff, vegetative use and transpiration, and evaporation.

Chemical nutrients, or the cycle of plant and animal consumption from, and natural and artificial return to, the soil of the chemicals necessary for life processes.

Ecological, or the cycle of interdependencies between various forms of plants, microörganisms, worms, insects, and higher forms of animal life.

Adaptation means not only the planning of agriculture to fit in with the natural or man-modified patterns of each of these four major cycles, but doing so in such a way that each cycle is considered as merely a phase of a common pattern of interdependence. Each must first be taken by itself, and then related to the other. Very great progress has been made in the United States and elsewhere along these lines, but, a few notable exceptions aside, barely the first steps have been taken toward that type of over-all planning which must be evolved before there can be established any lasting "symbiotic relationship with the land" capable of both permanently increasing agricultural yields and putting an effective stop to further loss of soil resources. That this is true can readily be shown.

ADAPTATION TO THE METEOROLOGICAL "CYCLE"

There is relatively little that man can do but adapt himself to weather "cycles." The possibilities of changing the weather are very narrowly limited. Some slight local changes may be effected in both precipitation and evaporation of water, and some still smaller changes may be effected in humidity by altering, in particular, forest growth.[15] But by knowing the pattern of changes that have occurred, and are in the process of taking place, it is possible to do a very great deal by adjusting in time. In meteorology the important thing is better facilities for fact gathering. The nature of the problem is such as to place this aspect of land utilization on a planned basis of widening magnitude.

Four aspects may be distinguished. In the first place, meteorological information has a multiplicity of uses, of which those for agriculture are but one. Aeronautical and marine transportation, for example, are dependent upon comprehensive, immediately available, and reliable weather information and weather-forecast data. Crop planting and harvesting share the need for these data with tourist and recreational travel and all related economic activities. The gathering of adequate weather information itself depends upon the most thoroughgoing coöperation of the wire and radio services of the various telecommunications networks. Weather information, that is to say, because it serves a number of industrial operations which require accurate, up-to-the-minute, comprehensive data projected into the future as far as possible, should be unified as a single service, and be gathered by means which consider telecommunications facilities as made up of a single and everywhere interconnected information-transmitting web.

Secondly, the instruments, methods of recording, range of coverage, nomenclature and modes of transmitting, regularity and circumstances of reporting, modes of analyzing, and ranges of reliable inference in interpretation should be as standard, uniform, and invariable as the current state of meteorological science and measurement techniques permit. Thirdly, records should provide a basis for forecasting as far as possible in the future, and for accurately tracing seasonal and annual cycles in the recent past. The latter is particularly important as a basis for estimating rainfall cycles in arid and semiarid areas devoted to grazing and to field crops. It is also very important in forest culture, flood control, hydroelectric power generation, and other activities heavily dependent upon the volume and distribution of precipitation.

Finally, all these data need to be gathered from, and broken down for the use of, local areas, regions, continents, and the world. Every attempt at greater precision in day-to-day reporting, and every attempt to lengthen the period of reliable forecast, widens the geographic scope of coverage, and every attempt to break this information down in a usable form for rainfall and temperature belts enhances the value of wide coöperative action. Adjusting agriculture to meteorological patterns, in short, means the planning of information gathering on an international basis. As Sir Osborne Mance has put it:

The operation of the Meteorological Service in any country depends on international co-operation primarily because weather forecasts are based on a network of observations covering a very wide area and arrangements have to be made for the interchange of the observations between different countries.[16]

The machinery for accomplishing this objective is formally quite complete. An International Meteorological Organization (O.M.I.), concerned "primarily with the administrative and technical arrangements necessary for the routine work of the official Meteorological Services," [17] has been established, with a series of five regional commissions, "for Africa (I), the Far East (II),

South America (III), North and Central America (IV), and the South Pacific (V), respectively." [18] The scope of this work is indicated by the three main divisions of meteorology affected by radio communications:[19]

(1) *Synoptic* meteorology which comprises the construction of meteorological charts over large areas as the basis for general weather forecasts. [When used for short-run weather forecasting—of special interest to agriculture at harvesting time—speed and comprehensiveness of reporting are of vital importance.] Great progress has been made in recent years; eight editions of these charts were issued daily in Europe, while the number in the U.S.A. was being increased to four. Messages and forecasts are being increasingly supplemented by wireless photographs and diagrams.

(2) *Meteorological Protection of Aerial Navigation;* communication to aircraft in flight of weather information, complete now from starting to landing, and universally available over all main traveled routes.

(3) *Radiosondage:* investigation of meteorological conditions in the upper atmosphere [—vital for all high altitude flying but also highly significant for all long-range (more than 24-hour weather) forecasting, and the basis, when combined with comprehensive synoptic meteorology, for "interpretation of the historic climatic record"[20]].

As these data suggest, the planning of the gathering and dissemination of meteorological data is far advanced. Given this information running over a considerable number of years, a great deal may then be accomplished in agriculture to adapt crop types, crop species, and agricultural methods. For example, frost- and rust-resistant species of grains of various sorts have made it possible to expand production into northerly regions previously closed to such crops. Reforestation and forest belts in semiarid regions may, to some small extent, modify climatic behavior. There are other limited possibilities.

Significant as some of these adaptations may be, in detail, it is still true that relatively little can be done to change the basic meteorological pattern for any given region. This picture is almost completely reversed the instant we turn to that feature of meteorological change of greatest importance to agriculture, adaptation to the hydrological cycle.

ADAPTATION TO THE HYDROLOGICAL CYCLE

The nature of the hydrological cycle—the "natural circulation of earth waters" from headwaters to headwaters—has been summarized by Person as follows:

a. The atmosphere absorbs water from oceans, lakes, rivers, the land, and other exposed surfaces—even from falling raindrops—(*evaporation*), and also that drawn from ground storage and exhaled by the leaves of trees and other vegetation (*transpiration*). Few people know what quantities of water are transported by evaporation and transpiration. Under varying conditions evaporation may lower a reservoir of water 15 inches (Ontario) to 8 feet (California) or even 12 feet (Egypt) in a year. A given area of conifers will transpire the equivalent of from 3 inches (pines) to 8.5 inches (spruce) of precipitation on that area; of hardwoods, from 5 inches (oaks) to 10 inches (beech).

b. Moisture-laden air is cooled as it moves upward, or as it comes in contact with other cooler bodies of air, and moisture is dropped in the form of rain or snow (*precipitation*). Fogs and dews are also forms of precipitation.

c. Generally the precipitated water, when it strikes the surface of the land, is absorbed and held by the surface soil (*absorption*), and when the water content of this layer has reached a certain point, depending on soil conditions, any surplus penetrates by gravity to underground strata of soil, gravel or porous rock (*infiltration*) where it is stored as *ground water*. The surface of this underground reservoir is called the "*water table.*"

d. When the rate of precipitation is greater than the rate of absorption and infiltration, part of the water runs along the surface of the ground directly into creeks and rivers, and thence into the lakes and the oceans. This is called "*surface run-off.*" . . .

e. Water exposed on the surface of the oceans, lakes, rivers, and land, including that transpired by vegetative cover, is again absorbed into the atmosphere and the natural circulation is continued indefinitely.[21]

Within a given region the hydrological cycle thus determines (1) the total amount of water available, (2) the distribution of this amount over the seasons and the years, (3) the availability for use because of the pattern of relationships existing among absorption, infiltration, and runoff, and (4) the means of utilizing this pattern to the maximum human advantage. The first two are given, and, in the short run at least, cannot be materially altered by the action of man except by diverting excessive supply away from wet soils by drainage or by gathering scarce supplies for irrigation on dry soils. With respect to the latter possibilities, it is now axiomatic that the unit of development should in all cases be coextensive with the area affected. Thus drainage of alluvial swamps such as those at the mouth of the Nile and the Volga, of depressed areas such as the Pontine marshes below Rome, or of such submerged lands as those recovered from the seas by the Dutch polders, is best handled by elaboration of a network of minor ditches and major canals which is unified throughout the entire area to be drained. The same holds for irrigation projects, as may be seen by examining the history of dry-land reclamation in the American Far West and the plateau land in Russia skirting the northern foothills of the Central Asian massif. The American experience in the Salt River and Imperial Valley developments is now prototypal for plans which embrace water utilization for major watershed drainage areas such as those of the Colorado River, Central Valley (California) and Columbia River projects.

Just as with the drainage district, so in irrigation, the unit of development has tended to become the river or watershed system as a whole, and this feature of land utilization should, on strictly engineering grounds, be planned on this basis. The areas to be recovered by these means are extensive and represent quite significant future additions to potentially cultivable land resources. According to a report of the Land Planning Committee in 1936, some 91,000,000 acres of land might be added to the land supply of the United States by drainage, and some 26,000,000 acres by irrigation.[22]

Somewhat less obvious and striking, but far more important quantitatively—because of the vastly greater areas affected and the rapidly multiplying demands upon water resources—are the possibilities of adaptation to and control over the general pattern of relationships existing among absorption, infiltration, and runoff. At this point we run into one of the most perplexing problems of water utilization in general: the fact that the interests of agriculture meet other demands upon water resources which make resort to comprehensive regional—if not national or international —planning of water utilization a necessity as imperative as that faced in agriculture by the depletion of soil resources itself.

Digressing for a moment, what are these other uses of water, and how important are they? According to estimates by the United States Geological Survey, the following water uses account for 14 per cent of the nation's yearly runoff to the oceans:[23]

	From ground water	*From streams and lakes*	*Total*
	(in billions of gallons per day)		
Irrigation	15	80	95
Industrial	5	65	70
Municipal	3	9	12
Rural (other than irrigation)	2	1	3
Total	25	155	180

The draft upon ground water is somewhat similarly distributed and is equally heavy. Nonagricultural demands from both resources are growing at a prodigious rate. A survey by the National Association of Manufacturers in 1950 showed a 36 per cent increase in industrial water-intake between 1939 and 1949.[24] Eighty per cent or more of this water is discharged as contaminated effluent into rivers and municipal sewer systems, where it not only represents a waste as far as further reuse is concerned, but where also it fouls up rivers, streams, lakes, and seaside waters into which it is discharged, with the result of multiplying still further the effective draft upon water resources.[25] Somewhat the same is true of the growth of municipal demands on surface and subsurface water. Not only are the cities growing rapidly relative to the population of the country as a whole, but also per capita water usage is rising rapidly. Furthermore, a whole series of changes in industrial technology—e.g., the shift over to light metals (such as aluminum), synthetic rubber, and synthetic fibers—are multiplying their needs manyfold.

Thus it comes about that in many large areas, as in southern California and around New York City, industries and agriculture are competing for ever scarcer water supplies, pointing up the need for comprehensive water planning for all uses within the region. Also, any further emphasis upon conserving water for the regulation of stream flow in order to eliminate floods and provide minimum channel depths for transportation, or to generate hydroelectric power, has a tendency once again to underscore this trend. In the case of southern California, some seven states, twenty-eight cities, the whole complex of power-generating plants and transmission lines serving that region, and a variety of the largest and richest irrigation districts in the world, are brought together in a series of closely coöperating agencies for the management of the waters of the Colorado River from Lake Mead south.[26] In England, so serious have competing demands for the limited water resources become that plans are now under way for the development of a comprehensive national water-utilization plan.[27] Despite the continental scale of the United States, the problem has become almost equally acute here—as the findings of the three-volume report of the President's Water Resources Policy Commission have demonstrated in great detail.

Severely competing demands for limited water resources tend everywhere to unite many different lines of interest in comprehensive water planning. But by the same token, these very same conflicting interests are bound to unite for improving the agricultural use of water, for it is in large part *the manner* in which agriculture takes its toll of the common regional water pool which determines not only how much of the pool it may use, but also how large the pool itself may be. There are two sets of relationships here. The first relates precipitation with surface runoff, soil absorption, and the changing level of the water table. The second relates soil type to slope and contour on the one hand, and to the seasonal concentration or scattering of total precipitation on the other. The two sets of relationships are linked together in such a way that they call for a type of land utilization which plans soil usage simultaneously in terms of (1) soil type, (2) the geophysical distribution of each type of soil over varying slopes and contours, (3) methods of cultivation which minimize surface runoff and maximize water absorption, and (4) the elimination of techniques which bring about long-run falling of the water table.

The first step in this direction is adequate soil mapping. An immense amount of work has been accomplished to this end in the United States in recent years, although the work has been greatly hampered by lack of agreement as to systems of soil classifications, some question about correlations between "observable features of the soil and its chemical character and productive ability," [28] and the lack of funds for publishing maps.[29] Some two-thirds of the arable land has been roughly surveyed, about one-half in fair detail. In recent years it has been possible greatly to extend the work by the rapid development of aerial photography. Not a great deal, however, has been done to relate basic soil types to slope and geological configuration.[30]

Given the appropriate geographic data, and some satisfactory mode or formula for correlating soil types, chemical properties, and configurational patterns, it should then be possible to construct maps of land resources which would at once determine the natural limits of the best land-use within each given hydrological cycle and the patterns of cultivation most appropriate to it. Within the climatic region, in short, the frame of reference for the best crop planning is partly soil type and partly elevation and slope. Drainage of waterlogged lands may also be important. The water objectives of cropping are then to improve drainage, absorption, infiltration, and underground storage. These four are interdependent. Whatever improves drainage helps to determine the precise amount of water required at the surface for various crop uses. Whatever improves absorption prevents surface runoff, and thus prevents soil erosion and the leaching of nutritive matter and essential chemicals. Whatever improves infiltration evens the supply of moisture to plants and increases the storage capacity of the underground reserves. Whatever improves underground reserves adds to the total which may be spared for nonagricultural uses, and equalizes the supply of readily available water over the seasons for agriculture itself.

The essence of best adaptation to the hydrological cycle is that water from precipitation not be lost. Agriculture holds the most important key. This key is vital to its own operations.

Even in the better watered sections the rainfall during the growing season seldom suffices for the production of a full crop, so that generally the productivity of this country is essentially dependent on the water stored in soil and subsoil and underlying rocks within reach of draft by the growing plants. Moreover this store is the chief source of springs and streams whence animals drink; it is the supply for wells whence men take the water required for domestic use; and it is the reservoir which holds storm waters and equalizes the flow of brooks and rivers.[31]

For each soil type in each part of every region, and for each characteristic hydrological belt, there are types of crops and cultivation which combine best use of water and soil resources with longest sustained yield. Within this framework, however, the key to the best cropping patterns is found in some adaptation to the ecological balance of plants, microörganisms, and animals which is natural to the soil type with the given hydrological cycle.

Before turning to this feature of land planning, however, there may be some point in attempting a summing up of the factors involved in making the best adaptation to natural hydrological cycles. When Lilienthal was Director of the Tennessee Valley Authority he spoke of the unity of land and water and men as a "seamless web." [32] This is no mere figure of speech. As pointed out below in chapter x, the TVA is a great pioneering achievement in multiple-purpose river valley development, which considers agricultural needs and uses as one aspect of a program embracing at once watershed control, navigation and power development, flood prevention, the supply of lakes, parks, and recreational areas, water supply for municipal uses, and so on *ad infinitum.* None of these uses need have a definite priority over the other. Though many compromises must be made in detail, each may be regarded as compatible with, and complementary to, the others. But reconciliation among such diverse programs means planning of each conjointly with the others, and the primary geographic scope of the multiple-purpose planning is of necessity coextensive, at least in the first instance, with the river valley system considered as a whole.

If, to employ the figure used by Person, we consider a river system to resemble "a tree with its trunk, large branches, small branches, smallest branches, twigs, and leaves," water control should begin with the leaves, twigs, and smallest branches of a river system,[33] embracing the whole fine veinous network of the various tributary systems and following the main branches and river sources down to the sea. At the headwaters, soil erosion is prevented by contouring slopes, shifting row crops from steep slopes to flatlands, planting eroded surface to permanent grass, shifting pasturage away from natural wood-growing areas, and increasing wooded acreage not readily adaptable to arability. By these means the soil is held in place, the stream below is not silted, the flow of water into the stream is equalized, and the capacity to store water is increased by the building of storage dams and by retention of water in surface soil and in subsurface reserves. The impounding dams provide small lakes which may be used for recreational purposes, water in the lakes may be kept clear so that fish may live in it, and small hydroelectric stations may supply power from the overflow for domestic and farm-machinery uses.

Preservation of a minimum of forest coverage may have an important bearing upon water supply. An interesting account of "changes in a wooded area of Cadiz township, Green County, Wisconsin, during the period of European settlement," reveals that along with a reduction in forest cover, went a decrease in the total length of the streams draining the area. The permanently flowing streams had decreased by 26 per cent in 1902 and by 36 per cent in 1935. This was due largely to the drying up of springs in their original headwaters, reflecting a decrease in subsoil water storage from the reduced infiltration on agricultural fields and pastured wood-lots.[34] Thus the structure of use at the headwaters will also determine the balance and the flow of downstream rivers.

Passing then, from these "leaves, twigs, and smallest branches" on down the main branches and to the trunk of the major river system, the same balances bring like, but also cumulative, benefits. "Every dam is part of a system for the whole river," [35] and the management of each watershed and smaller dam above in conjunction with each larger watershed and dam below cumulatively expands the capacity to handle flow and equally to serve a multiplicity of purposes—power generation, flood control, transportation, etc. throughout the river valley area. Supplementary, then, to the comprehensive plan for every small drainage area of all the tributary streams is the general case for integration of all these plans with a master plan for the major valley areas upon which the "little waters" converge.

Or, to put the matter the other way round, there should be a basic plan governing the use of waters for all joint purposes within each major river system such as the Mississippi, the Columbia, the Niger, the Danube, the Volga, the Yangtze. Within each major watershed are secondary and tertiary watersheds—such as those of the Ohio, the Tennessee, the Missouri, the Platte, and the Red rivers for the Mississippi basin—which should be planned on a unified basis and coördinated with each other. For each of their main tributaries, and for the veinous network of minor streams, creeks, ponds, and lakes, there should be formulated similar plans which relate to each other

. . . the amount and distribution of the precipitation of the area; the measured flow through its streams; the depth of the water table; the topography; the varieties of soils and to what crops each is best adapted; the areas of tilled soils and the proportions devoted to various crops; the distribution of forests, pastures, and other vegetative cover; the extent and nature of grazing by animals; the methods of cultivation; the extent of erosion and its causes.[36]

And throughout all areas, and at each level of significance, this complex of agriculturally significant relations should be balanced against power development, flood control, navigation, recreational, and similar projects which are inherently related to them.

It is against this background, and in this setting, that land culture must seek balances of the appropriate nutritive chemicals and of plant and animal life.

MANIPULATING THE RELATED CYCLES OF SOIL CHEMICALS AND OF PLANT AND ANIMAL LIFE

"The earliest stage of erosion," write Jacks and Whyte,[37]

is a loss of fertility. Whatever the cause of the loss, the result is invariably a corresponding loss in soil *stability;* the soil is deprived not only of its productive power,[38] but also of its capacity for remaining in place. Fertility is a term that should be applied to the soil and vegetation together, for the soil derives its capacity for producing life from the vegetation, as much as plants derive their capacity for growth from the soil . . . a deterioration in the physical properties and fertility of soil is the invariable precursor of actual erosion . . . an exhausted soil is an unstable soil; Nature has no further use for it and removes it bodily.

Given the soil type[39] and the hydrological cycle, a program for sustaining the physical properties of the soil is dependent jointly upon (1) taking certain mechanical measures, usually of but limited application, (2) maintaining or improving the balance of chemicals necessary for the maintenance of life, and (3) finding the right balance of plant and animal life which it may support. As for the first, leaving aside for the moment methods of cultivation, there is a considerable range of mechanical devices, such as banks or terraces suitably located on eroding slopes, dams across gullies, windbreaks, etc., which may be of great value in isolated cases. Once begun and allowed to continue, the process of erosion is cumulative in a geometric pattern:

The capacity of running water to hold soil in suspension depends upon the velocity of flow and the size of the suspended particles; doubling the velocity increases the carrying capacity no less than 64 times, and the size of the particle transportable 128 times.[40]

Closely related is the shift of row crops and other types of cultivation which leave the soil openly exposed to wind and rain action. On comparable slopes, according to one estimate, while land left in grass will show negligible erosion, wheat cultivation will result in a loss of ten tons per acre per annum; corn, 40 tons; and fallow land, 60 tons.[41] Table 4 illustrates the point more effectively than words can describe. High and concentrated precipitation, new crops, and rising slope of land serve only to multiply the speeds and scale of soil loss.

Far more important than these mechanical means, however, because more basic, is the problem of relating chemical balances with the ecological cycle. Chemically, the problem of maintaining the quality and fertility of the soil centers in various means for maintaining or improving the balance between "inexhaustible" and "exhaustible" soil properties. The combination of these two classes of chemicals varies indefinitely among types of plant and forest life. Yet in all cases, "inexhaustible" has a very special meaning. It means that carbon, oxygen, hydrogen, and nitrogen

TABLE 4

AVERAGE ANNUAL SOIL AND WATER LOSSES, 1931-1933
INCLUSIVE, EXPERIMENT STATION, BETHANY, MISSOURI
(Shelby silt-loam, 8 per cent slope, 33.54 inches
mean precipitation)

Item	Soil (tons per acre)	Water (per cent precipitation)
Continuous:		
Corn, plot 1....................	74.09	24.59
Corn, plot 2....................	60.80	27.41
Rotation:		
Wheat, clover, corn.............	10.36	10.68
Clover, corn, wheat.............	7.19	11.57
Clover (fertilized), corn, wheat...	3.74	8.64
Average of plots 3, 4, 5, and 6......	9.91	11.06
Continuous:		
Alfalfa........................	.21	3.41
Grass.........................	.32	7.74
Fallow:		
Spaded soil....................	112.06	26.02
Spaded subsoil.................	73.47	24.65

SOURCE: H. S. Person, *Little Waters; A Study of Headwater Streams and Other Little
Waters, Their Use and Relations to the Land* (Washington, 1935), p. 35, adapted from
H. H. Bennett, "Dynamic Action of Rains in Relation to Erosion in the Humid Region,"
in *Transactions,* American Geophysical Union, Fifteenth Annual Meeting, 1934, p. 4.
See also United States Department of Agriculture, *Soils and Men, Yearbook of Agriculture,
1938* (Washington, 1938), p. 594, table 3, showing "Annual soil and water losses per
acre from five widely separated types of land under conditions of clean tillage and dense
cover of vegetation."

are relatively very plentiful in nature, not that they are plentiful
in all locations or under any circumstances. Should, for example,
soil and wind erosion continue very far, nitrogen is leached from
the soil—taking with it the capacity of plant life and micro-
organisms fully to replenish the supply—plant life in turn cuts
down carbon resources, and the resultant increase in loss of surface and underground waters depletes usable supplies of oxygen
and hydrogen in their most vitally necessary combination. Soil
cultivation may thus result in slowly encroaching desert or other
wasteland, and for such areas "inexhaustible" resources are
steadily exhausted.

The "exhaustible" category also has a special meaning. It means "exhaustible" unless returned in whole or in part in the ordinary routine of farming. There are methods of cultivation which may return very large percentages of essential chemicals back to the soil. Principal among these are animal manures and crop wastes such as corncobs, stubble, and straw. Two developments in this connection are distinctly unfavorable to agriculture. One is the substitution of farm machinery for draft animals. While 30 per cent of the increase in food supplies for feeding an increasing population from 1920 to 1942 came from acreages released by the decline in horses and mules, and a further anticipated decline of horses from around 11 million head in 1946 to about 4 million head in 1975 would release some 27 million additional acres, yet unless other farm animals—such as hogs, cattle, and poultry—take their place, the soil-enriching manure of the draft animals is a net loss which must be compensated for by artificial fertilizer or the substitution of new and radically different crop patterns.[42]

The other trend is in the industrial use of agricultural by-products—the central object, for example, of the National Farm Chemurgic Council.[43] While it is probably true that roughly "as much organic matter remains in the field from production of an average crop as is removed in the harvested portion," [44] still, failure to return the waste by-products entirely removes enormous quantities of essential plant nutrients from the soil—possibly as much as half of the total utilized in the plant growth removed as productive crop. Much more important is the loss of these chemicals through the failure of Western methods to return "night soil" to the land. It is difficult to evaluate the over-all importance of this loss, but Victor Hugo was doubtless not exaggerating by far when he wrote in such colorful terms of "the land impoverished by the sea." [45]

It is possible that the chemical treatment of human sewage—and for sanitary reasons it must be chemically treated—may in the future make it possible to divert this colossal waste back to the land. This source is the chemical basis for most agriculture in the Orient, on the Mediterranean littoral, and for much of South American agriculture. It is true, of course, that when returned to the soil without chemical treatment, night soil may prove a net liability. "China," writes Buck, "can ill afford to use night soil unless it can be made sanitary. From an economic viewpoint, it would probably be cheaper to throw away night soil than to incur the losses concurrent with ill-health which result from its use." [46] But the methods for treatment to eliminate this hazard are already well worked out. The "aerobic oxidation process of fermentation" developed by Beccari has been in operation since 1927 in Cannes, France, turning "the garbage of a city of 60,000 population . . . into compost or humus." [47] Sewage-disposal plants employing somewhat similar methods are now widely established in the United States and elsewhere. Despite, however, some commercial use of the sewage sludges, it is still true that the most of this resource for agricultural chemicals is wholly wasted.

Among these chemicals, certain ones are highly strategic for all types of crops. Particularly important are nitrogen, phosphates, and potash. The first is contained in the organic material in the soil, and can be built up or maintained either by adding nitrogenous fertilizers to the land or by use of legumes and cropping methods which return nitrogen as a by-product of cultivation. Certain rare chemicals seem to be very essential in small quantities.

Many diseases of plants have been traced to the deficiency of certain soil elements. A lack of magnesium may cause sand-brown of tobacco or chlorosis of tomatoes. The addition of zinc to the soil and its use in orchard sprays remedies pecan rosette, peach little leaf, and similar diseases. More recently it has been shown that internal cork of apples, cracked stem of celery, and several other diseases can be controlled or prevented by small additions of boron to the soil.[48]

Major and minor chemicals must not only be present in the soil; they need to be in the right combinations. For all types of plants there is a proper "nutrient-element balance," and frequently this balance, once destroyed, proves extremely difficult to restore by the use of artificial fertilizers. Yet if the original balance is upset, artificial fertilizers offer the only quick remedy. For the long pull, however, far more can be accomplished by measures taken to prevent continued erosion and leaching from the soil.

On this point the experimental data are quite conclusive. In the estimated three billion tons of American soil lost during the

1930's—in 1948 Brune estimated that the rate of sediment production in the Ohio and the Great Lakes drainage basin was roughly fifty times the geologic norm, and in the upper Mississippi River, where 42 per cent of the land was idle, the rate was 75 times the geologic norm[49]—there were lost annually to agriculture through erosion,

. . . 90 million tons of phosphorus, potassium, nitrogen, calcium, and magnesium. Of this, 43 million tons represents phosphorus, potassium and nitrogen, the principal ingredients of commercial fertilizer. This is more than 60 times the amount of these elements of plant food used in the United States as commercial fertilizers during the fiscal year ended June 30, 1934. No other process or combination of processes is so destructive of valuable soil and its nutritive constituents as erosion. By comparison, the removal of plant-food constituents by cropping and grazing is relatively small.[50]

The loss of certain of these chemicals is particularly serious. For the purpose of maintaining an adequate chemical basis for soil fertility, "in the matter of phosphorus, the prospects are not so bright. Phosphorus is an essential constituent of all living creatures. It is, however, a rather rare element in nature, constituting only about one seven-hundredth part of the earth's crust . . ."[51] And, while known deposits of minable phosphates are quite large, it is true that, once exploited, this high-quality key and limiting resource is wholly gone. Even when exploited to the full, mineral deposits can, however, supply only a small fraction of what might be maintained almost in perpetuity by improved erosion and soil-leaching control methods.

This is the equivalent of saying that the addition of artificial fertilizers, though of great importance from the point of view of increasing soil fertility,[52] possesses its major significance where it is combined with methods of agriculture which prevent soil erosion—even when there exist severe shortages of necessary chemicals—in such a way as greatly to reduce the total amounts that must be applied. An outstanding example is the addition of phosphates to "acid" soils which makes possible the growth of legumes which will, in turn, replenish depleted reserves of nitrogen. (This is the basis upon which the Tennessee Valley Authority shifted its emphasis in production from nitrogen fertilizers to superphosphates.)

Continued neglect will mean mounting costs in the future:

The organic color is fading from much of our best grade farm lands. Rains and melting snow float away more and more of the top soil. . . . Our commercial agriculture, except what remains in animal husbandry such as dairying, is kept expanding by increasing overdraft on the fertility of our soils. Its limits are set by the economically available sources of purchased nitrogen, phosphorus, potassium, and sulfur.[53]

Erosion, soil fertility, and fertilizer replenishment are, thus, bound together in such a way as to make the planning of agricultural cropping the most important key at once to the maintenance of chemical resources and to land productivity. All experts seem agreed on this proposition. And this means that some way must be found of adjusting the needs of the population for agricultural products to the ecological cycle of each crop area, large or small. "In a general sense, the climate, vegetation, soil, and animal life of a natural area are closely inter-related." In this interrelationship,

. . . soil itself is not an inert medium . . . it represents a segment of the habitat more complicated than the air above it. Bacteria, minute plants and tiny animals . . . live in the soil. As many as 60,000,000 bacteria are contained in a single particle of surface loam, and the mycelial threads of many mushrooms and molds, the roots of grasses, herbs, shrubs, and trees pervade the earth's veneer. Investigations have shown that the earth of England harbors 50,000 earthworms to the acre, an acre of Maryland meadow supports 13,500,000 invertebrates at no greater depth than "a bird can easily scratch," and the soils of the Russian steppe maintain 415,000 ant nests per square kilometer.[54]

Most of this life is in some way "necessary," since each sort consists of a link in a chain of life interdependencies, which, if broken, can in many cases destroy, or at least badly damage, all the other links. The pattern of interdependence may change or be changed, but the fact of interdependence always remains. In all cases the rule holds that if a link is altered, a substitute must quickly be found which is either consistent with the maintenance of the balance of the chain, or which is made with appropriate changes in the other links in mind. From this general principle of ecological interdependence or balance there is rarely any easy or inexpensive escape. Attention to it is fundamental to both soil conservation and high crop productivity, and to it all agricultural methods need to be adjusted on pain of eventual weakening of both.

Such a chain of life interdependencies exists for all soils, in all climates, and for all types of hydrological cycles. It is possible, accordingly, to define more or less precisely the conditions under which good soil-cultivation can be placed on a long-term and sustained-yield basis. Avoiding further detail as far as possible, the conditions for combining conservation with scientific cropping methods may be outlined roughly in the following manner. Ideally:

1. *The farm cultivation scheme* should be coextensive with the native, or an altered but still generally balanced, pattern of ecological relationships, and with the bearings of these upon the maintenance or improvement of the chemicals balance appropriate to the given pattern. The *unit of planning* is not the crop, but the cycle of crops, not the given chemical but the entire chemical balance, not correction of a given deficiency or practice but the maintenance of the life processes of the soil itself.

2. The *ecological and chemicals program* of necessity varies with basic differences in the specific structure and qualities of the soil. *The unit of planning crop patterns,* accordingly, is the soil type.

3. *Planning cultivation to fit the soil type* should assume regional specialization of crops by soil types within each characteristic hydrological cycle. *The unit of reference in planning utilization of different soil types,* that is to say, is the areal configuration of land subject to each specific hydrological cycle.

4. *Scientific adjustment to the hydrological cycle* means finding that balanced use of water resources which is most natural to a given topographical configuration. *The unit of planning* water usage is then, first the watersheds of the tributaries (the "little waters"), and second, the watersheds of the tributaries with that of the major river systems.

5. *Planning agricultural usage of waters within minor tributaries and major river systems* should be conjoint with alternative

and complementary uses of water resources, such as municipal and industrial requirements, power generation, transportation, recreational fishing, and other uses. *The unit of planning* in the watershed, large or small, accordingly is inherently and necessarily multiple-purpose and multiple-function.

6. *Planning of watershed and multiple-purpose developments, finally,* must be adjusted jointly to (*a*) the limitations and potentialities of the underlying local climate and the hydrological cycle, and (*b*) intra- and interregional patterns of demand for agricultural products. The *unit of planning* for either or both is at least national in scope; in many respects, and with respect to many particulars, the basis is definitely international.

FITTING TOGETHER THE STRUCTURE OF DEMAND

AND A RATIONAL SYSTEM OF LAND USE

"Complete compatibility," write Bennett and Lowdermilk, "between the pattern of human use and the pattern of natural environment is, of course, impossible. Man must have cotton, corn, wheat, and other products from the soil, and he must till the soil to obtain them." [55] Given the proposition that man "must attempt . . . to adapt his culture to natural limitations upon land use" along the general lines sketched out in the preceding pages, the problem remains of how to distribute the land of varying types and qualities, with their different natural environments, among the alternative uses which the demands of society make upon it. This is not a matter, contrary to a widespread impression, that can any longer be left to chance. If there is a "socially best use" for "each acre of land," as L. C. Gray has stated, "it must be discovered through the process of land planning." [56]

Three levels of interest—and, consequently, of bases of land planning—may be distinguished: local or regional, national, and international. Each involves a triple set of policies which should be visualized on a comprehensive basis and with a view to its dependence upon parallel development of the others:

1. *The conservation interest.*—The power should exist, and the machinery should be devised, to implement the policy of preventing the planting of crops or resorting to methods of cultivation and land utilization which do not represent good adaptation

to soil types; do not prevent soil erosion and unnecessary leaching of valuable soil chemicals; are not in general harmony with maintenance of an adequate ecological balance; are not well adapted to hydrological and meteorological cycles; and are not consistent with multiple-purpose use of water resources.

This means, for example, removing land from open-field and row-crop cultivation when wind and water erosion hazards are high, preventing overgrazing on hilly and natural forest lands, preventing deforestation, and carrying through afforestation on lands clearly more suitable for this type of growth than for arable purposes. The Soil Conservation and Soil Erosion services of the United States made tremendous strides in this direction during the decade of the 1930's with respect to marginal and submarginal lands. They have been scarcely able to scratch the surface with respect to the far more important intramarginal lands which constitute the backbone of American agriculture.

2. *The priority interest among alternative uses.*—Facilities need to be provided for planning the best possible crop balance within each region consistent (*a*) with the structure of demand for agricultural products within region, (*b*) requirements for land uses of a nonagricultural character—parks, playgrounds, recreational areas—and (*c*) comparative suitability of land for supplying local needs as against the growing of specialized crops for export or the import of specialized crops grown in other peculiarly suitable regions.

This means definite programs for coördinating crop balances within each region and for specializing land utilization among interdependent regions. Very little is being done along these lines in the United States at the present time, with the result that, e.g., many districts which might supply the bulk of their own fruits and vegetables from local sources under favorable over-all cost and quality conditions rely largely on outside sources of supply.

3. *The interest in good farm-management.*—Facilities need to be provided for promoting those methods of cultivation and crop handling which are simultaneously consistent (*a*) with the foregoing, and (*b*) with high levels of net manpower productivity.

This means attempting to develop optimum-sized farming units for each type of crop and each mode of cultivation.

The first of these three lines of policy is obvious, and need not be further elaborated. The last is of a technical character, and will be taken up briefly in the following section. Something must be said here about the second, the planning of regional and inter-regional crop and land-utilization balances.

It would seem entirely obvious that, if "man must have cotton, corn, wheat, and other products from the soil, and . . . must till the soil to obtain them," land planning should provide for consistent readaptations of land utilization to the changing structure of demand for land products and land uses. Yet here again scarcely the first steps have been taken in the United States. The changes in the structure of demand now taking place, however, profoundly affect the uses to which the land will be put.

A few examples will suffice. A falling rate of population growth, particularly when coupled with rising material standards of food consumption and further changes in age distribution of the total population, may not of necessity mean net decrease in the rate of expansion of agricultural production, extensive or intensive. Dietary changes, mostly associated with rising standards of living, have brought about significant shifts from cereal consumption to milk, sugar, fruits, and vegetables. By one estimate, cereal consumption declined from "380 pounds per capita at the beginning of the century to 250 pounds in recent years," while the substitution of tractors, trucks, and automobiles for horses and mules between 1919 and 1929 "cut off the market for feed grains produced on 23,000,000 acres." [57] A like effect is obtained by better feeding of cattle, hogs, and other farm animals, requiring less food to produce desired increases in weight.

Any shift to higher dietary standards would affect both total acreage and the distribution of acreage by crops:[58]

It appears that the total acreage required to raise supplies of agricultural products sufficiently to enable the Nation to secure the moderate-cost good diet would be slightly higher than the total acreage required to maintain recent actual levels of per capita consumption. This diet provides for substantial increases in the consumption of a number of foods, including milk, certain fruits, and certain vegetables, which would necessitate an expansion in the acreage devoted to the production of feed crops and hay, to take care of the increases in milk, and in the acreages of fruits and vegetables. With the various adjustments

involved, the total acreage required for domestic food consumption
would be approximately 285 to 295 million acres, slightly higher than
the 280 to 285 million acres required for the maintenance of recent
levels of actual per capita consumption. This acreage is, of course,
greatly in excess of the requirements of the two lower standards—the
economical fair diet and the low-cost good diet.

If the Nation were actually able and willing to expand its consumption of food to conform with the "expensive good diet" it would probably be necessary to utilize about 30 to 40 million acres more than are
needed to cover requirements based on actual recent consumption.
This would not only result in a tremendous improvement in national
health, but would take us a long way toward a solution of the agricultural problem as a whole. . . .

As indicated . . . consumption of milk might be increased 10 to
20 per cent; that of butter, 10 to 25; of tomatoes and citrus fruit, 25 to
70; and of leafy, green, and yellow vegetables, 100 per cent. It is difficult to estimate the precise effects of such consumption on acreage.
Probably impending increases in the acreage of bearing trees will come
close to providing the needed increase in citrus fruits. Close to a
million additional acres might be needed for vegetables, including
tomatoes. The greatest effect on agriculture would come from the
desired increases in the consumption of milk and butter; probably 7
to 8 million acres more would be required to support the increased
numbers of dairy cattle.

These estimates, as experience during the Second World War
demonstrated in the case of milk products, meat, and fruits, are
probably too conservative. Yet they indicate roughly the nature
of the far-reaching changes in total acreage, and its distribution
among alternative uses, which a program designed to put a floor
under national food-consumption would bring about.[59] Any national wage and social security program having such an objective
in mind would doubtless be accompanied by other planks that
would vitally affect land use. Thus the incorporation of two weeks'
vacation with pay into the standard wage contract would probably quadruple the demand for park, forest, river and lake, and
other recreational facilities within two days' driving distance.
Raising this period to a month would mean further expansion of
local land use for these purposes, and would probably heighten
by another 100 per cent the demand for facilities within four to
six days' drive. Thus the amount of land to be set aside for such
purposes would mean vast changes in the use of nonagricultural

lands. Similar effects would flow from increasing growth of industrial raw materials and from more extensive use of agricultural by-products and wastes.

Of special importance is the development of chemical methods whereby products grown primarily as foodstuffs may be used as raw materials for industrial and nonfood uses. So important are these methods for increasing percentages of land products that the line between "foodstuffs" and "agricultural raw materials" is rapidly disappearing, permitting flexible and quick adaptation, with varying crop yields and changing demands, from one source to the other and in either direction. In the long run, as fossil fuels become scarce, reliance upon agricultural raw materials for industrial purposes is bound to grow in importance.

It is not too difficult to estimate the combined effect of conservation and the changing structure of demand for agricultural products and other land-utilization requirements on a national basis. The really tough problem arises in connection with the attempt to spell out such a broad national program on a local and regional basis. Here it is immediately apparent that some means need to be found, first, for effecting a satisfactory crop balance in both contiguous and distantly removed regions, part or all of which may have some peculiar natural advantage in the supply of specialized crops; and, second, for the balancing of farm land-use with the multitudinous, widely varying, and directly competing demands for nonagricultural land-use. Both balances must be maintained simultaneously, and in such a manner as to remain flexible and readily adjustable throughout.

Taken separately, a partial—and for certain areas a decisive—answer is found in the application of soil-conservation criteria. The percentage of hilly land from which row crops should be removed, for example, and the areas which should be reforested or allowed to return to grassland will vary greatly from one locality and region to the other. Much of this land may be used for nonagricultural purposes such as parks, factory sites, town locations, suburban developments, and the arranging of "greenbelts" and green wedges between residential and industrial areas in connection with the planning of both smaller towns and major metropolitan areas.[60] To this extent, application of conservation criteria to land utilization, intended primarily to assist maintenance of the final balance, might help in many regions to simplify maintenance of the second balance.

Aside from conservation, however, and assuming that each region will have available to it knowledge of the most advantageous modes of cultivation, handling, and processing of these crops most suitably adapted to its peculiar climate and other natural advantages, it is difficult to see how even interregional balances may be maintained without laying additional emphasis upon land planning on a national basis. The reasons for this are numerous, and they add up to a case which is virtually unanswerable by the proponents of old-line agricultural *laissez-faire*. A few examples will illustrate this.

For example, national and international planning of agricultural planting is strongly promoted by the problem of fluctuations in yields. Fluctuations in crop yields, due to climatological factors, pests, diseases, and similar causes, are difficult to anticipate and they bear unevenly upon the economic fortunes of various regions. The more heavily specialized the region, the more serious the incidence. Should heavy specialization happen to coincide—as is frequently the case—with widely varying weather hazards, the effects are doubly serious. The answer to this predicament is not "diversification" to lessen the hazard locally (unless such diversification is consistent with best crop patterns) but "evening" the risks by mechanisms for interchange between surplus and deficit areas taken on a more comprehensive, interregional basis.

Another example of need for more comprehensive crop planning is the growing importance of agriculture as a basic source of industrial raw materials. Further, some by-products, such as alcohol, plastics, and artificial fibers from wood and other wastes may constitute important measures of national conservation and may be able to compete with the identical product produced from better sources of raw materials elsewhere as long as the waste is paid for at a rate anywhere above mere cost of handling. For example:

Alcohol-gasoline blends . . . are good fuels; they differ only slightly in certain respects from gasolines in general use today, on the whole giving fully equivalent performance. . . . The best available information indicates that the production of alcohol from farm products would have to be subsidized [because the cost exceeds that of gasoline]. There is no such thing as "the cost" of making alcohol since it may vary with the size of the plant, cost of raw materials, process used, and the utilization of by-products. [But] petroleum reserves are being used up and cannot last indefinitely, and it may be argued that the time has come to use more of the annual income (farm products) and less of the stored capital (petroleum and coal).[61]

The admixture favored is 10 to 20 per cent of alcohol in the blend with the gasoline.

There are many examples of factors which make local agricultural production—even when it may be highly diversified and where the net advantages of producing for local supply are high—still a matter of national concern. To an increasing extent, that is to say, advancing technology plus cheap transportation favors relating regional agricultural production to marketing on a super-regional basis. Even when production may be specialized for, and primarily designed to cater to, local and regional needs, developments of the type indicated mean that local land utilization can rarely, if ever, be organized on the basis of complete local self-sufficiency.

A third example of the need for regarding local crop patterns as a component of larger regional, national, or even international crop patterns is found in national concern over population relocation and decentralization, which carries with it the need for balancing the occupations within each region. Thus all processing methods—whether canning and preserving, quick-freezing, use of agricultural waste materials, or primary uses of basic crops—tend to promote ruralization of industries close to the raw-materials site, to shift and redistribute the population, to alter the patterns for the dovetailing of seasonal agricultural work and industrial occupations, and to change the nature and content of the problems of local and regional town-planning in a way which carries far-reaching implications for interregional balances. Trends and plans looking toward decentralization, scattering, and ruralization of industries, occupations, and populations can rarely be confined to any definite region, and they are, of course, everywhere dependent upon interregional power grids, and markets for specialized raw, semiprocessed, and finished products. They constitute, in brief, problems which favor a national land program as clearly as do those centered in the issues of soil conservation and adaptation to natural cycles of weather, precipitation, and ecology.

It is consequently no accident that growing concern over agricultural prosperity is everywhere reflected in plans for unifying soil conservation and land utilization on a national basis. While there are very important differences in social objectives and attitudes toward planning in different countries, the trend of expert opinion in general has been unmistakably the same as far as the technical aspects of the problem are concerned. This can readily be shown by tracing developments in official policy both at home and abroad.

In the United States, for example, there has occurred a rapid rounding-out of state and federal agencies for the supply of expert counsel for practically all phases of land utilization, and this is available to almost any community, however small:

Most States have agricultural, engineering, conservation, planning, and similar technical bureaus. Immediately at hand for consultation is the county agent—probably the first one whose advice should be sought. The Federal Government has many agencies established to render just such assistance. Information and advice may be obtained from such agencies as the Geological Survey, the Bureau of Reclamation, and the National Park Service, of the Department of the Interior; the Office of Experiment Stations (and the nearest experiment station), the Bureau of Agricultural Economics, the Bureau of Agricultural Engineering, the Bureau of Biological Survey, the Bureau of Chemistry and Soils, the Forest Service, the Bureau of Plant Industry, the Bureau of Public Roads, and the Soil Conservation Service, of the Department of Agriculture; the Bureau of Fisheries of the Department of Commerce; . . . and the Federal Power Commission. Although located in Washington, many of these agencies have regional or State representatives . . .[62]

Impressive as such a listing may appear at first blush, official American activities in behalf of land planning show four basic weaknesses. In the first place, there exists little by way of an over-all plan, however tentative, which may serve as a point of departure or blueprint from which to coördinate the activities of the various agencies. Secondly, no consistent or successful effort has been made to unify and integrate the work of the agencies themselves. Thirdly, relatively little has been done to define the meaning of the several lines of expert counsel in the actual operation of an economically "optimum"-sized farm, or for "optimal" combinations of farm functions. And finally, the bulk of this counsel ends with advice giving only. There exists no real power decisively to manipulate and guide land utilization in any comprehensive way even where, as in soil conservation, the public interest is of overriding importance, as long as the land is privately owned—as the bulk of American agricultural land is. In the United States this power is weak even with respect to public lands—as witness the continued overgrazing of the national forests and various publicly owned watershed areas.

We have, in other words, the bits and pieces of a national land utilization program, but no program, and no plan for achieving one. There exists a common problem, but no common purpose. We appear not even to have understood the obvious truism that, as Lilienthal has so well pointed out, "skills are not self-coordinating," nor do we appear to have grasped "how rarely these different groups of specialists seem to care about anything beyond their own specialties." [63] *Caveavemus expertum,* an expert in management has written,[64] is the first rule in making use of experts. And surely a plan as a basis for seeking "collaboration amongst men of highly special responsibilities" and skills is the second. But even a plan is useless unless there is some way of implementing a program which is at once consistent with the goals of good science and engineering on the one hand, and with democratic participation and popular institutions on the other.[65]

No consistent effort has been made to achieve either goal, beyond such partial efforts as those of the TVA and the outlining of plans on a more comprehensive basis as, for example, in *The Future of the Great Plains* by the now defunct National Resources Planning Board. Confusion in the top governmental circles is paralleled by the "eleven attributes of mind characteristic of the prairie settler" that stand in the way of even an adequate understanding of the problem at the farming level. These attitudes of

mind, as summarized by Jacks and Whyte from *The Future of the
Great Plains*, indicative of

. . . limitless optimism and the deceptive sense of power that comes
from wealth too easily won, are: that Man conquers Nature; that
natural resources are inexhaustible; that habitual practices are best;
that what is good for the individual is good for everybody; that an
owner may do with his property as he likes; that expanding markets
will continue indefinitely; that free competition co-ordinates industry
and agriculture; that land values will increase indefinitely; that tenancy
is a stepping-stone to ownership; that a factory farm is generally desirable; and that the individual must make his own adjustments to
calamity.[66]

Somewhat paradoxically, major efforts at comprehensive land
planning have occurred abroad in two countries which represent
the extremes in population pressure, extremes in the scale of land
resources with which to meet domestic needs, and extremes in
social institutions and background, viz., England and Russia.

In England, as an alternative to the long-advocated nationalization of land the Labour party carried through a series of postwar
measures for introducing comprehensive control over all rural
and urban land values, methods of land and agricultural utilization, and marketing of farm crops. The two most important acts
were the Town and Country Planning Act, and a general enabling
law "to make further provision for agriculture," both passed in
1947. Neither involved, interestingly enough, an unduly sharp
break with the past. The first was largely based upon a series of
earlier peacetime and war-emergency investigations, of which
the more important led to the coalition-minded Barlow and
Uthwatt reports. The second was largely an effort to codify, unify,
and revamp a miscellany of laws, regulations, and *ad hoc* measures which had cropped up from time to time over the last half
century. Britain is now in a position, while still standing as a leading world proponent of *laissez-faire* economics and policies, to
carry through a comprehensive land-planning program coextensive with regional and conurbation population relocation, with all
land and water resources used for agricultural and nonagricultural
purposes alike, with methods of land management, and with

methods and machinery for processing and distributing agricultural produce.[67]

At the opposite end with respect to size, economic development, and social philosophy, the Russian scheme, to cite a single example of water-resource development,

. . . consists in bringing the principal rivers and water resources of the Soviet Union into one interlocking system under complete human control. By means of locks, barrages and canals it is proposed to link together the north-flowing and south-flowing river systems as well as the separate rivers in each system. Similarly the east-flowing and west-flowing systems of the Ural Watershed are to be united. If water which is required to fertilize and populate the steppes, to be converted into power, to be utilized for navigation or to check the advancing desert is being wasted in the wilderness of the northern swamps, a turn of a key or the opening of a sluice will bring it to its proper place. . . . The technical and administrative problems presented by such a scheme are immense. They were considered by a plenary meeting of the Academy of Sciences in 1933. . . . The main scheme was to be completed in the fourth five-year plan. . . . The scientists assembled at Moscow took into account not only the water requirements of farms and farmers, of power stations, of industries and of navigation but also the effects of their controlled water régime on the level of the Caspian Sea, on the lives of fishes and on the distribution of insects. . . .[68]

Largely because of the authoritarian manner which characterized the inauguration and continuance of the Russian scheme, Jacks and Whyte and other foreign experts have expressed serious doubts regarding the Russian plans. The doubts, however, are not on the scientific, engineering, and agronomic side. With respect to the technical facts and plans, the picture looks, in the main, quite sound and thoroughly in line with the best practice in the United States and elsewhere. Conversely, in the case of England, although the scientific and technical side of the national land-planning program is still in a preliminary stage of development, there has been little evidence to show that the operation of such planning, as it has thus far been carried through or is in prospect, deprives farmers or other agricultural interests of the opportunity to pursue their own welfare. Clearly, they may not waste resources or oppress the public, but what has happened is simply

that the resources of science and political power have been placed
at the disposal of farmers to the joint advantage of farmer and
public alike. Private interest, efficiency, and ingenuity are supposed to take over from there.

When one turns from general environmental conditions and limitations affecting land utilization to the actual farming operation
itself, he meets up with a variety of defenses centering about the
time-honored right of the farmer to farm as he pleases. Actually,
this argument shields from scrutiny the existence of a large and
growing number of uneconomic dwarf holdings which have little
to do with either "farming as a way of life," or with the strong
popular predisposition to defend the "family-sized farm." The
case for both commonly appears as a defense of waning rugged-
individualistic virtues and the traditional American family. Yet,
it is interesting to note that such an argument is rarely made
any longer for any other productive unit of society—such as
handicraft or small-factory production or the "papa and mama"
stores. Is it really a valid defense here?

The sentimental and cultural sides of the issue must be bypassed here; they are too far removed from the central context of
this study. But something must be said about the mistake of
taking them too seriously. In the case of the TVA, for example,
political propaganda concerning the "family-sized farm" deprived
the agricultural experiments of much of their economic significance. Yet clearly, over most of the area covered by its experiments, the TVA was dealing with subsistence and European-type
peasant farming—which on the social side meant poverty, sloven-
liness, isolation, loneliness, lack of intellectual opportunities and
access to the social and cultural amenities, and, furthermore,
meant this primarily in the "piedmont" or "Tobacco Road" type of
country, where land was poor, soil was being rapidly eroded,
crop yields were small, and the future seemed hopeless—whereas
in the richer valleys, just as in other developed agricultural sections of the country, farming was undergoing its own swift technical revolution. To scientific agriculture, the "family-sized farm"

may represent what the regime of the handicrafts was to the Industrial Revolution.

Without seeking to deal with the very real problems lying behind the sentimental clichés, it may be remarked in passing that the "family-sized farm" does not, popular legend to the contrary, represent the traditional American way. Early farming in this country was large scale, and much of it was at the outset consciously organized and operated on the basis of the best scientific information available. Outstanding among the popular heroes of this country, Washington and Jefferson would have been entirely at home with the huge scientific farming operations which have come so rapidly to the fore in recent years. It was Lincoln, the great champion of the homesteader, who was responsible for the establishment of the Department of Agriculture in 1862 for the purpose of making available to all farmers, large and small, the full range of scientific and technical information which had previously been the privilege of large landowners like Washington and Jefferson.[69] Even on the frontier, coöperative efforts in clearing land and raising buildings, agricultural experimentation, putting in and harvesting crops, and pooling expensive equipment such as combines and threshing machines were very strong in American agriculture.

The central problem for scientific agriculture concerns the optimum combinations of manpower, machinery, acreage, and types of crops. As for machinery, in general it appears that the size of the area to be cultivated should be as large as (a) the most economical type of equipment for each planting, cultivating, and harvesting operation can handle on the optimum capacity-factor basis, or (b) the nature of the complementary uses of the equipment may allow—as with the "all-purpose tractor," in either case using the best combination of equipment, of the various types necessary for the different farm operations to be served, which may be centrally operated, repaired, and most efficiently managed by especially skilled staffs. These are the conditions for keeping the capital cost of farm equipment to the minimum per dollar-value of crop, and they spell typically a very large unit. Thus, introduction of the power tractor in the high plains cotton area of Texas has increased the average amount of land a farmer

can cultivate from 100 to 450 acres.[70] Introduction of the cotton
picker, capable of reducing the average cost of picking a bale
from $32.14 by hand to $5.83 by machine (in a Mississippi experiment), is conditional upon large fields, straight rows, a minimum
of turnings, etc. A method has been developed for sowing rice by
airplane—applicable to other crops—which will sow 20,000 acres
per hour.[71] Over the six-year interval of 1924-1929, mechanization
of wheat farming meant a doubling of the wheat acreage a man
could handle.[72] Examples might be multiplied for specialized
crops of all types.

It is difficult to add up the factors bearing upon the efficient
utilization of agricultural machinery in satisfactory manner. But,
keeping in mind investment cost, utilization or capacity factors,
repair, and maintenance, it seems reasonably certain that the bulk
of the heavy-duty and more highly specialized machinery could
serve several farms and might advantageously be grouped in
regionally spaced machinery parks.

One investigation showed that the range of annual use of two-
row tractors for row crops was from 20 to 250 hours (out of an
annual daylight total of some 5,000), and that the average use of
each piece of equipment was only 76 hours, or 30 per cent of the
upper figure of the "usual range" for various types of equipment.
The actual range was from 14 per cent for manure spreaders
and 16 per cent for tractor mowers and grain drills, to 34 per
cent for milking machines and a high of 43 per cent for peanut
pickers.[73] It would seem possible in many cases to pool this machinery so as at least to double the annual hourly use. The
machinery will wear out faster, but investment will be better
utilized. Similar economies are possible from specialized servicing
and repair of machinery and equipment. For plowing in stony
ground the percentage range of time lost for servicing and repairs
during use was 18 to 22 per cent. Comparable figures for seeding
are 26 to 31 per cent; disking, 12 to 22 per cent; harrowing, 11
to 15 per cent; combine harvesting, 29 to 38 per cent—the more
mechanical the power equipment, the higher the ratio. An increasing amount of servicing and repair requires expert mechanics.[74]

Only on the very largest farm units, such as the huge "factories

in the fields" of California, Texas, and a few other highly specialized mass-output areas is the machinery park large enough
and sufficiently well balanced with equipment and service men,
and efficiently operated, to obtain the best possible economies in
use which the newer methods have opened up. Nevertheless,
the trend is there, and such mechanization means large-scale
regional organization and pooling of high-cost farm machinery;
this machinery, in turn, becomes very economical to use and maintain when servicing very large and specialized crop areas.

Turning from machinery to the crop area, accordingly, we meet
with the conditions for introducing the economies of scale. "American farming," an expert writes,

has become more than just a way of life. Agriculture is operating on a
gradually shrinking number of farm units. Against a drop of nearly
a million farm units since 1935 is a considerable rise in the average
size of the individual farm [indicating that] large-volume production
is here to stay. Everything is geared for mass production on a big-
business scale.[75]

Estimates made by the Department of Agriculture suggest how
extensive were "labor savings" from mechanization, scientific agriculture, and increased size of farm units in the United States from
1917-21 to 1944.[76] These figures, while somewhat out of date, may
be further extended by recent agricultural data, and may be
duplicated from the history of Britain, Argentina, Australia, Brazil,
Russia, and other areas where attention is being paid to agricultural efficiency. They signify that the individual fields should first
be laid out in patterns most consistent with soil types, land contours, and ecological factors, and then be made large enough so
that large-scale equipment can be used in any given operating
cycle with optimal or near-optimal efficiency. Such fields, further,
need to be located in relation to each other so that they render
easy the movement from field to field of plows, harrows, cultiva-
tors, various power equipment, etc., with a minimum loss of time,
with the least amount of change-over in equipment, and with the
widest possible variety of uses which can be arranged in a given
time-sequence. A parallel rule holds for the size of each crop in
most cases where varied crops—as with dairies, cattle ranches,
hog farms—are grown for feed or to be used to some extent for

by-product purposes; i.e., the crop should be large enough to permit supply adequate for the optimal size of feed installations in the form of storage bins, hay barns, silos, etc., and the volume of by-products should be sufficiently great to make possible economical handling with mechanical equipment.

There are very few cases where simultaneous consideration of these variables does not lead to what would be, by most conventional American practices, a super-sized farm—running into the thousand-acre size and above for most staple food and industrial raw material crops. The efficient area-unit of operation, as far as engineering, agronomical, and accounting features are concerned, should, in short, be a large-scale farm, regionally or centrally managed.

Finally, with respect to *manpower*, it is entirely clear that the advance of agricultural techniques is promoting here, as elsewhere, both a steadily increasing specialization of labor and a greater emphasis upon coöperation between tasks and interdependent skills. This is, of course, precisely what is already being done on the larger cattle, dairy, wheat, and other types of specialized farms. When to this are added plans for the location of plants for first processing of agricultural products at or near the farm, or for establishing similar plants for working up by-products near the sources of supply—or even plants located in rural areas to make use of farm labor during otherwise unoccupied seasons— the opportunities for further specialization may be coupled together in such a way as to enhance full employment within the area as a whole. If, within this framework, the family-sized farm continues to exist, it will do so increasingly as a unit of reckoning in a scheme of division of labor and of proceeds, and not as a unit of management in the utilization of land. Centralization of farm buildings and machinery parks and relocation of first-processing, by-product, and other ruralized plants might then lay heavy emphasis upon shifting residence from the countryside to the village or town with its attendant social and cultural advantages. And this, in turn, means that farming and industry might then become related in such a way as to promote a regional reorganization which unified village, town, and city life with that of the countryside. Farm planning at the operational level, in other words, would heavily reinforce the local shift in emphasis onto a regional development basis just as regional development in turn requires heavier emphasis upon "grass-roots" participation.[77] With such a series of shifts, farm planning would tend more and more to become an aspect of regional planning, being joined in all the varied and multifarious activities of a coöperative nature which might characterize civilized existence in a society determined fully to absorb and realize upon the productive potentials of science and engineering, with a view to broadening the material foundations of the "good life."

SOME WIDER IMPLICATIONS OF AGRICULTURAL RATIONALIZATION

Just as a rational basis needs to be found for fitting local agricultural planning into that of other aspects of life within the region, so also should the plan for the minor region be fitted into that of the major river valley or other major region, and all of these into the national plan and ultimately into such international plans as broad social objectives may envisage. All levels, as with concentric circles having a single focal point, are being given attention in most countries where a farm problem has been found to exist, and where the resources of science and engineering are being brought to bear in its solution. In only one or two countries does anything beyond a paper plan exist for comprehending the whole. But to the Soviet Union, with perhaps too rigorous a plan, are rapidly being added others. Venezuela is evolving a plan for developing the llanos; Argentina, for developing the pampas and for redistributing industry; South Africa, for saving the veldt; India, for river valley developments of the TVA type with heavy emphasis upon agricultural modernization.

While the problems, the patterns and programs, and the first results shape up differently for different areas, yet, as far as the technical and engineering aspects are concerned, they appear to be evolving quite uniformly along the general lines sketched above. In the international sphere, also, considerable effort is being directed to bringing some order out of chaos.

The leading agency in the latter field might operate along lines similar to the original plan for the Food and Agricultural Organization (FAO) of the United Nations. The FAO, made up of representatives of members of the United Nations, was to serve as a clearinghouse and planning body for all aspects of food supply and trade in agricultural commodities of a definitely international character, but it has been greatly weakened since its inception. A few examples will show how far-reaching the implications of this work might have become.

Statistical services of the FAO were to include the collection and analysis of data on food production, trade, and consumption. Staffs were to be available to member governments for improving their statistical methods. To achieve comparability of data, an initial inquiry was being made into statistical methods and budgets of member countries. Regional conferences were to be held to establish standards of nomenclature, definitions, units of measurement and of conversion from one system to another, uniform methods of handling and presenting data, etc. FAO has suggested to the United Nations Educational, Scientific, and Cultural Organization (UNESCO) the establishment of a world information pool which would provide facilities for the exchange of information by means of photographic reproduction for the entire field of science and technology, and for the compilation and supply of a running list of all published documents in all fields of science, regardless of source.

SUMMARY AND CONCLUSIONS

The world-wide "race with famine" can be won in the foreseeable future by agronomic science on certain specific conditions. These conditions embrace conservation to maintain or extend the productive potential, and the methods of cultivation applied to maximize output within the limits of that potential. These conditions may be arranged in descending order of generality and of man's capacity through developing technology to control, alter, or adapt.

At the top, the major outlines of world crop specialization are determined by the meteorological facts. Here man can do relatively little to alter the physical environment, although he can do a great deal through special seed selection, methods of soil cultivation, etc. to adapt crops and animals to conditions outside their "natural" habitats. Success there depends in large part upon capacity to foresee and to adapt to varying meteorological facts, and this depends upon climatological research and the most extensive and reliable weather-reporting system possible. Weather reporting, in the interests of both economy and effectiveness, should be global in coverage, and set up to serve simultaneously all other activities—shipping and navigation, aerial navigation, radio broadcasting, resort and recreational interests—heavily dependent upon weather forecasting.

Within the framework of the meteorological patterns of the world, the next important variable for crop production is the nature, seasonality, and geographic distribution of the hydrological patterns of precipitation, ground absorption, ground storage, run-off, and plant transpiration. Demands of industries and urban users for water are increasing along with the water needs of agriculture. Agricultural and nonagricultural uses, combined with technological advance in hydroelectric power, internal water transport, and irrigation methods, tend strongly to favor unified multi-purpose planning of river or other major drainage basin systems. This planning is already recognized as necessary and valid in the great river valley developments of the TVA type. When surplus water areas are juxtaposed to large deficit areas, there is already a definite tendency to extend this type of planning onto an intervalley, interregional basis, as with the program for unified water development of the Great Lakes–St. Lawrence network. Another example is found in the projected interlinkage of water use of the major West Coast river basins. In England, water planning has already fanned out beyond this onto a truly national basis. The Report of the President's Committee on Water Policy suggests similar planning for the continental United States.

Within the given meteorological and hydrological patterns, the major determining factors for agricultural science are soil types and geographic lay and contour of the land. Good agricultural practice favors extension of crop differentiation by gradients, where level lands are specialized on cultivated row crops, medium gradients on grains and grasses, and higher slopes on permanent pasturage and forest cover.

Within the pattern of soil types and for each gradient there exist natural balances of soil chemicals and of plant and animal life (ecological balance). Land utilization should be planned with a view to the entire range of each, and with an eye to the obvious interdependencies between both. While in most cases both are subject to a great deal of manipulation, yet any given agricultural program which fails to maintain either the original or an appropriate substitute balance for each will soon exhaust the soil and render it unfit for cultivation.

The next problem of scientific agriculture has to do with the optimum-sized farm operation in terms of over-all efficiency for each pattern of crop rotation, and this in turn is dependent upon the crop patterns of all other regions. Given the crop or crop rotation system, it is very difficult at present to say just what does comprise an optimum-sized unit. Certainly the historical facts point to a steady increase in the scale of farm operations, and this increase has been paced by an increasing mechanization of farm operations. But it appears to be true that the unit of good farm operation may not necessarily be coextensive with the most economical combinations of machinery and equipment. In most cases, farm machinery and equipment can or should be pooled over a much wider area than that provided by what appears to be the most economical size of over-all farm operation—although the reasons for the latter are unclear and may be more of a social than of a technical character.[78]

As for supply of market data—supplemented as it may be by inducements in the form of loans and subsidies or prohibitions in the form of acreage and other types of limitations—as a basis for actual crop planning, the crop patterns in all countries tend everywhere to develop more or less along similar lines. In the planting of crops, a multitude of technical services are supplied by the central government relating, in the United States for example, to virtually every phase and facet of cultivation. In the selling and marketing of crops, similar information (and, in some cases, machinery) is supplied to provide up-to-the-minute information on prices, market trends, surpluses, and plans for handling each and every untoward circumstance which may arise. At the world level, some tentative efforts, largely through the machinery of the United Nations, are being made to extend similar services on a global basis.

Rarely, to be sure, are the social, political, and other institutional conditions of national life favorable to full orientation of agricultural production along the lines adumbrated. Over most of the earth, uneconomic small or dwarf holdings are the rule; deep-rooted habits of soil robbing are general; complicated and oppressive systems of land tenantry inhibit change for the better; poverty, malnutrition, and low man-hour productivity among the agricultural population go generally hand-in-hand.

But also the generality and massive scale of the difficulties standing in the way of scientific agriculture are, by virtue of these very same facts, paralleled everywhere by the increasingly recognized need for decisive and far-ranging changes. Perhaps more money, more thought, and more comprehensive planning are going into agriculture than into any other line of human activity. This holds for countries like India, China, and Argentina where the population is still overwhelmingly rural and agricultural. But it also holds for highly developed countries like Britain, Canada, and the United States where—though for widely contrasting reasons—agricultural development continues to maintain a highly strategic position.

Before all other human needs comes the demand for food. Adequacy of supply—particularly in the face of a rapidly increasing population—will everywhere become steadily more dependent upon the scientific revolution in agricultural methods. If and when the preliminary steps of "rethinking through" are once taken, the newly developing sciences of climate, soils, plant and animal growth, and agronomic technology are certain to promote a continuing revolution in both methods and theory. What we have seen above is probably a bare beginning.

VII

The Chemical Revolution in the Materials Foundation of Industry

When due allowance is made for the conceits of the times, it is still possible without exaggeration for this generation to speak of a "chemical revolution." What is involved is a radical transformation of the entire materials foundation of industrial civilization as a whole. The "revolution" rests on two main supports. One is the direct linkage of chemical processes with exact scientific research into molecular and atomic structures. The other is the immediate introduction of new methods and processes on a mass-output basis.

The results of this wedding of laboratory research and mass production ramify throughout the industrial system. They have given rise to quite a new conception of the nature, structure, and available quantities of essential resources. They have multiplied the range and variety of new and substitute end-products many-fold. And they have served to introduce problems of technical cost theory and developmental planning of an extraordinary and challenging nature.

Consider briefly the meaning of "chemical industry." The trade, and sometimes even the technical, terminology is frequently confusing. The classification "chemical industries" commonly refers to industries producing industrial salts, acids, gases, dyes, pharmaceuticals, and other products not classified under some other materials-producing industry. Some classifications will include rayon, plastics, fertilizers, miscellaneous synthetics, and, occasionally, products of refining processes such as ferments, yeasts, antibiotics, and various other activizing agents which employ, or result from, bacterial and other biochemical action.

Yet no such classification has any meaning unless it has reference to the distinguishing characteristic of chemical processing in the sense of the sifting-out of physical-chemical components, or the changing of the molecular substances of the basic raw-materials employed. "All industrial production," a famous German inquiry into chemical processing stated,

takes place either through fashioning or transforming materials. Most industrial production consists in reshaping of crude materials; iron is used for making machines, and textile products are fashioned from animal or plant fibers. In contrast, other industrial branches are characterized by the process of altering substances as such [and,] consequently, production which involves shaping and fashioning is called mechanical, while those processes which alter the materials themselves are called chemical.[1]

In the latter sense, chemical industries include practically all metallurgical refining; all refinement of fuels such as petroleum, natural gases, and coal; the processes of refining materials leading to the production of cement, rubber (whether "natural" rubber or other basic raw-materials), glass, etc.; and all industries, in short, engaged either in breaking down the molecular or atomic structure of materials into their physical components (analysis), or in reassembling them to make new compounds or materials (synthesis). The emphasis is on the *nature of the process*, and not upon the type or state of raw or finished materials. It makes no difference whether the activating agents be heat, electricity, catalysts, or bacteria; so long as a change is effected in molecular or atomic structure—so long as the material undergoes inner transformation—the process is a chemical process.

It is worth noting further that this characterization of chemical processes goes far beyond the once traditional limitation of the term "chemical industry" to solely *molecular* structures and molecular compounds. Converging lines of research and industrial practice have brought together the fields of chemistry, physics, and biology on a wide range of central problems dealing with both molecular and atomic phenomena. As Watson Davis put it,

The exploration of the atom has progressed with such rapidity that physicists and chemists have been plunged into a new branch of knowledge. It is "nuclear chemistry." . . . Within it physics and chemistry blend, fuse, merge, and lose their separate identities. . . . It is no longer meaningful to apply the tags of "chemist" or "physicist" to the scientists who are pushing energetically at the new frontiers.[2]

A similar, and intimately related, fusion has been reflected in the field of industrial chemistry itself. Thus, many of the plastics and the bulk of the synthetic-rubber industries involve inter-atomic as well as molecular changes. Chemistry and biology are similarly linked by the study of substances affecting such processes as body growth, functioning of the endocrine glands, cell-wall construction, and the production of food extracts and other products for the control over malfunctioning and disease. Similarly—in the study of such agents as enzymes, of the action of nonfilterable viruses, and of the nature of electrical and radio-active action in and on the body—biology and physics, and the industries translating the results of their investigations into usable products, are bound together in a complex of common problems. Quite literally in an increasing number of cases the laboratory has grown into an industrial producer.

In general, chemical processing has spread out to encompass more and more basic raw materials. As a writer for the National Resources Committee once put it in a now famous document:

Just as the science, chemistry, is one ministrant to sciences, so the chemical industry is one which serves all other industries. Fully to grasp the truth of this statement one needs only remember that few of the raw materials provided naturally are ready for use and that in most cases a chemical change takes place before they are suitable.[3]

In speaking of the scientific organization and development of the chemical industries we are, then, speaking of an industry —frequently closely linked with extractive operations and mechanical processes—which is engaged in the transforming of the inner substance of materials used by all other industries.

Scientific organization of chemical industries, accordingly, has three major criteria which may serve as guides: (1) the *components* patterns provided by the nature of the molecular and atomic structure of its principal raw materials; (2) the *materials* patterns required in the process of combining, by formulae, substances previously separated by chemical decomposition with chemical components from the same or still other materials; and

(3) the *nature of the methods* introduced to place all processes of breaking down (analysis) or building up (synthesis) on a mass-output basis. The first two might be thought of as introducing the patterns of the "ground plan of nature," modified, as it may be, by current scientific understanding of ways of altering the constitution of matter. And the third might be considered as the current level of the industrial arts in adapting the modes and techniques of mass production to the changing picture of the "ground plan." The industrial planning of the chemical industries, that is to say, must reconcile the last with either or both of the former—depending upon the extent to which analytic processes are combined with synthetic—as they are given at the current level of scientific knowledge.

Where chemical industries have been most fully adapted along these lines they show the following common characteristics:

1. *Raw materials.*—The raw materials (coal, oil, ores and metalliferous earths, wood pulp, etc.) are of standard physico-chemical composition when introduced to the first steps of chemical processing. If the process is analytic, the preparatory step is known as "beneficiation"; if synthetic, it is taken care of by specification and test for chemical purity, specific gravity, and other determinate properties. Within specified limits of permissible deviation from standards, the materials are, that is to say, standard, uniform, and invariable at the introduction of the process, as well as at each succeeding stage.

2. *Process.*—The bulk, or in some cases the entirety, of the process of breaking down or building up (analysis or synthesis) is by continuous and automatically checked, tested, and adjusted flow (i.e., complete automation). Typically, regulatory devices are to some extent or other electrically synchronized. Due allowances being made for repair and maintenance interruptions, the automated plant operates 24 hours a day and 365 days a year. If the process is electrolytic, electrothermal, or bacterial, the load factor approximates 100 per cent. A thoroughly rationalized chemical plant approaches the ultimate goal of completely automatic, continuous-flow production.

3. *Joint or by-products.*—Whether or not there are one or more main or joint products to which all other components are by-

product, all principal by-products are utilized, either in their original chemical form or further split down into simple molecular compounds (or "reassembled"). Nothing, that is to say, is thrown away for which any use can be found unless the cost of utilizing it is such that, considering the by-products as a "free good," it would cost more to use it than the alternative product made from other sources for which it was a substitute.[4] The same holds for chemical utilization of industrial wastes, such as, e.g., Thomas meal (an important source of fertilizers) from the lining of acid-base open-hearth furnaces, casein from by-product milk, and industrial alcohol and various other by-products from wood and agricultural wastes.

4. *The size of the plant* for separating out each primary product or products, as, for example, coke or gas from coal, should, quite obviously, be optimum[5] for that product or process. Conversely, the size of the plant for synthesized main products should be optimum for the final assembled product or products. The principle of full by-product utilization may then follow several patterns. If the volume of a given by-product is too small to permit utilization in plant of a size which is optimum for the appropriate process, a multiplication of primary process plants may add the necessary volume. Or, this volume added to other quantities available in the near vicinity may permit erection of the proper-sized plant at or near the by-product source. Or, undersized plants might be utilized as long as the small-plant "diseconomies" were less than the waste of throwing away the by-product. Or, finally, the volume being too small for on-site utilization, it can be shipped to other users.

5. *Location.*—On all except the fourth criterion for by-product utilization, the principle of complete utilization of all by-products tends in most cases—particularly in heavy industrial chemicals and in fuel and ore refining—to promote plant agglutination, or multiplication of more-or-less optimum-sized plants to utilize each major by-product in the neighborhood of each primary raw material, such as coal, petroleum, or iron. The fourth criterion may under appropriate circumstances promote plant scattering, as does also the general principle of utilizing waste raw materials from nonchemical processes at the source, such as agricultural

and forest products at or near the farm and lumber camp. Plant agglutination favors regional industrial concentration, or the evolution of the industrial "complex" or "combinat." Plant scattering promotes decentralization and even, in many cases, ruralization of chemical industries.

The case of chemicals does not provide the only criteria for plant agglutination or plant scattering. Others are provided by the mechanical processing industries,[6] for using low-grade, waste, or small quantities of local resources, and by factors involved[7] in conservation. Nor are the factors in the chemical industries favoring either pattern due solely, or in some cases even primarily, to the reasons given above. In ferrous, and in some cases of nonferrous metallurgy, chemical processing (e.g., of fuels and ores) may be vertically linked with such subsequent mechanical operations as rolling, casting, and even the production of finished end-products. It sometimes happens, notably in the case of iron and steel technology and in the refinement of aluminum, that plentiful and low-cost power is a dominating force in plant concentration at a particular site. Conversely, the presence of an extensive and finely meshed power grid may promote plant scattering since, if the level of power consumption is not excessively high, grid lines may be tapped at any particular point.

Nevertheless, the above factors—particularly when taken, as they should be, in combination—always provide two major patterns of plant growth in the chemical industries, and, hence, two types of development problems. One is associated with the growth of the industrial "complex" or "combinat"; the other is tied up with industrial decentralization and localization. In the remainder of this chapter we shall be concerned primarily with the former. As for the latter, given short shrift here, to deal with it at length would sidetrack analysis onto more detailed problems of plant location.

While it is true that there are only a limited number of cases in which this major development of chemical industries has been carefully thought through and the plants have been located and constructed on a scientific basis, yet there has been considerable adjustment to this end, and it is possible, accordingly, to project

from the past history of the chemicals industries the broad outlines of rational organization and location.

AGGLUTINATIVE PATTERNS: WHERE THE "GRAVITATIONAL PULL" IS
ASSOCIATED WITH ANALYSIS OF BASIC RAW MATERIALS

The Schuman Plan for the international rationalization of the
huge North-Central European steel industry illustrates in a rather
spectacular way the degree to which technological developments
and cost considerations—along with political and other similar
factors—favor industry-wide planning in steel. Most of the plants
included in the plan, whether located in Germany, France,
Belgium, or Luxembourg, are part of an "industrial complex"
which includes coal mining, coking processes, heavy chemicals
production, and other allied chemical products along with the
refining of iron and steel and the production of a bewildering
variety of iron and steel products—raw, semifinished, and finished. It is here frankly recognized that no one can tell where
chemical processes begin and nonchemical processes end, on the
one hand, and that there is no effective way of carrying through
the type of most economical coördination without taking in some
or all of the whole congeries of directly related industries in the
"industrial complex," on the other.

The heart of the steel industry, so considered, is chemical processing, and for this reason steel and the complex series of technically related chemical industries associated with it provide one
of the best examples of the bearing of the "chemical revolution"
upon long-range and comprehensive industrial planning. While
the primary purpose is to produce iron and steel commodities,
goods which are, in this context, "by-product" to steel are also
produced in a wide range. The most important raw materials are
coal, iron ore, and limestone. If an iron and steel "complex"
were being planned *de novo*, or if an effort were being made
fully to modernize an existing regional pattern, there are four
major types of "planning balances" that would have to be resolved
simultaneously.

1. The *first balance* that would have to be struck would be
plant location with respect to the volume and location of more
important raw materials on the one hand, and markets on the

other. In the case of the iron and steel industry, the latter can be, for all practical purposes, omitted since it weighs but slightly against the former, largely due to the ratio which freight costs of bulky raw materials typically bear to those of refined products. Besides this, the sheer scale on which optimum-sized units of iron and steel industries operate creates a local demand for a sufficiently large volume of important primary and secondary products to tip the scale in favor of location near the most important raw materials. Location, in other words, is dominated by the regional distribution of the basic raw materials. With respect to these, historically the tendency has been for ores to move to fuels, particularly if fuels are found, as is quite commonly the case (for example in the western Pennsylvania and southern Great Lakes iron and steel centers), in close proximity with good-quality limestone.

There are a number of reasons for this. For one thing, iron ore deposits are typically more widely scattered than coal, and are of more widely varying concentrations and chemical composition. An adequate and reasonably accurate geological investigation of these resources constitutes an important early step in planning location.[8] A second reason is that techniques of beneficiation of ores, whereby they are made more nearly uniform as to chemical qualities and the metallic ratio to total volume is materially enhanced, decrease the volume of ores that must be shipped. A third reason is that a fairly large and growing percentage of metal input takes the form of old or new scrap and is, hence, available at principal points of population concentration and metalworking industries instead of at the ore pits.

A fourth reason is that interprocess fuel and transportation economies—such, for example, as are incurred in the making of steel out of molten pig iron, thus bypassing the cold pig-iron stage—favor vertical integration from the raw materials to the finished or semifinished product, and the production of the latter exerts a strong pull toward large industrial and ultimate-consumer markets that have previously grown up around, or in close proximity to, massive sources of cheap fuels. Thus ore has increasingly flowed from the French Minette reserves and northern Sweden to the Ruhr coal basin, and from the Mesabi and other

Great Lakes deposits to Pittsburgh, Buffalo, Cleveland, Gary, and South Chicago. Water haulage versus rail, ability to strip mine ores and thus to decrease the cost of handling, etc., may also play important roles.

There may, also, occur a counterflow of coal to ore if two primary conditions can be met. First, if large markets for primary and secondary products exist at or near the ore fields, and, second, if freight-handling equipment is usable for fuels as well as ore. If, as is typically the case, it costs but very little more beyond mere loading and unloading expenses to carry back, by rail or water, full loads of fuel than it does to take the carriers back empty, then coal may move to ore. Even, that is to say, if it were much more expensive to move coal to ore than ore to coal, it would still pay to do the former as long as (*a*) anything at all were contributed to lower overhead freight costs by the coal shipments, and (*b*) markets were available on the other end. Examples are provided by the growth of a large iron and steel center around Duluth near the Mesabi ores, and by the linking of the Russian industrial centers of the Kuznetsk, producing coal, and Magnitogorsk, producing iron. In this case, the coal cars moving westward to the Urals were returned eastward to the Kuznetsk Basin with beneficiated ores, with the result that major iron, steel, and by-product utilizing "complexes," using varying mixtures of local and imported ores and fuels of roughly the same general character, are found at both ends.

2. A *second balance* must be struck among the main products, iron and steel, and the primary by-products. Typically the two former have been united in a single continuous process with the result that ironmaking, except for certain specialized purposes, is merely a step in steel processing, and is, hence, linked with the latter in continuous-flow production. Here the iron goes directly in molten form from the blast furnaces to the Bessemer converters or, as is now more commonly the case, open-hearth furnaces, and from thence, via the soaking pits, immediately to the rolling mills. It would be interesting, were space available, to go into this development at some length, for it provides one of the best examples of the fusion of previously unrelated processes in such a way as to convert a series of hitherto independent industries

into a single, continuously flowing complex of confluent processes.

This *second balance* provides the heart around which all the other balances must be struck. Three phases, each of which favor widening the arc of integration, may be distinguished: the pre-preparation of the raw materials, the actual process of refining, and the first working-up of the iron or steel into finished shapes.

(1) Ore and limestone typically come ready for introduction to the blast-furnace process. The primary considerations are that chemical properties be standard and uniform, the metal content of the ore relatively high and invariable, and the flow to the plant sufficiently even as to reduce to the minimum the need for storage space and excessive rehandling. Planning extends backwards, that is to say, to ore and limestone extraction, beneficiation, and shipping, and, in practice, this unification has been effected in almost every major iron and steel center whether located in the United States, Germany, or the U.S.S.R.

With respect to coke, however, the picture is somewhat different. Here the actual process of prepreparation is typically done within or in immediate juxtaposition to the iron and steel plant, and the flow of the main product, coke, must be coördinated with that of the other materials fed into the blast furnaces, the ore and limestone, and in the manner indicated above for these two materials. The main object is the supply of coke, but the use of processes of distillation also supplies enormous quantities of by-product gas, tar, light oil, and ammonia. The production of these materials provides a complex of problems in itself, to which we will return in a moment, below.

(2) The second phase has to do with the unification of the actual process of refining itself. Here the ideal is the closest approximation to continuous flow from the blast furnaces to the rolling mills to produce a single, uniform product. The process in its most advanced form is still far from the theoretically ideal, but important steps have been taken. A battery of blast furnaces, tapped in series, supplies an approximation to continuous flow beginning at the source of refining. Elimination of the cold pig-iron and the billet-steel stages has converted the balance of the process into one requiring no alternate cooling and reheating steps[9] prior to the rolling mills, with a resultant enormous saving in over-all heat requirements. A ton of crude steel which required an average of 15 million B.T.U. (British thermal units) around the turn of the century now uses 6 million or less. Revamping mill layout in compliance with flow principles and continuous heat has also eliminated much rehandling at intermediate stages, and has welded formerly separate industries into a new series of unified processes which must be planned as an integrated whole.

(3) In the third phase, rolling mill operation is unified with crude-steel production, in itself a purely mechanical operation, with the result that the arc of coördinate planning is further extended. This step carries with it some very interesting implications. The previous steps, linking the volume and the timing of flow back to the blast furnaces, promote a type of close synchronization which favors—due allowance being made for reserve and repair (such as relining of furnaces and converters)—operation 24 hours a day and 365 days a year. If heat losses are to be avoided between the soaking pits (which equalize the heat throughout the billets coming from furnaces and converters) and the rolling mill, then the former must feed directly into the latter. The alternative is to build warmer and rolling-mill capacity to a multiple of previous stage capacity. That is, if blast furnaces and further refining capacity are able to deliver 500 tons per hour, evenly distributed over the 24-hour diurnal cycle, or 12,000 tons per day, and rolling mills operate but 8 hours per day, then the capacity of the latter per hour will have to be three times that of the former, or 1,500 tons per hour. This part of the plant would then require an investment somewhere near three times as great, relatively speaking, as is needed in the earlier stages. Since the case is very strong for eliminating all except supervisory night work, pressure has been strong for converting rolling to a fully mechanized, automatic or at least semiautomatic basis operating around the clock. The advances made in this direction in recent years have been phenomenal. Continuous steel casting—which bypasses the soaking-pit stage—provides a method of flow production which increases output per molder more than 100 per cent and is now being widely installed. In another process, that of the strip sheet-plate mill, all processes from billet to finished

plate have been made completely automatic. Such a mill run by the Jones and Laughlin Steel Company in 1948 was able to turn out strip at the rate of 70 miles per hour by a process that required nothing more than continuous engineering supervision.

Extension of this principle to other rolled products—pipe, tubing, etc.—raises one very interesting question which has called for the application of planning and control in still another direction. Faced with getting the utmost out of steel capacity during the war, it was found that much delay in output arose as a result of widely varying steel formulae, each new or different formula involving separate treatment, which necessarily interrupted production in various stages of processing. Over 3,000 formulae were found. Not over 200 could be justified in terms of the specified properties required of the end products, and, of these, it appeared possible to concentrate around 95 per cent of demand upon a half-dozen or so basic formulae. This investigation, carried out through the machinery of the American Standards Association for planning the structure of industrial standards, made possible a high degree of mill specialization upon given formulae, and thus has cleared away another obstacle to complete mechanization of rolling mill operations.

When complete mechanization is achieved, the need for long-range planning is multiplied. For the individual mill, it means adapting the mechanical end of steel production to the closest possible approximation of a 24-hour, 365-days-a-year basis. For the industry as a whole, it means planning the production schedules of each plant with regard to the production schedules of all the other plants, and an effort to adjust the total output of specialized mills to the changing structure of demand. The more completely a mill is mechanized, the more important does a steady and adequate demand for its products become, since mechanization greatly increases the ratio of investment cost per ton produced, and tends to convert large percentages of labor and other operating costs into overhead expenses. It not only costs, consequently, nearly as much to produce at any fraction of capacity as at full capacity, but it also becomes difficult to produce at less than capacity without laming the process from beginning to end.

The result approaches a condition where the major alternatives are simply to produce at full capacity or to close down entirely; to extend planning to embrace production schedules of the bulk of the steel industry or revert to a simpler technology; to effect, on the part of the principal industrial, transport, and other volume users, a structure of demand which is most consonant with the general pattern of output of an industry made up increasingly of specialized mills turning out standardized products on a continuous basis, at or near full plant capacity, or to continue the wasteful proliferation of products from unspecialized, high-cost and batch-production plants.

3. A *third balance* included in this complex of industrial operations is that of water, heat, gas, and power. Water was once solely a locational factor, the large quantities of water required for steel processing compelling the location of plants on or near large lakes or rivers. Electrometallurgical methods, continuous-heat processing, and growing objections to dumping industrial waste waters into rivers and lakes have resulted in a series of changes which require less water and provide for purification and reuse of water supply (recycling) on a unified basis throughout integrated operations. Heat conservation is further extended through continuous processing and the use of bleeder steam and hot water for plant purposes. Utilization of blast-furnace stack gas for plant purposes tends, depending upon circumstances (German experience) to release part, the bulk, or even all of the coke-oven by-product gas for public sale. With the shift of mechanical operations onto an electric power basis, there is also a general trend to turn from power generated on the site to the purchase of part or all of the power needed for normal operations from public grid networks.

The process balances of water and heat call for unified plans for the use of each on an interconnected basis throughout the whole of the complex of unified operations. Those of gas and power raise rather special questions which have far-reaching implications for industrial planning.

If gas is produced as a disposable by-product from continuously functioning coke-oven batteries, operating on a scale to provide an adequate flow of coke to optimum blast-furnace combinations, there may be nothing to do with it but make it available for public consumption through long-distance gas mains. Another possibility is to link together a series of other industries which use large quantities of gas, in which case the cost of constructing long-distance mains encourages movement of user industries close to the supply plants. Or, both public and other industrial users may be supplied over a common network.

The latter possibility tends to favor further integration of industries using manufactured gas near the supply source, and both possibilities tend to convert supply into a public-utility function. The most extensive schemes along this line have been proposed, and partially developed, in Germany and Britain. In Germany, during the early thirties, a main network, gathering up by-product gas from cokeries located mainly at or near the Ruhr steel mills, was extended eastward as far as Hanover and southward beyond Cologne. It was supposed ultimately to extend still further in both directions, but was stopped by realization that conversion of fuel supply throughout the areas of use necessitated continuous pressure for unbroken operation of the coke ovens, and hence of the whole complex of fuels and metals refining with which it was interlaced. Similar principles govern the British postwar scheme for a ten-thousand-mile grid serving manufactured gas to some 5,000,000 people, and covering "an area from the coast in the west, the Pennines in the east, and the northern borders of the Lancashire cotton area in the north, to the saltfields and chemical works at Nantwich in the south." [10] It appears that if one phase of a chain of functionally coördinated processes is under public pressure for continuous supply, then all the other phases integrated with it also must continue to function. In effect coal must then be mined, coke ovens must operate, blast furnaces must keep going, furnaces must supply billets, and rolling mills must turn out end products. As long as such unified operation can be maintained, the advantages in over-all economy are enormous. If it breaks down for long at any essential point, then the damage tends to widen in proportion.

In actual practice there is much more flexibility in these adjustments than our brief sketch would indicate. Some storage is possible at a number of points—coal mines to the cokeries, coke ovens and ore pits to the furnaces, furnaces to converters or ovens, etc. It is also true that gas can be stored to some extent over the daily cycle and to fit adjustments in demand for various industrial uses. Furthermore, while the volume of gas supply from by-product furnaces can be very great, in most cases it is apt to be supplementary to some extent to other supply, and hence can be made to serve in part in a stand-by capacity. Yet in the main the limits to adjustment are very narrow in both timing and volume, and it is bound to narrow still further as the foregoing types of scientific organization in steel processing are more fully and carefully carried through.

With respect to the power balance, a number of factors favor purchase rather than plant generation. Among these are the increasing size of the optimum generating unit, the possibility of purchase of power at base-load rates from unified grid networks, and the sale of some or all of by-product gas for power-generating purposes, where the grid's market is capable of indefinite expansion. The iron and steel processing plant then becomes a major factor in the grid power pattern. The grid, that is to say, must be constructed to handle this demand; and the volume and diversity of demand will heavily influence power capacity, load, and diversity factors and hence the structure of power rates to all other types of users. Conversely, the possibility of using by-product, plant-generated electricity or gas for public power-generation purposes can have an important bearing upon the size and nature of public generating facilities. In any case, if these interlinkages are effected, the planning of iron and steel production should be carried out in close coöperation with the planning of the public fuel and power supply.

4. The *fourth balance* in metallurgical refining referred to above has to do with the primary by-products. Listing only those coming from coke ovens,[11] the more important are coke, tar, light oil, gas, and ammonia. In a steel plant, coke supply is apt to be used entirely for blast furnaces, and gas may be used to some extent for heat- or power-generating purposes. Tar, light oil, and ammonia, however, will appear as pure by-products. Gas, before being used for fuel purposes, will have to be refined, and will thus give rise to several secondary by-products. The latter, and the

primary by-products, are then available for sale or for use by closely juxtaposed plants. If the volume of supply is great, these plants will constitute a series of further satellite refining industries, dependent for their raw materials supply in whole or in part upon the coke ovens attached to the steel plant or plants.

On the engineering economics side, and irrespective of the structure of ownership and management, if the volume of supply from a single battery or a series of local batteries is adequate, then each of the primary by-products industries should be located at or near the cokeries, and each would form the nucleus of a complex of further refining processes. Thus, for tar there are six main products from further chemical analysis; from light oil there are seven; from ammonia, twelve. Most of these joint products can be further "split downwards." (For example, the very complex aniline-dye industry uses tar as its principal raw material.) How important coke-oven by-products may become in the national chemical industry can be seen in the fact that in 1946, coke ovens associated with steelworks produce some $800 million worth of by-products used by the steel companies themselves and sold some $122.9 million to other industries.[12] In 1948 the United States Steel Corporation alone possessed 4,289, or 29 per cent, of United States coke ovens, and produced 30 per cent of the nation's output of ammonium sulphate, 30 per cent of the benzol, 30 per cent of the tar, and 10 per cent of all the toluol and xylol combined.[13]

If, to refining "downwards" (analysis), synthesis is added, then each of the primary and many of the secondary or further-process by-products become starting points and nuclei for the further extension of satellite industries. The fourth type of *balance* in iron and steel refining becomes, consequently, interlinked with technically related industries. If materials supply from the primary source exercises a dominant locational pull, then these industries will be drawn toward the iron and steel complex. If not, they will set up chemical-process "complexes" of their own where the determinants of agglutination or scattering will be similar in principle to those which operate in iron and steel.

An outstanding example of the nucleational pull of combined analytic and synthetic processes is provided by petroleum refining, which in 1954, in addition to its oil products, supplied around

one-fourth of the United States chemical output.[14] In such refining centers as Bayonne-Bayway, Hammond and South Chicago,
and Richmond (California), refining methods tend to run the
gamut of analysis and synthesis in all the steps from crude oil to
end products. We then have the picture of several major plants
agglutinated as nuclei, supplying a variety of products as additional links in a chain of concatenated processes. The flow of
supplies, and the process interlinkages that characterize the concert of operations within the nuclei, come, then, to spread
throughout the refining center to link, in reciprocal dependence,
(*a*) the nuclei to each other, (*b*) these to the satellite industries,
and (*c*) the satellite industries to each other.

AGGLUTINATIVE PATTERNS: WHERE PLANT NUCLEATION IS PROMOTED
BY SYNTHESIS OF A DOMINANT END-PRODUCT

In this case the "raw materials" may come from several different
sources as by-products from other processes, but plants are centered in the production of a single or closely related group of
synthesized end-products. The factors favoring plant agglutination in such cases are similar to those based upon analysis of
primary raw materials such as coal, ores, and petroleum, except
that the process is reversed. The illustration of nitrogenous fertilizers may be cited.

The primary raw materials are "by-product coal" and "synthetic
hydrogen and nitrogen," and the secondary raw materials are
nitric oxides, calcium cyanide, and urea. From these come the
more important fertilizer components of synthetic sodium nitrate,
ammonium nitrate, ammoniated superphosphate, ammonium sulphate, and ammonium phosphate. These are then brought together
in fertilizer combinations with by-products from various vegetable
and animal protein sources, and may be supplemented by natural
sodium nitrate, drawn from Chilean *caliche*.

The tendency is for all primary and secondary raw materials
processings to be planned as a single complex of continuously
flowing chemical processes. By-products unrelated to this central
process are then available for sale as chemicals. Yet, the volume
handling of them may favor branching out into industries where

these chemicals play the role of raw materials for further analysis or synthesis.

AGGLUTINATIVE PATTERNS: WHERE THE CENTRIPETAL FORCE IS FOUND
IN BALANCE OF HOMOLOGOUS PROCESSES

This situation is little more than a combination of the previous two types, and may be dismissed with a single illustration. The Commercial Solvents Corporation has a "diversified output [which] includes penicillin, vitamin feeds, dry ice, antifreezes, hand creams, and the alcohol that cheers as well as the kinds that dissolve paints." [15]

Here, in effect, two different chemical industries, based upon two types of raw materials—corn and molasses on the one hand, natural gases on the other—have been interlaced to produce two closely interrelated types of products falling, respectively, into the three alcohol groups and the nitroparaffins. Roughly half of the 150-odd products are derived from both types of raw materials. The processes are similar, and the end products are joint to each other. The complex of plants required to carry out the balanced concert of refining and synthesizing operations is similar, though smaller in scale, to the nucleated patterns previously discussed.

AGGLUTINATIVE PATTERNS: WHERE REGIONAL INTERLACING IS PRO-
MOTED BY COMMON FUEL AND POWER SUPPLY

Whenever chemical processing is both large scale and heavily dependent upon electric power as a major cost item, there is a tendency for an "industrial complex" to be built up around sources of cheap and plentiful power supply. Good illustrations are supplied by the aluminum and magnesium industries. The former is, perhaps, the more striking of the two. The largest single complex of aluminum-refining and aluminum-using industries was probably the one constructed by the Russians near the site of the gigantic Dneprostroi dam. Similar complexes have been evolved in the United States based on TVA, Columbia River, and St. Lawrence water-power.

In the case of the Dnieper industrial group—as it was planned years before the 1939 war, and largely with the aid and counsel, incidentally, of American engineers—aluminum processing was combined with ferroalloy and alloy steels production to form a balanced metallurgical unit drawn together by a combination of process interdependencies and common reliance upon cheap and plentiful hydroelectric power.[16]

The aluminum plant, which produces metallic aluminum, aluminum oxide and electrodes, is technologically independent of the other enterprises in the Dnieper industrial group. Its importance as a consumer of Dnieper station power is shown by the following figures. It consumed 274,000,000 kwh. in 1934, in its second year of operation, and 588,000,000 kwh. in 1935. After it reaches ultimate capacity its consumption will rise to 1,200,000,000 kwh., i.e., about 45-50 per cent of the entire output of the Dnieper station. . . .

The geographical combination of the production of metallic aluminum, aluminum oxide, and electrodes under a single management offers a number of . . . advantages. The electrode department, for instance, supplies the aluminum plant and the Zaporozhe steel works as well. The coke required for the production of aluminum oxide is obtained from the by-product coke plant located near by. Low content ferro-silicon is obtained as a by-product of aluminum oxide production. The principal nucleating factor in this case was power. "Electric power supply," the report goes on to say, was the general principle underlying the uniting of enterprises using modern technological processes within a given territorial area. In addition to electric power supply, plans were made for a number of additional tie-ups which increase the economic advantages of the entire group. Most of these have already been realized. Each enterprise makes use of the products produced by the other enterprises located on the site. The steel for the rolling mills of the tool-steel plant comes from the 30-ton electric furnaces of the Dnieper steel works. The iron and steel plant, the open-hearth furnaces and the tool-steel plant get their ferro-alloys from the ferro-alloys plant. The ferro-alloys plant gets its electrodes from the electrode department of the aluminum plant. The slag-cement plant gets its slag from the blast furnaces. Very close power coordination has been established between these enterprises. In addition to the power coordination that usually exists between the various units of iron and steel combines (the use of a mixture of coke-oven gas and blast-furnace gas for heating open-hearth and rolling mill furnaces, the use of blast-furnace gas for heating coke ovens, etc.), a number of additional tie ups have been realized in the Zaporozhe industrial group. Coke, which is one of the constituent parts of the electric furnace charge in the manufacture of aluminum oxide, is supplied to the aluminum plant by the by-product coke plant. The coke plant also supplies the ferro-alloys plant with metallurgical coke and coke slack, which are part of the oven charge in the manufacture of ferro-alloys.[17]

In this case the planning of power utilization of the aluminum group—in turn tied up with and largely dependent upon multiple-function river development which promotes river navigation, flood control, irrigation, etc.—at the Dnieper dam site is correlated with the coke-oven, chemicals-processing, gas-producing, and ferroalloys complex of the near-by heavy industrial center of Zaporozhe. And these are, again, closely coördinated with similar combinations at the principal ore base, Krivoi Rog, and the principal fuel base, the Donets area. The only major change in this process of plant nucleation by the introduction of atomic power would be in the location of sites. The nature of the general complex of plants centered in chemical analyses or syntheses of basic raw materials would otherwise be unaltered. The power source would still be multiple purpose.

Quite similar, though originally not planned on a unified basis, has been the evolution of the Ruhr and the Pittsburgh heavy-industry areas. Another interesting example of a regional industrial complex is found in the "chemical valley" of the Kanawha River, in West Virginia, based on the "rich trinity of power, gas, and coal." Water power generated in the hills and along the main stream supplies the industries via a unified regional transmission grid. The industrial raw materials are natural gas, coal, and ferro-alloys, and by-products from coke ovens, natural gas refineries, oil refineries, and allied industries. The complex of industries built up around these raw materials and by-products is so closely interlaced as to constitute a balanced and interdependent unit of operations, the functioning of each of which is closely dependent upon the continuous and properly balanced functioning of all the others.

Strung out for miles upon the few available flats along the river are du Pont's great ammonia works at Belle, Monsanto's big rubber-chemicals unit at Nitro, Westvaco's giant chlorine plant at South Charleston, probably the biggest in the world, and various smaller alkali and coal-tar works in between. And overshadowing them all,

there is Union Carbide & Carbon Corp.'s vast city of chemicals, raising
its silvery tanks and towers over the river at South Charleston . . .[18]

In addition to these there are ferroalloy and glassmaking plants.
All are dependent upon the same basic raw materials; all share a
common dependence upon unified development of the valley's
water resources for power generation, transportation of heavy raw
materials, and industrial processing purposes; and all are dependent—either upon prior raw materials processing or for the
sale of important by-products—upon other plants in the valley for
their separate functioning.

A single, though perhaps the most spectacular, example will
suffice to illustrate the binding character of the technological
relationship. At South Charleston, located on an island in the
middle of the river and covering an area of 88 acres, sits a plant
which

. . . uses more water a day than the city of Buffalo and contains
more piping than a city the size of Rochester. The main raw material
is gas. Gas pipe lines converge on this hub in a vast underground network, feeding in some 15 million feet of mixed gases every twenty-
four hours. The gas comes from surrounding wells, from du Pont's coke
ovens at Belle, from the Pure Oil refinery and a small oil-cracking
unit on Carbide's own property, and from three raw-material plants
dotted around the country. These substations sit athwart natural-gas-
company lines, sifting out the heavier gas fractions for Carbide's special use and passing the bulk of the gas stream back into the mains,
little the worse for wear.[19]

From the complex of operations located at this one point comes
some 160-odd chemicals from the "great chemical tree" of the
hydrocarbons, possessing among them a bewildering variety of
ultimate-consumer and further industrial-processing uses.

In summary, each of these plants is dependent upon the functioning of the others. All are bound together in a complex of operations which unites them in a pattern closely analogous to that
which binds together the different operations feeding into an
assembly line in a single mass-production plant. The technological
interdependence covers raw materials, by-products, transportation, water utilization, and power generation and transmission.
The volume and timing of the flow and requirements of each

plant, and of each major operation in each separate plant, must be closely and directly adjusted to that of all the others. Stoppage at any one point tends, like the breaking of a link in a chain, to arrest the functioning of all the other links. Ideally, the whole concert should be planned and operated as a unified whole, and practice appears in certain sectors to have closely approximated this goal in the Kanawha Valley. The continuous and automatically synchronized operations of the individual plant and its various joint and by-products processes[20] provide the patterns which govern the broad relations binding the several plants of the region into a balanced regional chemicals-complex. The unit of appropriate technological planning, accordingly, is not the plant but the concert of plants; not the local plant grouping but that of the region as a whole.

NUCLEATIONAL PATTERNS AND AUTOMATIC PLANT OPERATION
IN CHEMICALS INDUSTRIES

As a little familiarity with the evolution of chemical industries will quickly show, the four types of agglutinative patterns do not exhaust the variation, and they are not mutually exclusive. Thus, the use of petroleum-refinery by-product gas in the mixed gas supply for plants such as the South Charleston works in the Kanawha Valley may serve to link together the first two types described above. Power plays a fairly important role in all chemical processing, and the "gravitational pull" of plentiful supplies of low-cost power—using the example of the Dnieper dam—merely combines with the "pulls" associated with chemical breakdown and by-product utilization of coal, ore, nonferrous metals, and ferroalloys in centers located at Dneprostroi, Zaporozhe, Krivoi Rog, Rostov, and other satellite regional complexes. As indicated briefly above, plant nucleations centered in analysis may be combined with nuclei centered in synthesis. Many other combinations are possible, and any of these associated with chemical production may, in turn, be combined with factors (to be discussed in the following chapter) which favor nucleation of certain types of mechanical and manufacturing industries, such as machine, machine tool, and textile industries.

Two main points emerge from an examination of these developments. First is that each plant of a complex, just as with every process within the plant, tends increasingly and throughout to be placed on a continuous-flow basis, where all steps in analysis or synthesis are controlled by automatically operating, self-correcting control instruments. The ultimate is reached when all such control devices are linked into a series of interlocking control panels, and these in turn into a single central panel (automation). This has actually been achieved already in a number of outstanding cases—in most of the new petroleum refineries, and in the plants at South Charleston referred to above. Where this has been accomplished we are faced with the "automatic plant"— operating continuously 24 hours a day, and every day in the year. The biggest "cat-cracker" (catalytic cracking) plant of the Esso Standard Oil Company, built in 1949, was capable of producing 41,000 barrels a day, ran entirely on instruments, and needed a crew of only seven men.[21]

Such a plant will achieve its theoretical ultimate in over-all operating efficiency in proportion as it is able to combine these features: (1) standardization of the input of raw materials if the process is analytic, and of chemical components if the process is synthetic; (2) continuous flow from process to process, with no inventoried or stored batches awaiting further processing, and with each step adjusted in terms of timing and volume of flow; (3) a system of gauges and recording and control devices which automatically test the flow (e.g., for chemical purity, pressures, and volume) and which employ "feed-back" principles in making corrective adjustments; and (4) interconnection of all such gauges and devices by electronic methods into control panels for each major segment of processing, and even into a central control panel.

A second main point is the interlinkage of separate plants on something approaching the same principles as those governing within the plants themselves. As this happens, the unit of direct reference tends, in the engineering sense, to become the complex of plants. Here again the case of the Kanawha Valley network of plants will illustrate. Similar are the huge complexes of by-product plants operating over the stream of oil and natural gas coming from the earth at either end of the great pipeline networks—

taking by-products from the flow and returning oil or gas to the lines for ultimate users—wherein each separate plant and each separate process from the well to the ultimate user is part of a synchronized web of interdependent plants. Flexibilities may be built in so that breakdown or alteration of the processes of analysis or synthesis of chemicals may be changed at will at any given and specific point. But the operating ideal is continuous, unbroken flow between plants similar to that obtaining within the single automatically functioning plant.

Even where the engineering links are less directly binding—where, for example, the separate plants are not linked by direct panel-board control—the ideal is the closest possible approximation to the situation where they would be so interlocked. The ideal, that is to say, is a unit of production planning which is no longer the plant nor even the enterprise. Just as once the separate and discrete steps which broke up the processes of production into several production units in the handicraft period were combined in the factory in the early days of the Industrial Revolution, so now, and in an analogous way, separate plants in the more important chemical industries are united in vast combinations which are increasingly planned and integrated as unified, interlocked, and continuously functioning complexes. As long as factors of an engineering and cost-accounting nature are allowed to dominate, this mode of reorganizing the materials foundation of a modernized industrial system will be deepened, widened, and generalized over the bulk of the mass-output chemical industries.

There is a point, however, in most chemical industries where factors promoting plant agglutination begin to give way to influences which promote regional decentralization and scattering. These do not so much run counter to the foregoing tendencies as they tend to supplement and round them out. Nor do they decrease the emphasis upon long-range development planning. Rather do they favor extension of a different type of planning—one that silts off the maximum range of analysis and synthesis from these nucleating cores and scatters them widely in keeping with quite other considerations which play significant roles in the broad program for putting the organization of production onto a thoroughly scientific basis. Two or three examples will suffice.

DISPERSION OR SCATTERING PATTERNS
IN THE CHEMICAL INDUSTRIES

In general it follows that where power grids exist, and where refining methods of the less bulky and smaller-volume chemical
by-products are largely or wholly dominated by electrothermal
and electrolytic processes, chemical industries may be widely
scattered. Where some of the processes are large scale, such as
in some of the metallurgical branches, they will tend to be sucked
into the major industrial complexes discussed above. Comparatively small specialized plants, however, will best be located
wherever cheap power is available. Since the ratio of power cost
may be relatively high, but the total volume of electric use both
comparatively low and evenly distributed throughout the days
and seasons, they may be located at any point not too far distant
from a regional power grid.

Within any given grid these plants, because of their high-load
factors, tend to raise the level of off-peak power usage by increasing the ratio of base to peak load, and hence to improve the
factors promoting most efficient use of power facilities.

If, then, power is available from the grid, plants may be located
with respect to chemical nuclei depending upon the combination
of several factors. For example, if the electrothermal or electrolytic process uses one or several by-products from a major nucleated chemicals complex such as that of iron and steel, or of
petroleum, and markets for the finished product are near, then
these industries may be located at or near the major plants.
Otherwise, markets or sources of raw materials will dominate,
and plants will be scattered without regard to proximity to the
nuclei.

Markets will tend to dominate particularly where highly specialized end-products are produced from several highly refined
chemical components which may be shipped considerable distances at low cost from a variety of widely scattered major chemical industries. Conversely, raw materials will tend to dominate
where the scale of optimum-size operations may be comparatively
small, and where either bulky and low-value raw materials, such
as sugar beets, may be put through an initial refining process, or

where the end product is high in value and low in bulk, as in many of the pharmaceuticals and the more recent antibiotic industries.

There are a good many other locational determinants in addition to these, and they may combine in many different ways. In general, chemical industries tend to scatter if one or more of such factors or conditions as the following are dominant:

First, wherever resources are widely scattered geographically, the optimum-sized unit of operation is comparatively small, and the ratio of shipping costs of the finished or semifinished product to shipping costs of the raw materials is relatively low. Good examples are found in various forest and agricultural by-product industries. Thus the production of rosin and turpentine in the longleaf slash pine belt of the southeastern United States is conducted in some "1,018 plants that distill pine gum and in 26 plants that use pine stumps." [22] A similar possibility is found in the plans for extensive by-product utilization of forest waste in the pine, fir, spruce, and hemlock forests of the Pacific Northwest, where it is estimated that at present some two-thirds of tree growth is thrown away in lumbering and milling operations. Small plants located near foresting and milling sites can turn the waste into plastics, turpentine, alcohol, and numerous other commodities. National and regional plans for building up local forest resources will tend further to widen the possible scattering of small chemical plants for making plastics, rayon, paper, soaps, paint, and similar forest products.[23]

Other fields are the initial processing of agricultural commodities such as beet and cane sugar, soybeans, cottonseed, and olive oil; the quick-freezing of fruits and vegetables; and use of surplus milk and agricultural wastes for making products ranging from cheese to plastics. Still further possibilities are provided in the use of local earth, mineral, and clay products for making sulphur, salt, lime, brick, glass, fertilizer raw materials, etc.

A second condition exists wherever by-products from major and large-scale chemical industries are adaptable to the production of many different products having a wide range of highly specialized uses, and where most of the production processes require specialized but small plants. Such are the various alcohols, materials out of which are made paints, varnishes, lacquers, soaps, and solvents, cosmetics, caustic soda, ammonia, many pharmaceuticals, and a large number of similar chemicals.

A third is that which exists wherever (a) fuel, power, and transportation facilities are widely and intricately meshed, so that plants located at any point may be assured of adequate continuous service, (b) rates are adjusted to favor local industry and promote either continuous local service or off-peak usage, or both, and (c) local markets are capable of absorbing all or the bulk of local products—as with canned and preserved foods. In most cases the centrifugal pull of these factors will simply be added to those indicated above.

A further category, hardly to be termed a "factor or condition" for small-sized plants in the chemicals industry, perhaps can be called a "mood" or a "state of mind." If research and engineering were specifically and deliberately directed toward the discovery of processes and methods appropriate for small-scale plants which would make use of local and limited resources, many additional possibilities might turn up. For example, new developments in the very old sponge-iron process of ore reduction may make it possible—in a unit having a daily capacity of not more than from 100 to 200 tons—to produce iron at costs competitive with or possibly even cheaper than those of the huge blast furnaces. (In contrast, one blast furnace produces around 800 tons a day.) The Brassert process would require no coking coal at all. The Humboldt process, developed by the Kloeckner-Humboldt-Deutz Company in Germany, is not, like the blast-furnace process, a batch process, but a completely continuous process which uses "Non-coking coals rich in gas and tar" and ore fires to produce pig iron in a "low-shaft distillation furnace" which is "only one third the size of conventional blast furnaces, yet tonnages of iron from both units are equal." [24] The use of electric furnaces, where the economical unit of operation is even smaller, only 64 tons a day, also favors small local plants using local ores and catering to local markets.

There are other examples that might be offered. The turbo-hearth is a method of making steel in some 12 minutes instead of the 12 hours required by the ordinary open-hearth furnace, and the economical-sized unit is only about one-tenth as large—30 tons as against 225 tons. Continuous casting may mean that the economical size of a steel mill can be reduced from something like 1 million tons annual output to about 100,000 tons. Research might turn up many similar examples. Some of this research might be extremely simple, and some might be confined wholly to economics. Thus, beer is mostly water. When it is brewed at large central establishments, vast amounts of water and glass bottles or metal cans are unnecessarily shipped about the country. Almost any local water under proper chemical control—contrary to commonly accepted opinion—is good enough for making beer, and a very small local plant can now be mechanized completely so as to compete effectively with quite large central plants. Similar considerations hold for wineries and distilleries. There may be numerous other examples.

In addition to the engineering and economic factors, there may be a number of supplemental considerations of a broadly social character which will tend to favor geographic scattering of chemical industries. Among these are (*a*) conservation measures which require making use of valuable forest, agricultural, and mining by-products and wastes; (*b*) the building up of renewable local resources in agricultural and forest products which have been declining in the past; (*c*) the obtaining of a better balance in rural districts between industrial and agricultural or other seasonal employments; (*d*) health and cultural reasons for favoring the ruralization or shift to small towns of industries without serious prejudice to costs (perhaps, on the contrary, with gains in the form of lower costs), in order to reverse population concentration in major metropolitan areas; and (*e*) the decreasing of crosshaulage of raw materials and finished products, thereby reducing also the demand for transportation facilities.

The development of chemical industries which may be widely scattered geographically, in consequence, is apt to be thought of in connection with such problems as planning of river valley multiple-purpose projects, agricultural and regional land planning, the planning of transportation and power-transmission grids, and plans for the general decentralization of population, industry, and trade. The heavier, however, the emphasis may be along these lines, the more careful must be the planning of the relationships between decentralized chemical industries and the major nucle-ated chemical combinations briefly outlined in the foregoing pages. The technological and other interconnections among these various branches of the chemical industries are so close, so intri-cate, and so binding that a long view in the planning of any one necessarily demands a long view in the planning of the others. Within the chemical system, the possibilities of duplicating and overlapping are seemingly infinite. At the same time, the chemi-cal process itself is one which advances by steady shifting of the bulk of costs onto an overhead basis where continuous produc-tion at full capacity becomes the manufacturing ideal. The pri-mary means of lowering costs is to step up capacity and load factors, and to force down to the barest possible minimum all unnecessary storage, transportation, and other expenses.

Whether the plant be small or large, local or part of an indus-trial complex, the primary process is typically on a continuous-flow basis. To accomplish this calls for a continuous flow of raw materials to chemical plants, a continuous flow from one step or stage or plant to the next, and from each unit to its consumers or markets. The central core, and many of the peripheral off-shoots, of the leading chemical industries must, accordingly, tend more and more to be planned as though they were made up of single, intricately balanced, meticulously dovetailed, flexible, and synchronized productive complexes. And the balance of the smaller, local, and more specialized plants come then to be devel-oped in relation, at once, to these central nuclei and to other plans which deal with other utilities and industries in which analogous considerations favor similar planning efforts.

SUMMARY AND CONCLUSIONS

For social scientists the swiftly spreading chemical revolution in the materials basis of the industrial system prescribes a new and radically different view of the nature and limits of resources, ma-terials, and possible end products. It is as though a limited and cramped world had suddenly discovered a vast new continent where not only all the old materials were to be found in great abundance, but where also myriads of new and exotic minerals, lands, plants, and animals were to be found on all sides. Here the scientific laboratory plays the role of discoverer and explorer, while engineering stands by to transmute the new possibilities immediately into useful products through the medium of a new type of mass-production system.

This new type of mass-production system is rapidly becoming prototypal for all processing and manufacturing methods of this type of industrial order. In its highest expression, (*a*) plants are automatic or near-automatic; (*b*) new and different factors favor plant agglutination and plant scattering patterns, irrespective of property lines or corporate division of ownership; (*c*) the rationale of interplant flows is adapted after and, in effect, modeled upon the pattern of intraplant flows; (*d*) capacity and load factors approach the 100-per-cent limit; (*e*) all articles and their components are enveloped at each stage in systems of rigorously formulated standards and specifications drawn in keeping with physical chemical characteristics and so as to be functional to use; and (*f*) all or nearly all costs—investment and operating alike—tend cumulatively to take on an overhead character.

In the following chapter we will attempt to see how far these same patterns apply to the manufacturing industries.

VIII

The Permeation of Automation Processing

From its beginning the machine has been the heart of the industrial system. It is the object first brought to mind when one speaks of the Industrial Revolution. But this expression is no longer merely a way of delimiting a historical epoch. Clearly, the industrial system has no definite beginning in time, for the fundamental technical developments underlying its most important factory applications date far back in human history. More obvious still, it has had and probably can have no end. In scarcely any field has it even experienced a significant tapering-off in growth, change, and development. A "machine civilization," such as we are coming to know it now, is one of continuing, and possibly accelerating, revolution. Owning to the spread and permeation of machine methods throughout the productive operations of the economy as a whole, the revolution goes on simultaneously in technology per se and in economic life.

These two aspects of the "continuous revolution" are closely related. The revolution in technology tends generally and cumulatively to place production on a mass-output basis, and to find ways of applying machine methods to more and more materials, processes, and objects. These interact to cheapen production, widen markets, raise material standards of living, and focus increasing attention on the need and desire for further spread and application of machine methods. And, with the permeation of machine processing throughout the economy, the physical means of life undergo a continuing transmutation which changes attitudes toward industrial methods themselves while at the same time raising vast new problems which promote still further adjustment of manners and morals, work habits, and outlooks. But, also, there arise equally vast new problems of the methods and organization of the very machine operations themselves. These problems are of such a complex and difficult order that there is little poetic license in referring to them as the problems of developing a *scientific factory system for society as a whole*.

Here we are concerned solely with the latter set of problems— with the production problems raised by the scientific and technological advances in machine methods. More specifically, we are concerned with the interactions among three specific types of developments: first, with the perfection of the individual machine until it becomes completely automatic; second, with the weaving together of individual automatic or semiautomatic machines into continuously operating and automatically controlled processes— the "automatic plant"; and, third, with the problem of interprocess coördination of separate plants, each of which has been placed largely, or fully, on an "automatic plant" basis. For reasons which quickly become obvious, it is the last of these three which is coming, sometimes furtively, sometimes openly, to dominate analysis, research, discussion, and policy as a whole. In the larger industrial sphere, what appears to be shaping up, with the inevitability of glacial action, is the gradual *de facto* application of one or another of the aspects of automatic machine-operations to the industrial system at large. And whatever is accomplished along this line has the reciprocal effect of bringing about further radical alteration in machine construction and plant operations.

A word of warning is in order. As elsewhere throughout this study, descriptive details are not offered as typical or characteristic of the current historical facts, but as foreshadowing a coming structure of things which is in line with past developments of a significant character. Such analysis of facts and trends as may be offered is limited to an establishment of the larger social-science implications of continued developments along such lines. The problem at this point is to outline the implications of an injection into the sequences of manufacturing of the sorts of rigorous controls and timing schedules associated with production at or near the level of complete automation—not only upon the

individual plant, but upon congeries of plants and the manufacturing system as a whole.

The idea, furthermore, is not one of mere "relatedness" or
market "interdependence." In effect, the end result of the continuing industrial revolution, as we may view it now, is the extension outward of the design and operating rules governing the
individual automatic or semiautomatic machine not only to the
entire round of factory operations within the given plant, but
to a widening concert of related and coöperating plants. Veblen,
in the passage quoted early in this book, appears to have had
something of this sort in mind when he wrote that "By virtue of
this concatenation of processes the modern industrial system at
large bears the character of a comprehensive, balanced mechanical process." [1] There is doubtless some poetic license in this characterization. Yet, within most modern industries, groups of plants
are becoming interconnected in such a way that, just as the adequate functioning of the individual machine means that part must
be adjusted to part, process to process, and the volume, timing,
and flow of materials and energy synchronized, so it is coming
to be with congeries of plants themselves. Everywhere and
throughout, each step in mechanization, dovetailing, and intersti-
tial adjustment within and among plants favors taking the next
step. And every such step still further widens the arc of useful
interprocess and interplant coördination, integration, and unification.

Certain of the essential facts in this picture were brought home
sharply to the American public during the Second World War and
its aftermath. Wherever subcontracting took place on an extensive scale, as with the aircraft and shipbuilding industries, there
were as many potential bottlenecks, as many operations schedules
to be coördinated, as there were plants subcontracting. It became
apparent during the war that a single bomb might knock out a
single ball-bearing plant and thereby cripple a large segment of
the German war machine. More recently, strikes in steel, coal,
automobile, and other so-called "key industries" have demonstrated the sensitive interdependencies which link the American
productive mechanism together. Disruption at any key point
might spread interruption widely and rapidly to a thousand and
more points. But the central fact is not that the industrial system

is becoming inflexible, as some alarmists feel, but that it is becoming so increasingly sensitive in interprocess and interplant adjustments as to call for new types and levels of organization. More than that, the nature of the adjustments is such as to call for interplant coördination very similar to the type gradually being evolved for the purpose of linking all processes together within a balanced, automatically controlled, and continuously functioning mass-output plant. Development, organization, management, administration, and policy must then accept planning on an extensive and exacting scale.

The productive potentials of success in such an outward extension of planning are enormous—far beyond the dreams, in fact, of even an efficiency-minded people such as Americans in the middle of the twentieth century. But the conditions for this enormous output are also exacting in the field of the relevant technology. They are made doubly—not less—exacting by any effort to build in, as a basic technical component, the highly desirable feature of flexible adjustment to future changes in engineering methods, products, the structure of costs, or the needs and wants of the consuming population.

Here, although the technical details are extremely complex, the larger picture of forces coöperating to promote planning for long-range development are readily within the grasp of the layman. Attention to a few of the more important details is inescapable—while holding these to the minimum—yet it will be found that most of them already have a familiar ring. It is only the revolutionary implications for human organization that are but little understood.

Consider, first, the product of a logical extension, rounding out, and rationalization of the engineering and cost laws governing machine operation per se.

INTERLACING IN THE FACTORY "MICROCOSM": FROM AUTOMATIC MACHINERY TO THE AUTOMATIC PLANT

Among the several interesting ways in which the evolution of the factory system might be traced, of central importance would be the gradual shift away from the situation where the machine was introduced as a helper in an otherwise handicraft system to the place where the roles of man and machine are reversed. The term "manufacturing"—meaning literally "hand-factoring"—has been carried on from the earlier stage when the machine took over certain limited and especially heavy, or arduous, or simple, or entirely uniform and repetitive operations. As long as the bulk of the operations were handicraft, the machine remained essentially an auxiliary. Even where this was less true, as in early mechanized spinning and weaving, yet in the main the attendant operator set the machine pace and continuously serviced many detailed operations of the machine itself. In the early steam engines, even the inflow and discharge of steam from the piston chamber were regulated by hand.

The perfection of the machine, however, tended everywhere to reverse this role. There were two main steps. First was the step of reducing the operative to a mere attendant whose pace of work and specialized functions were set by machines. Charlie Chaplin's motion picture, *Modern Times*, caricatured this state of affairs for all time.

The second step was associated with the first, and grew out of it. It was the transferring of the machine into a self-feeding, self-operating, and self-discharging mechanism. It is very easy to accomplish in some cases, very difficult in others. There are some fields where it may never become entirely complete. But where it *can* be carried through, the roles of machine and operative are radically altered. The operative ceases to be the robotized, exhausted, bedraggled, and dehumanized hero of *Modern Times* and becomes the supervisor who guides, oversees, repairs, and redirects the machine. And the machine takes over, step by step, the entire round of factory operations.

How? Consider first the machine itself. Take a single example from contemporary experience: the ribbon machine for the automatic production of glass incandescent-lamp bulbs. This machine, capable of turning out 600 to 800 bulb blanks per minute, represents a fusion of a series of processes which were performed heretofore by separate machines and required considerable auxiliary labor. Now the one machine runs endlessly and continuously, and requires a single attendant and no more than occasional repair work to keep it going. When not producing light bulbs it can turn out Christmas-tree ornaments, radio tubes, tumblers, and other glass products. Each shift requires but little time and expense.

The ribbon machine offers a fairly complex exhibit of phenomena common to all completely automatized processes. A few of these are of crucial importance. (1) At the highest level, from the point of materials feed to discharge of the finished product all operations are completely automatic. Each component operation is simple, repetitive, and continuous; variations within the complex of machine operations in volume and timing do not occur from operation to operation but are completely synchronized; and the concert of synchronized operations is under the direction of gauges, recording instruments, and controls which may at will be reset and manipulated by the operator at the control panel board. (2) The motive power is electric; internal synchronization is affected by gears, pulleys, or shafting driven by power from the same source or by separate motors subject to common panelboard control, and the control panels themselves are electronic. (3) The material fed into the machine is (relatively) standard, uniform, and constant in size and shape or in physical and chemical properties; and output is standard and uniform with respect to size, shape, chemicophysical content, and variety within the tolerance limits built into the construction of the machine. (4) Flow of material into the machine is as regular, as constant, and as variable as is the output, but the ideal is continuous, mechanically or electronically regulated inflow and outflow at the highest level of capacity of the machine throughout the entire length of the run. (5) The fewer and the longer the separate runs, the closer does capacity operation come to mean 24 hours a day and 365 days in the year.

Suppose, now that each stage in the total process of production were similarly mechanized, what then would we have? Simply, the "automatic plant." The ideal in machine operations, that is to say, is the equivalent in mechanical processing of what we have already found general in mass-output chemical processing. The A. O. Smith Corporation's Milwaukee plant for turning out automobile frames will illustrate an early application (1921) of these methods of manufacturing. Here, in a plant covering two city-blocks, is found a large mass of highly specialized machines geared together so as to operate as though parts of a single "machine." Strip steel, picked up from boxcars on the siding where it is inspected and accepted or rejected, is then twisted, punched, and trimmed, and the members are pressed together, riveted, finished, and tested, in one continuous series of mechanical and completely automatic steps requiring but 90 minutes from boxcar to storage yard (or other boxcar) at the end of the production line. At full speed the plant will turn out 10,000 frames per day, and requires but 200 men, only 50 of whom ever come in contact with the steel in process. The working force was decreased by 95 per cent per volume of output over nonautomatic methods. The over-all cost, when high obsolescence and development costs were added in, and although the plant has rarely been able to operate continuously at full capacity, was still about one-third under that of alternative methods.[2]

Because of built-in flexible systems of jigs and fixtures, the process is highly adaptable, and relatively short interruptions are required to make the necessary change-over before beginning to turn out different sizes and types of frames. At a time when it could have supplied all the frames required for all the automobiles produced in the United States the plant was turning out over thirty different sizes and shapes. But the process per se is capable of even further adaptation. For example, this plant can be adapted to form sheet steel into butt-welded pipe at the rate of 35 miles of pipe a day. Other products that can be turned out are high-pressure steel vessels for oil, chemical, and brewery industries, and hot-water storage tanks. For any of the products, furthermore, the machinery is adaptable in terms of an extraordinarily wide range of combinations of widths, lengths, thicknesses, shapes, and qualities.

There are many other fields in which approximations to this plant have been effected. An outstanding and spectacular example is the automatic strip mill for making sheet steel referred to in the previous chapter. With benefit of a little romancing,

. . . a hand-mill is a hot, noisy place, crowded with old style equipment [and] squads of workers waiting about while others relieve them for short periods at the furnaces. In one such mill of this character the "iron" is handled more than fifty times by tongs and hands before the process is finished.

In a modern strip mill all this vanishes. The place is cool and spacious. A few workers, some scattered about in over-head control booths pushing buttons, handle the "iron" in one operation. Here a huge slab as big as a mattress but weighing several thousand pounds is automatically released from a furnace, rolled into a coil a thousand feet long like a thread on a spool, placed on a conveyor and put through more continuous operations until it is cut into sheets for your automobiles or plates (later tinned) for your canned soup. All the horde of men who once were employed in the making of steel are swept away, leaving a few watchful men guarding controls.[3]

In testimony before a United States Senate committee, in 1940, it was estimated that these mills had already displaced some 38,470 workers, and, when further change-overs then in prospect were carried through, would eventually displace a grand total of 84,770.[4]

Essentially the same picture holds for papermaking, seamless tube production, a wide range of small but essential components-parts production—such as gears, screws, ball and roller bearings—and many other types of industrial operations. There are few cases of mass-output and general-utility producers' or consumers' goods where it may not apply in whole or in large part even now. Just as with chemical processing, in the mechanical industries this is the dominant pattern for future plants.

It is worthwhile pausing to note more precisely just what is involved, for the productive potentialities of such plants—in many cases without much or any additional capital investment per volume of output, and in all cases with drastically reduced general operating costs—are enormous. Norbert Wiener, in his epoch-making book *Cybernetics* (derived from the Greek word for "steersman") believes the change-over of such momentous importance as to justify describing the present time as the "age of servo-mechanisms." [5]

In general, the change-over to the automatic plant is merely an extension, as remarked above, of the internal organization of an automatic machine. But let us note carefully what this means.

First, here also, as with the individual automatic machine, power-plant generation and transmission are separated from the power-using or working operations, and the entire concert of productive operations is electrically driven or electrically controlled, or both. With the electrification of machine operations, power is separated in far-removed electrical generating plants, and transmitted to the factory user over a grid network. Power generation and transmission have been technologically collectivized. Only half of the former plant—the machine-working part —remains a technically individual unit. There are exceptional cases where large power generation on the site may supply part, or on occasion all, of the electricity used in a given plant, but in the main the trend is overwhelmingly in the other direction.

Second, the individual machine is itself designed and scaled in size to serve as a mere link in a mechanized *process*. The concert of steps is dovetailed among the machines just as are the individual parts within the separate automatic machines. In detail this means that (a) each stage or phase of production is in turn mechanized, (b) each mechanized process is rendered automatic, (c) materials handling between processing operations is mechanized by use of automatic "transfer" devices and synchronized with the machines served, and (d) at every step and with respect to every phase of materials handling and processing, all materials, all machines, all materials and machine components, and all methods of rating, operating, testing, and controlling are enveloped in a system of standard terms, sizes, dimensions, qualities, and rules for operation and use.

Finally, the actual synchronization of the servo-mechanisms guiding each individual automatic machine is effected by electronic devices gathered together on a central control panel-board. What does "control" mean? A special study of this problem in connection with the automatic plant summarizes the concept this way:

Fundamentally control is the sending of messages which effectively change the behavior of the recipient. When dealing with control mechanisms (or communication machines) we can classify these messages into two broad categories, (1) the messages which direct the machine to initiate its operation, state what that operation is to be, and determine the extent of the operation—these are messages originating with man or another machine—and (2) the messages which inform the control device of the extent and direction of its own action. The first type of message is called the *taping* (derived from the frequent use of paper or metal tape, with punched holes or magnetic areas acting as a coded form of input message) and the second type is called feedback.[6]

How this operates in detail has been described in the report of the Harvard group in the design of "An Automatic Piston Factory." It will suffice to say here that the taped messages are instructions from the control device to individual machines to operate at given speeds, or in a certain manner, and that feedback involves a method of reporting and checking on accomplishments which automatically corrects speed, flow, and quality of performance. This means the elimination of all storage of materials in process. Production runs are long, but over-all adaptations can be made in most cases for relatively short runs. All or nearly all of the staff occupy supervisory, repair, research, or other office positions. Salary and wage costs tend to become overhead in character. Drastic reductions are made in space and number of employees per unit of production (see table 5 for some interesting examples). In the pioneering A. O. Smith Corporation plant, 200 men were needed to operate the plant at virtually any level of production from zero output to the limit of capacity, while several thousand additional employees—mostly engineers, scientists, and allied technicians (working in a $1,500,000 laboratory)—were engaged solely in perfecting and refining existing methods and in development work on new methods and applications.

So much for the individual automatic plant. But just as automation of individual machines and part processes tends to encourage the evolution of the automatic plant, so do automatic plants tend to become interlocked in a direct engineering fashion with other plants related in the larger sequences of production. Before turning to this larger problem, let us note how it is forecast by the development of the automatic plant itself. If, for example, the materials fed into the plant, raw or semifinished, must conform to the plant standard with respect to sizes and dimensions, or physical purity and quality, then the conditions have been determined for the plants supplying these materials, and these conditions are precisely the ones also favoring at the same points the

TABLE 5

PERCENTAGE CHANGE IN REQUIREMENTS FOR SPACE AND EMPLOYEES
IN PROCESSES WHICH WERE AUTOMATED

Process	Percentage change (per unit of output)	
	Space	Employees
Grain sorghum plant[a]	−62	−50
Continuous-flow napalm	−45	−77
Printed-circuit fabrication	−12	−13
Lard rendering	−94	−83
Chocolate refining	−83	−85
Bottling line	−76	−82
Plant maintenance, lubrication	...	−87
Univac computer	−86	−92
Belt conveyer[a]	−81	−85
Centralized traffic control[a]	−20	−62
Railroad classification yard[a]	−20	−20
Electricity generation	−68	−58

SOURCE: David G. Osborn, *Geographical Features of the Automation of Industry* (Chicago: University of Chicago Press, 1953), p. 73.

[a] Cases marked thus were measured in terms of acreage; other cases, in square feet of floor area.

automatic plant to turn out standardized products or components.

Or, again, if a good case is to be made for the elimination of storage or rehandling between machines in a plant now being made automatic, so also is there a good case for the elimination of storage in the supply of materials to the plant and in the commodities produced by it. Thus the automatic plant tends to favor a condition where the railroad cars, or trucks, or other supply media bring materials to the plant and carry products away from it in a smooth and continuous flow which is adjusted in terms of volume and timing to avoid, as far as possible, all accumulations or storage. Transport media come then to serve as though they were endless belts or parts of automatic conveyer systems connecting interprocess materials-handling within the plant itself. It is not at all inconceivable that something like the automatic and electronic devices employed in power-plant generation of electric current and grid-line performance, alluded to below in chapter x, might not come to be applied to concerts of coöperating successive- or complementary-step mechanical plants.

How far are we dealing here with a mere figure of speech?

INTERLACING IN THE INDUSTRIAL "MACROCOSM":
FROM AUTOMATIC PLANT TO AUTOMATIC FACTORY SYSTEMS

It was not difficult to see in connection with the chemical industries how automatic processing led directly to the interlacing of such plants on an "automatic" or at least "semiautomatic" basis. The cases of the metallurgical-chemical complexes of coal, coke, iron, steel, and by-products, or of the Kanawha chemical complex (chap. vii) will illustrate. In these, quite clearly, each more or less fully unified and separate automatic plant becomes, so to speak, a self-regulating "organic" unit in a larger "organism" of which it is a component part.

The analogy itself requires some explanation. The organic analogy, of course, is always extremely dangerous. In this context it is in danger of implying, if not used with the most clearly expressed reservations, a sort of technological "corporativeness." It is the nature of the "corporative" concept that it gratuitously adds to interdependence the concept of utter regimentation of parts by a superior authority governing arbitrarily over the whole, and that its characteristic mood is that of the static, the fixed, and the changeless. This is the opposite of what is meant here. The basic technology itself is highly dynamic. It can be shown that it is difficult, if not impossible, to make it function effectively at any given level without the maximum freedom of initiative of that type of informed, participating, and coöperative-minded "free-roving intelligence" which we commonly associate in its highest expression with the scientific outlook. Furthermore, the purpose of all the vast activity and change leading to the analogy of the "organism" in this context can become the freeing of the entire human race—not just a privileged few—from the life-and-death struggle with personality-degrading toil, giving it both the material perquisites and the freedom for really living "the good life." The problem here is one of technology, not of men. Machines cannot enslave or regiment men; only men and society can accomplish that inversion.

With these reservations clearly in mind,[7] however, the organic analogy has a limited usefulness. In the human body, the brain—as the biologist sees it—is part of the nervous system; the lungs, of the respiratory system; the heart, of the circulatory system; the stomach, of the digestive system. Each of these systems is, so to speak, an internally unified and wholly interdependent system throughout all its parts. And each of these systems is related to and interdependent with the continuous functioning of the other systems that constitute the body as a whole. In a general way the individual automatic machine may be compared to the separate organ indicated in each of the foregoing systems. The interlinkage of electrically synchronized and automatic machines may be compared to that which unites the separate organic processes that in each case make up the circulatory system, the respiratory system, etc. But the final type of interlinkage, comparable to that which unites in a common web of mutual interdependencies the several circulatory, respiratory, digestive systems, etc., also takes place in the mechanical industries as a whole.

It takes place on the technological level in two different ways. In the first, each of the separate plants is centered in the completion of a major stage or step in the processing from raw materials to finished product. This is the common case of vertical integration—though the expression generally refers to ownership rather than to technological integration. An outstanding example is coordination among the spinning, weaving, and dyeing plants in the textile industries. In the second, the separate plants produce component parts which are separately assembled either in a centrally located plant or in a series of widely scattered assembly plants (as with the automobile, farm machinery, machine tool, aircraft, and, to a limited extent, shipbuilding industries). These two types are, quite obviously, not necessarily mutually exclusive, and may be combined in a number of ways.

In general, it may be said that any consistent attempt to think through the nature and implications of these confluent trends will show that they consist, in effect, as pointed out above, of an outward extension of the functioning rules governing the operation of the individual automatic machine in such a way as to embrace whole series of plants and industries.

But what is not so obvious is the fact that these changes, enormously advantageous as they are in terms of net gains in productivity,[8] do not mean a single, frozen pattern. On the contrary, paralleling the requirements for closer synchronization is a series of possibilities which are capable of introducing a high and growing degree of flexibility and adaptability without sacrificing—in fact, while enhancing—the capacity to produce under conditions of falling costs. But these, in turn, cannot be realized without a strong emphasis on long-run and comprehensive planning in the manufacturing industries as a whole.

Once again, it is necessary to be explicit. Referring back to the preceding chapter, we have shown the tendency for the bulk of the raw materials supply of the leading manufacturing industries to be placed on a chemical basis employing mass-output, continuous-processing, and automatic-control methods. These plants must now be synchronized both with the plants of their principal users and with each other. This is not, as it might well seem at first glance, a mere matter of purchase and sale of the requisite supplies from whatever sources may be available. What is wanted is less a knowledge of alternative supply sources and more a definite and carefully defined flow of standard, uniform, raw or semimanufactured materials from a variety of plants, all or the bulk of which are organized, or are being transformed, along the aforementioned lines. If at each step the plants forwarding products, as well as the plants receiving them, are organized on the automatic or semiautomatic basis, then supply becomes more and more a problem of engineering control over the properties and volume of the flow. The problem becomes one of securing an interplant linkage of production processes, in which volumetric adjustments and the timing of flow may be said to resemble the production process within the separate plants.

To the extent to which this happens, where once there were a series of discrete steps between plants, now there is continuous flow from one to the other. Where once inventories were largely made up of goods in storage between steps in production, now inventories are primarily, if not wholly, made up of materials in process or in continuous movement between manufacturing or processing plants at spatially removed sites. Where once adjustment of schedules and output with each other was a matter of chance, now they are technically linked directly together. In a simple figure, the numerous little rivulets from the minor first-processing plants combine with the larger tributaries flowing from the major supply pools of the more important components, and, via these larger tributaries, all are woven by conscious plan into the great "river system" which dispatches end products from the assembly lines in an immense and widening flood.

But with this figure, the value of this analogy also ceases. What must be imagined is that the "little waters" which flow into the major tributaries, and the tributaries themselves, are dependent upon each other in three additional senses. In the first place, the types of products flowing into the main stream at various points are not, like the confluent waters in a river system, the same, but are numerous and varied.

The fact that these streams supply different products, none of which is dispensable, means, in the second place, that each must supply a designated amount in a smooth and even flow, and that the failure of any one flow to enter the larger stream with the precise type of goods, in the precise amount, and at the precise time, necessarily means reduction in the flow of all the other streams. In the limiting case, total "drying-up" of any one flow would mean the complete choking-back of all the others. In actual practice, to be sure, no dovetailing is ever quite so demanding as this, since the possibilities of even severely limited storage, materials substitutability, etc., provide considerable flexibility in adjustment. Nevertheless, the whole general trend in manufacture is toward ever closer interlacing in type, volume, and timing of flow, and hence, toward the conditions that hold for the limiting case.

Finally, this interdependence is gradually becoming too tight, too necessitous, too rigorous, and too exacting to be handled as a problem of marketing adjustment. Whether integrated vertically or "confluently" through ownership relations or not, the plan which oversees and supervises the meshing is slowly being rationalized throughout the mass-production industries into the patterns of architecture and engineering. The model, so to speak, is the mechanized factory at the automatic level, and as far as factors of engineering and cost accounting operate in this direction, these patterns show the following general characteristics:

(1) Each separate machine-factoring operation at each level or stage of production and for all supply components is placed on a close approximation to the automatic plant.

(2) The types, shapes, varieties, properties, qualities, methods, and controls over supplies produced in each plant whose output is confluent with, or effluent to, other similar plants are embraced in a single, comprehensive, and unified system of engineering standards for the whole of the product which converges toward any given assembly or semi-assembly operation, or which constitutes a step in a series of interlinked processes running from raw materials to finished products. Each part, or quality, or dimension, that is to say, is complementary or supplementary to all others, and constitutes an interchangeable unit or property within a framework which is, for each given part of property, for the moment fixed and unalterable for each given assembly model. Given a change in the model as designed in the drafting room and tested either in a pilot-plant operation or on the experimental field or proving ground, or both, the portion to be changed is "unfrozen." The change may relate to only a subassembly operation, or to all parts and all assembly. Usually, as in automobile and aircraft production, such changes are narrowly limited at any one time. Once the change-over has been made, however, the process is once again "frozen," and once more the concert of operations flows on as before.

(3) The production schedule of each separate contributing plant, being confluent with those of other component suppliers, is geared to the "master production schedule" of the assembled or end product. The same holds for a plant, such as a weaving mill in the textile industry, which is woven in as a unit with an integrated series of preceding and following operations.

(4) The "master schedule" governs at once (*a*) the technical properties of all confluent products (i.e., the product is covered by a specifications formula from which deviations are not permitted beyond narrowly defined margins), (*b*) the volume of production, and (*c*) the timing of delivery. Every new step taken in the direction of greater dependence upon interchangeable

parts, of closer control over supply specifications, of reduction of
warehousing space and the elimination or even temporarily
bunching of materials inventories between processing steps, and
of the regularization in the flow of supplies promotes the rigor of
this three-phase control.

Such automatic interplant coördination may occur, as indicated
above, either with vertical integration of successive steps of production or with assembly-plant operations, and in either case it
may eventually occur with contiguous plants in an "industrial
complex" as well as with distant plants. A chemical example of
automatic interconnection of processes at spatially removed plants
is provided by the "push-button" operation of the Shell Oil Company, whereby any one of its 22 different petroleum products
from any one refining plant in its Midwest operations can by
teletype be put into its 850-mile-long pipeline network and directed to any other plant or distribution point within the system.
Most of the refining plants in the system are almost or entirely
automatic, as are also the pumping stations. The latter maintain
at each station one man only, for stand-by and maintenance purposes.[9]

Nothing quite so completely automatic as this is to be found
linking spatially removed plants in the mechanical industries as
a whole. However, very important steps in this direction have already been made, and many more are in the offing. One step is
the frequently forgotten interplant unification by automatic devices of power generation and transmission. A partial step is
provided by the combination of teletype interconnection of newspaper printing with electronic devices for setting type photo-
graphically. Similar examples are provided by mechanisms for
transmitting and receiving telegraphic and facsimile messages.
Another partial step has been taken in the quality-control end by
the installation of instruments for showing rejects all the way
along an assembly line. Such a system as the one introduced by
the General Electric Company in 1950[10] is capable of being used
in plants feeding into an assembly line whether the plants are
grouped closely together or are spatially removed by some distance.

Assembly industries raise some very interesting possibilities along this line. The ground for introducing the elements of inter-plant automatic coördination has been prepared by the rise of the occasional "superplant," combining parts production, subassembly, and assembly. One of the earliest, and perhaps the most highly publicized, was the famous River Rouge plant of the Ford Motor Company. Much of it was quite scientifically laid out. Some of it appears, according to best engineering knowledge, to have grown up like "Topsy." But the principles underlying its organization appear to be fairly simple.

This motor-car plant, or, rather, web of coöperating plants, covers over a thousand acres and employs, as one writer has put it, "almost every trade known to man." [11] Schematically, all the parts-producing plants are immediately juxtaposed to the several subassembly plants which use their entire output. The latter are juxtaposed, in a similar manner, to the main or final assembly line, at the end of which the finished car rolls off under its own power. All the plants in this industrial complex were built of a size or in multiples of size necessary to supply the required amounts of materials or parts to each subsequent or confluent operation, and most of them were interconnected with the continuously moving conveyor equipment. The capacity and the movement of the final assembly line govern those of the subassembly lines, and these in turn, those of all parts-supply plants. Volume and timing are unified throughout, and a single unified system of specifications and standards obtains at all levels and stages of production.

Actually, not even the River Rouge plant produces all the parts required by the final assembly line, though it did come fairly close to doing so at one time. There soon arrives a point, however, when it is no longer practicable to bring all the plants together in a single limited area. For various reasons it may pay, when all necessary costs are considered, to scatter components plants and even, in some cases, the subassembly plants. This does not mean, however, any relaxation of the need for interplant coördination.

That this is true can be seen by reference to a case which received considerable attention in the immediate post-World War II period in the early plants of the Kaiser-Frazer corporation. In developing plans for producing their new automobiles, the corporation, it was pointed out, could take one leaf out of the experience of the old Jordan car and another out of Kaiser's war-time experience in the shipbuilding industry. In the case of the Jordan car, all parts were handled by subcontracting, and assembly took place at several sites. The company had, in legal fact, practically no "plant" of its own at all. Yet the operation was a reasonably efficient one. What happened, in effect, was that the subcontracting plants were, for the purposes of supply to the Jordan Company, woven together through a system of specifications and supply schedules *as though* they were separate parts of a single system.

The other strand in policy was taken from Kaiser's wartime shipbuilding experience. In this case shipbuilding was made up primarily of assembly operations at tidewater locations. Some final operations preparatory to assembly, mostly connected with plate and pipe shops, were performed on or near the assembly site, but increasingly, as the war years passed, more and more of the separate parts going into the ships were manufactured or prefabricated elsewhere. (This finally became true for all engine-room equipment, for most cabin and mess installations, for life-boats, and for many deck, bulkhead, superstructure, and other installations.)

Both lines of experience drawn upon by the Kaiser-Frazer corporation followed a pattern very similar to that employed in England during the war and commonly termed "shadow plant production," wherein a wide variety of plants manufacturing various products for peacetime use, usually scattered geographically and relatively small in size, were converted to the production of parts for ammunition, ordnance, airplane, tank, shipbuilding, and other types of assembly operations. The plants were grouped to feed into a given assembly line or group of assembly lines *as though* they were departments of a single unified plant. It was found that the "shadow" plants could achieve very nearly the same types and amounts of economies as those organized along River Rouge lines.

"Shadow plant production" appears, consequently, as a rather sharp contrast to the nucleating pattern of the River Rouge type of plant. During the war it became common in most of the belligerent countries. The Germans used it, e.g., in connection with airplane construction, splitting up parts production in a widely scattered series of plants, with subassembly of engine, fuselage, and wings taking place at a number of points and final assembly almost anywhere. The Soviet Union, after the destruction of the leading industrial centers of the Ukraine, began to apply similar methods on an extensive scale. The United States employed similar methods in both the new wartime industries and in adapting peacetime plant facilities to war production purposes.

Many different reasons may be given for the wartime resort to "shadow plant production": the desire to scatter plants widely so that no militarily essential industry could be knocked out by enemy attack, particularly from the air; the effort to use the maximum of existing plant facilities, however small, so as to avoid the diversion of materials and industrial capacity into new construction (in England close to 50 per cent of all war production was carried out in plants employing 50 men or less); and the necessity of avoiding housing congestion in a few major industrial centers. These and other reasons relating to problems of health, food supplies, and morale played roles of varying importance. But perhaps in the long run more decisive was the fact that "shadow plant production" could be adapted to achieve many if not all of the more important advantages of mass-production plants grouped closely around a single central-assembly operation.

It achieves this, however, not by negating the principles that underlie the organization of nucleated plants, as at River Rouge, but by adapting them to widely scattered plants. As the detailed reports of the British Ministry of Labour and National Service and the Ministry of Production[12] make clear, even very small local plants were reorganized to produce specialized component parts on a mass-output basis by the introduction of automatic machinery, flow production methods, assembly and conveyer equipment,[13] quality-control devices, electric synchronization, and the like. These plants were then woven into a supply web in such a way that their output flowed directly to subassembly operations in the aircraft, shipbuilding, ordnance, and other industries. Usually it was found that in the neighborhood of an assembly plant there were plants already existing which could, thus reorganized, produce or be adapted to produce one or more parts in circumstances approaching optimum efficiency, and some pattern of these plants could be worked out to supply most or even all the parts needed for each major assembly operation. Where these results could be achieved, there was nothing to be gained, and in most cases a great deal to be lost, by nucleating in the River Rouge fashion.

In terms of efficiency of production, when all real costs are added into the picture,[14] "shadow plant production" earned its way. This result should have surprised no one, for it was no more than a rapid and generalized improvisation, superimposed on older manufacturing methods, of techniques which were already well known, particularly in the United States, in various branches of the manufacturing industries. The automobile industry, for example, had slowly been moving in this direction for a number of years, and the advantages realized from the trend may quite possibly make the River Rouge type of "Superplant" obsolete. The General Motors Corporation represents, possibly, the highest development along this line in America. Somewhat more than a thousand plants are woven into the General Motors parts-supply system. Still, the widening of the network of interlaced production schedules does not involve any fundamental departures from the organizational pattern that underlies the River Rouge plant. On the contrary, the attempt to plan and unify these schedules is insensibly, but swiftly, transforming the automobile industry into a single, internally balanced, and closely interlaced engineering "structure" which is already to some extent organized as an engineering whole throughout most of its parts, in order to make possible adequate functioning in each and every segment. The development of electronics indicates a steady tightening of the pattern of interprocess coördination. How true this is may be seen by extrapolating from past trends in the evolution of the giant corporate complexes, which have, to date, governed the unfolding pattern. This pattern already approximates, in the macrocosm of the automobile industry as a whole, the prototype of the automatic plant and the general scheme underlying the mechanized "superplant."

In any such intricately interlaced balancing of production processes, malfunctioning may occur. Aside from disproportions in plant capacity (in itself a technical problem of investment), these may be of two main types: those which are due to unforeseen contingencies of a natural or technical character, and those which are due to institutional causes. The former, which include such events as snowstorms, ice blockades, floods, railroad accidents, fires, etc., can usually be anticipated to some extent and, consequently, safety factors may be introduced which provide due allowance for their occurrence without appreciably interrupting production. The latter are those we commonly associate with labor conflicts and business depressions in countries organized on a capitalistic footing. But they may arise anywhere and under any type of economic or social system where interindustry relations are not embraced within a common framework of policies designed to come to grips directly with this entire class of problems.

Even where the disadvantages which arise from malfunctioning due to institutional factors are obvious and spectacular, as they may be at times in a country like the United States, they have not nullified the productivity gains from such partial synchronization as may have been effected. So, here, with carrying the process to its economically justifiable limits and without reaping the full benefits from such coördination, the cumulative process of unification goes on apace. Nevertheless, as successive steps are taken in this direction, and however hesitant and laggard the process may be at any given time, it is not the plant or the industrial process, but the industry as a whole that tends to become the unit of reckoning.

INTERLACING IN THE MACROCOSM: INPUT-OUTPUT IN THE ECONOMY AS A WHOLE

A major step in the direction of actual management of the industrial system of the United States *as though* it were "a comprehensive, balanced mechanical process" was taken with the adoption by the defense administrative authorities in late 1948 of the Leontief "input-output" method of planning industrial mobilization. Leontief devised what has been referred to as a "20-by-20 grid" of 20 major industrial groupings. A portion of such a grid is reproduced in table 6. As will be observed, the figures given

TABLE 6

INTERINDUSTRY FLOW OF GOODS AND SERVICES BY INDUSTRY OF ORIGIN
AND DESTINATION, 1947*
(In millions of dollars)

	(1) Agriculture and fisheries	(2) Food and kindred products	(3) Chemicals	(4) Iron and steel	(5) Nonferrous metals	(6) Motor vehicles
1. Agriculture and fisheries.........	10,856	15,048	1,211	...	11	...
2. Food and kindred products.........	2,378	4,910	685	3	...ᵃ	...
3. Chemicals.......	830	1,451	2,655	99	85	111
4. Iron and steel....	6	2	5	3,982	33	1,102
5. Nonferrous metals	...	...	189	324	2,599	176
6. Motor vehicles...	111	3	...	...ᵃ	...ᵃ	4,401
7. Coal, gas, and electric power....	61	193	188	242	104	62
8. Railroad transportation........	440	548	287	423	100	228

SOURCE: W. Duane Evans and Marvin Hoffenberg, "The Interindustry Relations Study for 1947," *Review of Economics and Statistics*, May, 1952, table 4.
* Each row shows the distribution of the output of the producing industry named at the left. Each column shows input distribution for the purchasing industry named at the top.
ᵃ Less than 0.5 million.

after each classification indicate the amount of the products (output) of the industries shown in the left-hand stub (Agriculture and fisheries, Food and kindred products, etc.) absorbed by the industries (input), similarly classified, ranged across the top of the columns. Thus in 1947 agriculture and fisheries consumed $10,856 million of its own products and sold over $15 billion worth to food and kindred products.

These categories might be broken down into 50 instead of 20 industries, or even further. The Bureau of Labor Statistics has developed a "96-by-96" grid, and even a "300-by-300" one has been proposed. But with any size of grid, the point is that change in output of any given industry can then be related to change in all other industries, and this change may be computed for the total production of each industry, for the separate products of each industry, for average or specific prices, and for employment, plant capacity, investment need, or other specific data as desired. Furthermore, theoretically, it should be possible to trace the impact of any given program, such as foreign aid, or the amount of public-works products required to achieve any given increase in employment, stimulus to purchasing power, or other desired result. When the basic economic data are collected they can then be fed into an electronic computer and this computer might then, as one popular exposition put the matter, "take over the job of planning industrial mobilization" for the entire American economy.[15]

There are still numerous weaknesses, statistical, methodological, and theoretical in the program. On the statistical side, data are frequently not available in the necessary detail, and there is no currently valid way of handling variations introduced by the passage of time. Beyond the statistics are certain large problems of a more abstruse character. It takes the economic system "as given," and pays no attention to productivity ratios. It does not give any check on efficient use of resources. It assumes—as did its early historical inspiration, the system of n-simultaneous equations in n unknowns for the determination of prices as devised by Leon Walras—something approximating a largely nonexistent perfect competition in the demand and supply of homogeneous goods, investment funds, labor, and other resources. It also assumes as given the whole structure and distribution of costs, prices, incomes, spendings, savings, and taxation as they appear at a particular moment. It leaves totally out of the picture the possible bearing on output of such technological and organizational factors as we have been dealing with in this study thus far, and it ignores entirely conditions and principles of bureaucratic organization, public reactions, labor morale, social and political movements, ideologies, and institutions.

Yet despite these limitations—severe and comprehensive though they may appear at first—their enumeration also serves to make clear the area where the method of input-output analysis may claim merit. Without denying in the least the necessity of paying attention to these other factors, yet the method has the great significance of finding a technique of relating for any given industry the bearing of its output, prices, degree of capacity utilization, level of employment, wage scale, or other important quantifiable data on change within that industry upon all other industries of the economy as a whole. The method is no less useful if it assumes entirely different conditions relating to efficiency of production, structure of business organization, or social institutions than if it merely assumes the picture as currently given. Allowance for other conditions than those found valid for a particular moment in time would in many cases involve new and important modifying variables—an outstanding example is the case of "time"—but that is all.

The important point is that we have here a powerful tool which, though limited to the analysis of data and the supply of information, yet provides the basis for interindustry coördination of capacity, rates of production, employment, prices, etc., and is designed to supply this information on a continuing, precise, and, in effect, "automatic" basis. Whether the larger national objectives then be viewed as "defense production," full employment, or maximum output (or any other given level of output) for any other purpose, it still has the same potential value. The problem thereafter is one of instrumentation.

As far as the technological data are concerned, much has already been done. As indicated above, the tendency toward internal unification along industrial lines at the technological level, and to some degree at the broad policy level, is found in practically all leading industries, in every major industrial country, and in every country attempting to evolve from the beginning an industrial modernization scheme. In this respect, for example, what appears as a trend in the United States is used directly—and as an obvious principle of organization, as the basis of planning—in the Russian trusts, which follow more or less strictly industrial lines and whose unified management includes technical, planning, finance, supply and sale, construction, manpower, and accounting departments.[16] The industry, in other words, is managed as an engineering and accounting as well as a policy-implementing unit. Whatever the differences of opinion on the long-run merits of the larger objectives pursued—those which guide policy in a socialist as against a capitalistic economy—there can be little dispute among experts on the engineering and accounting aspects of this process. Consultation with American, German, and British engineers who served as consultants to the Russians in various lines of industrial development under several Five-Year plans has elicited the general comment, that, "from the engineering point of view, this is the way to do it."

Much the same general intention lay behind the various British reorganization schemes in coal, textiles, steel, engineering trades, and other allied lines.[17] This pattern is not greatly different from the converging "rationalization" measures in the several industrial reorganization schemes in Germany during the interlude between the two World Wars, particularly as they were being shaped up on the eve of the Nazi *coup d'état*.[18]

Industry-wide "rationalization" was implied or (on occasion) openly declared to be the object of the various British development schemes[19] and of the French Monnet Plan.[20] But the "logic of the situation" in industry is not confined to such formally outlined development plans. Evolution along similar lines can be traced in its detail in the history of American industrial development over the past half-dozen decades.

PATTERNS OF FORMAL COÖRDINATION AND PATTERNS OF MANAGEMENT DECENTRALIZATION

Just what does "industry-wide" coördination mean? An analogy may be of assistance. If steel filings are spread more or less evenly over a sheet of paper between two magnets, and the paper lightly tapped, the filings will group themselves in "lines of force" which are parallel to each other as straight lines in the direct line of force between the two magnets and as concave lines of deepening concavity and less clear outlines from thence outward. If, in a second experiment, the same procedure is followed but only one magnet is used, and this magnet is placed upright with its magnetized end resting on the paper, the result will be "lines of force" centering as clear cut lines at the point of the magnet, and from thence radiating outwards, spreading fanwise and becoming less distinct the farther the distance from the magnet.

The first might be likened to the "lines of force" which, with varying degrees of potency, promote industry-wide organization horizontally along industry or trade lines. The second might be likened to those which promote some combination of horizontal with vertical "lines of force," a range of industries integrated from raw materials to markets and having nucleated centers but affected some by factors favoring plant specialization along hori- zontal lines. Where the deepening concavity and fading lines of the first and the fanlike outer diffusion of the second become marked, the nucleational or centralizing pulls begin to give way to centrifugal or localizing attraction. There is never a clear line to be drawn between the two. Rather there exists what might be called a *band of indifference* of varying width for different indus- tries.

Beyond this *band* or line the localizing, or diffusing and re- gionally scattering, forces are dominant. In this area there will be three general types of industry. First are those (*a*) of a strictly local character, catering only to local needs, or (*b*) based upon local resources or supplies which exist in quantities sufficiently large to justify plant operation at or near optimum size. (If the plant is less than optimum size, the resulting inefficiencies are still less costly than the transportation charges incurred by ship- ment from more efficient plants elsewhere.) Such are local furni- ture and woodworking plants, bakeries and various types of food- processing plants, laundries, in many cases brickworks and glass- works.

Second are those which are fixed *in situ* as coördinate parts of multiple-purpose projects or multiple-product processes. Thus the industries and services built up around one or more of the related functions integrated into the TVA project—power de- velopment, river transportation, reforestation—are indissolubly linked together within the locale as though coördinate parts of a single productive mechanism. So also are industries which use as their principal supply materials which are by-product to some major industry built up on some peculiarly valuable local primary material such as coal, iron, copper, or soybeans, but where the primary product is produced in such quantities as to require inter- regional, national, or international markets.

Third are those plants which produce a highly specialized

chemical or component in comparatively small plants (where the optimum-size plant is small), either as the sole supplier to a specialized assembly operation which, in turn, caters to national or international markets, or as one of a large number of small plants supplying standard parts to regionally spaced assembly plants, as in the pattern employed by the Ford Company.

For all three types of local industries, there are, in some combination, a number of technical advantages to be derived from planning. With respect to the process, very nearly every factor of economical production favors use of industry-wide or "nationally formulated" standards and codes in building, in equipping with tools and machines, in safety methods and work procedures, in the organization of materials and energy supply, and in the basic routines of job organization and supervision. With respect to both the raw materials used and the *product* or *service* supplied, very much the same holds for compliance with standard dimensions for component parts, qualities, workmanship, modes of packing and shipping, etc.

With respect to *location* within the community, a great deal is to be said for assimilating the workplaces, living quarters, and recreational and cultural facilities of every community into an over-all village, town, or regional planning scheme, but only when long-run net productivity to the community is the goal, and not short-run competitive gain. Such experiments as those of Greenbelt, Radburn, a number of the English "garden city" villages, and the planning of suburbs around a major metropolitan nucleus as in London, Amsterdam, and some of the newer Russian towns, indicate clearly that adequate planning of the structure of local industry is reconcilable with long-run low cost.

Returning to the industries within the *band of indifference* the possible combinations and permutations are seemingly infinite. In general, however, the following are valid:

(1) In industries producing either a primary raw material or a semifinished (or unfinished) product used for a wide variety of purposes, the units of planning for industrial purposes expand horizontally, unifying production policies and practices within each given stage of production. This is the case with coal and most mining industries, the timber and lumber industries, cement

and most of the glass industry. The unit of planning in these industries is industry-wide, with a strong resemblance to the unified
planning of public utilities. Thus, for example, the schemes advanced by the British Labour government for a unified administra-
tration of both the nationalized coal and communications industries are cut of essentially the same cloth and in this respect
closely resemble the Russian schemes for the heavy and light machinery, aircraft, coal, machine tool, paper, rubber, and construction industries. Both the British and the Russian schemes represent
the culmination of a process of unification and planning which
appears as a logical result of the coöperative efforts along engineering lines of many leading American trade associations. It was
clearly toward some such end result that the more important
pre-Nazi German industrial "rationalization" plans were leading.
Planning here does not necessarily mean that all plants must be
tied in with a single central management, so as to lose all management autonomy. It means merely that the technical terms, conditions, and relations of production need to be so organized that
each plant functions *as though* it were part of such a scheme;
this holds as long as the overriding object is maximum economy
of production.

(2) In partial contrast, the complex of vertically integrated
operations is the *primary unit of planning* in those industries
where the leading plants center in big units whose technologically most advanced method of organization favors juxtapos-
ing different stages of continuous-production processes. This
is true whether the interdependence is *convergent* to a single
product, as with automobile production and similar assembly operations, or *divergent* (joint product) from a single raw material,
as with cattle in packing plants, or with nonmetallurgical plants
utilizing metallurgical by-products such as gas and coal tar.
Within such a complex or *combinat*, technological and economic
factors favor an arrangement where all plants are proportioned
to each other with respect to capacity and the volume and timing
of flow of output, and this holds through all stages of production
and for all the plants which are complementary or supplementary
to each other.

In case of vertical integration, the unit of planning within the manufacturing industries parallels that of the heavy chemical industries referred to in the preceding chapter. A single example, combining both chemical and mechanical processes, must suffice. In the reports by the British Iron and Steel Federation and the Joint Iron Council of the Minister of Supply on reorganization of the British Iron and Steel Industry—reports which subsequently became the basis of the British steel nationalization scheme—the following proposals are made:

The first essential is the manufacture of hot-rolled strip in a plant integrated as fully as possible from the raw materials, ore and coal, to the hot-rolled product.

To secure the advantages of a seaboard location with existing pig-iron and ingot capacity, the proposal is to erect on an available site adjacent to the G.K.B. Works at Margam a new 80″ continuous hot strip mill with a capacity of 1 million tons of product, suitable for processing into plates, sheets and tinplate.

This mill will be preceded by a new slabbing mill capable of handling 1.25 million tons of ingots, and by a new open hearth furnace shop with an initial capacity of 800,000 tons of ingots. The existing Margam open hearth furnaces are to be improved to furnish 200,000 tons of ingots, giving a total of 1 million tons of hot ingots direct from the steel furnaces to the mill.

The new melting shop will be laid out to enable extensions to be made to provide all the steel required as hot ingots, but in this first stage it is proposed to draw up to 250,000 tons of cold ingots from the existing steel works in West Wales.

To provide the 750,000 tons of pig iron required for this enterprise and the adjoining Port Talbot steel works, the existing blast furnaces at Margam, one of which is already under reconstruction, are to be enlarged, the ore dock is to be extended, and facilities installed for the preparation of the iron ore to secure the maximum economy in coke consumption. These developments will give an additional pig iron capacity of 300,000 tons.

An additional coke oven battery is to be erected to meet the increased demand for coke, and to provide a total supply of 600,000 tons, representing an increase of 280,000 tons.

This is an exceptionally interesting example since, although it was drawn up by the industry as part of a counterproposal to nationalization, the proposal showed a clear appreciation of the necessity of planning all the related production processes in each major location *as though* the several plants were merely separate parts of a single synchronized plant. In fact, the industry proposal was subsequently used against them, as a case *for* nationalization.

(3) Finally, where the "gravitational pull" of the complex or *combinat* becomes unmistakably dominant, the tendency is cumulatively to embrace both horizontal and vertical units in comprehensive industry-wide planning in the fullest sense of the term. This is already the case in the principal metallurgical industries, particularly in the steel and iron industries. It is also, to cite another example, the case with the cotton industry, where the tendency is increasingly to combine carding, spinning, fulling, weaving, dyeing, etc. into single, functionally integrated engineering units. The analogy here with public utilities is the interdependence between the several types of traffic media, which require the planning of each facility—in transportation: rail, highway, waterways, airplane; in communication: telephone, telegraph, radio, postal services—as a coördinate and interlaced segment of a single system.

Here again a single instance must suffice. For purposes of clarity it is drawn from the British metallurgical reorganization scheme referred to above. "The general plan," the report continues,

involves the building of 4¾ million tons of blast furnace and about 6 million tons of steel ingot capacity. The precise rate of building will depend on a number of factors, including the extent to which part of the rolling mill plant can be imported. The aim, however, is to start construction progressively on the whole of the plan within the five years from 1946 to 1950 and to complete it by the middle of 1953, i.e., within about 7½ years. . . . The total cost of the plan is estimated at £168,000,000.[22]

So far as scale is concerned, it is interesting to note that the entire British steel industry, as projected under this plan, has just about half the steel capacity of the United States Steel Corporation—which also manages its plants as component units in a national scheme of production.

Various proposals for reorganization of the British cotton, woolen, engineering, and transportation industries have proceeded along similar lines. Though preferring again to maintain the separate identities of the 1,750 business establishments in the various branches of the iron-founding industry, the report of the Joint Iron Council to the Minister of Supply paid at least lip service to the need for over-all planning by the industry as a whole.[23] Thus we are faced with the very interesting spectacle of British industry in one of its oldest and most highly individualistic branches, and in perhaps the most ardently individualistic country in the world, itself interpreting "modernization"—a term which is scattered all through its report—as planning, on a basis to some degree coextensive with both horizontal and vertical limits of the technically related industries as a whole. One can well imagine what strictly engineering and economic considerations alone would make of the proposals once they were divested of the incubus of outmoded systems of business organization. In the case of Britain, of course, this cannot be read from the run of subsequent developments. The language of coördination and planning was not very heavily reinforced by operational plans or achievements in either the nationalized industries or in the private sectors under the development councils. Technical rationalization has been at best haphazard and mostly confined to internal plant operations. Nevertheless the potential of "modernization" is still there.

The economies from "modernization" in the proper framework of policy are striking. Those which arise from purely technical modernization, as with fuel savings,[24] are paralleled by those which arise from plant specialization, interplant production dovetailing and proportioning, plant relocation, and the like. Most important of these for the industry as a whole are (*a*) the planning of the several subordinate complexes to specialize on a narrow range of end products which permit "full line loading" of all plants within the coördinated complex as a whole, and (*b*) the relocation of part or all of the plants in each *complex* with respect to other plants and plant complexes and with a view to over-all reduction of freight costs to plants, among plants, and to the principal consumption centers.

The full benefits of either of these types of economies can be reaped only when industry-wide planning, within the manufacturing industries which show strong *agglutinative* patterns, are coördinated with other plans which are coextensive with the economy in general. Specializing the several complexes, for example, means carrying over into the industry as a whole a pattern of plant specialization which has first been slowly evolved with the technical progress of industry between individual plants in a given region, or among plants belonging to several independent private companies. The earlier and smaller-scale specialization, however, is consistent with business competition, while the later and more modern specialization is well-nigh unthinkable in these terms. In private hands it means all-inclusive monopoly, or, lacking this, unification of policies with respect to basic cost and price variables between independent firms in such a way as to produce a like effect. To place such a mode of organization in private hands is no longer easily reconcilable with political democracy. But quite aside from this, to plan any key industry means, in effect, to plan significant costs of all other industries using its end products, and thus the planning of one means unification with the planning of the others.

The same holds for location. Two points may be mentioned in passing. First, all schemes of reorganization which embrace the industry concerned as a whole—such as the German "rationalization" of the late twenties, the Russian "trusts," the British and the French (Monnet Plan) reorganization schemes—tend to make definite assumptions about the nature of transportation which are inconsistent with anything short of the unification of transport media. And, second, the "isotims," or lines which trace the "divides," and thus outline what might be called the economic "watershed area" for each plant or complex of plants, are determined primarily by the structure of freight costs. Within limits, these are, in turn, determined by the pattern of space relationships among the various raw materials, distances from markets, and various factors of a more purely technological character governing agglutination or scattering of plants. But even here there is a wide margin for shifting the "isotims" where precise location depends purely upon freight-rate policy. Here, as with most other costs, it is policy that determines the cost as much as costs that determine the policy. And so it happens that any reorganization scheme which is coextensive with a major industrial grouping can be planned most effectively only when planned in coördination with the transport system as a whole.

But this is only to conclude that manufacturing shares this in common with other segments of a fully modernized industrial system, and that with the shift of the primary unit of reckoning from the individual plant to the industry, adequate planning on the latter basis becomes impossible unless it is conceived within the framework of over-all plans coextensive with the major segments of the industrial system. That is to say, this is true *as far as* technological factors contributing to mass output at lowest cost are concerned. Given, in other words, a carte blanche on the drawing board and in the designing room, such will be the result on the sheer merits of the industrial case in manufacturing, as clearly as in the several public utilities—where, as we all know, the case is no longer contested among experts.

SUMMARY

In the chemical and manufacturing industries most processes may now be made entirely or almost entirely automatic. Each major step taken in this direction stresses the value of "rethinking through" the entire round of both intraplant and interplant operations. A great deal has been done on the first, relatively little on the second. Yet the two are not really separable. To introduce automation in major plants inevitably requires the revamping of operations of related plants, and in such a way that the effect is *as though* the entire concert of such plants were (a) converted to an automation basis and then (b) proportioned in size, scheduled in production, and synchronized on a quasi-automatic basis.

To carry out both is still largely the task of the future. But all the major "pilot plant" ideas and methods have already been worked out. The "rethinking" is required largely in the application of continually expanding scientific principles to further links in processing and further extension of automation.

In the few pioneering cases where initial methods have been more or less fully developed, regularization of flows to and from plants in successive stages of production come to resemble those internal to each plant. There arises the same need for precise dovetailing of volume and timing between these successive steps; for minimum storage or inventory at any given point; for feed to and from each step of materials and supplies of standard dimensions and of standard physical and chemical properties; for complete interchangeability of parts for all equipment and assembled products; for such a degree of plant specialization as to provide each unit with a "product mix" low enough to require little or no time for change-over; for extending operation toward the eventual (although never quite realized) goal of 24 hours a day and 365 days a year; for conceiving each specialized plant *as though* it were a single functioning unit related to the rest in somewhat the same way as the separate parts-producing units within the plant are interdependent at the assembly line; for interplant operations equipped with continuously functioning energy and transport services and serviced with continuously functioning communications systems which at all such points guide, synchronize, and correct flows and schedules by feed-back controls in an automatic or quasi-automatic manner.

The "rethinking" involves the development of comprehensive standards for properties of materials and for equipment and product design; new criteria for size and capacity proportioning of related plants; new factors in plant location; universal resort to energy drawn from a common power pool; further steps to reconvert transport facilities into the equivalent of intraplant automatic-transfer machines and conveyor equipment; development at all points of internally consistent systems of nomenclature, devices, and codes for the automatic conversion of basic routine information into a form usable for automatic guidance, control, and correction of operations.

Thus the replanning, and the subsequent reorganization move outward from the automatic plant to the raw materials and the finished product; to the industry, to congeries of technically related industries, and in some instances to the nation or even the whole industrial world (e.g., standards and properties of control devices; materials balances as with "input-output" analysis); and to transport, power, and communications networks.

The productive potentialities accompanying changes along such lines are, in many instances at least, phenomenal. No clear limits except those set by human ingenuity and science are in prospect. Science is once again "the endless frontier."

IX

The Problem of Inter-Media Traffic Unification

THE LOGIC OF TRANSPORT UNIFICATION

The monumental report of the National Resources Planning Board on *Transportation and National Policy* constitutes an elaborate detailing of the case for an "integrated transportation system" for the United States as a whole. The Board laid no claim to originality. Nor could it, for in outlining its far-reaching proposals the Board has merely spelled out policy[1] which was supported by well-nigh unanimous expert opinion throughout the world.

The idea of a unified transport web has governed developments as far apart as those of the London Passenger Transport Board and the New York Port Authority. In the larger sphere of international air, sea, and rail transport, the various international pooling arrangements, committees, commissions, and permanent operating companies and regulatory bodies are engaged in applying the same basic principles on a regional and global footing. The Transport and Communications Commission of UNESCO is continuously engaged in the promotion of transport coördination of all types throughout the world.

"Transportation," wrote Kipling at one time, "is civilization." It is the carrier of men and goods, the leading agent in the integration of community and national life in a machine age, the lifeblood of the industrial system based on mass production and mass distribution, the weaver of interdependencies in resources, material goods, experience, and ideas, and it provides the most essential means for bringing peoples, civilizations, and cultures into close and living contact with each other in the burgeoning "one world" of these tempestuous times. It is all these things and more, however, in direct proportion as integration of transportation takes place on an ever-widening scale. The laws of growth which govern the maturation of the "nervous system" of telecommunications are shared by the spreading arterial and veinous networks of transportation.

Complex though the transport media have become, yet it is still possible to grasp the principles underlying their general development without great difficulty. This may best be accomplished by considering briefly the development of each principal medium in turn.

LAND TRANSPORT UNIFICATION

Though rapidly declining in relative importance, railroads still constitute the backbone of both freight and passenger land-transport systems all over the world. Railroads have begun to specialize and in so doing they bid well to hold their own for a long time to come. In certain areas, such as continental North America from the Ohio River north, and in Asia above the iso-thermal line where winterlong freezing is the rule, there is no good traffic alternative to railroads for long-distance bulk freight movements throughout the year.[2] In the Great Lakes region, the huge shipments of iron ore and coal by water, which sustain the bulk of the heavy steel-manufacturing industries of the continent, are suspended for from three to six months of the year because of freezing, and whatever freight movement cannot be postponed must be made by rail.

But successful specialization and economy of operation, both where railroads have something like a natural monopoly and where this is not the case, require unification of the rail network. This is no new need. Almost from the beginning railroads have been developed on the basis of a regional network, and their experience has provided the patterns for expansion of other forms of transport. A sketch for a German system made by the great railroad pioneer Friedrich List in 1833, compared with a map of the German autobahnen (superhighways) as they had developed by the middle 1930's, reveals an underlying pattern which is the same for both. Extend List's web outward to the limits of the European continent and supplement it with a meshwork of secondary and feeder lines, and we have the general outlines of the European rail network in the midst of the Second World War. Roads and railroads are agents of national and regional unification par excellence; each performs this function in proportion as it takes on the all-embracing weblike pattern.[3]

As far as the engineering and operating facts are concerned, the picture for both road and rail networks is basically the same. In a few places technical difficulties, most important of which is difference in gauge—as in the broad gauge used by Russia and Spain, and the different gauges of Brazil—inhibit complete interchangeability of rail rolling stock. In other places varying patterns of public and private ownership or of competition prevent full realization of the possibilities provided by the existing level of technical rail unification. Confusion due to duplicating and overlapping administrations in both rail and highway systems frequently has a like effect. While the validity of the pattern of unified networks is everywhere conceded, practice in many cases is still far behind the best levels of achievement.

With respect to *mileage of lines,* in various places in the world (most notably in Europe) lines paralleling each other have been built on both sides of national frontiers for defense purposes, and for tapping common pools of traffic for which one line alone would be fully adequate.

Competing lines have a similar effect in the United States. For example, it is possible that the trackage connecting the Midwest with the Pacific Northwest is double what would be needed on a unified basis. It is interesting to note that the Sun Yat-sen plan for a national integrated railway, highway, and waterways system for a future fully industrialized China—one-third larger than the United States in area and with close to three times the population—called for 100,000 miles of heavy-duty rail trunk-lines, as against 237,000 miles of rail trackage in the United States (in 1938).[4] Russian plans would require but little more than half of the American rail mileage for comparable areas and levels of industrial development.[5]

Heavier reliance on highway facilities would not necessarily mean correspondingly greater extension of road networks. This is because of the heavy concentration of trucks and buses on short hauls (around 80 per cent in terms of truck ton-mileage in the United States) for which they are best adapted.

As for the problem of amount and type of *rolling stock,* during the war (1940-1944) the railroads of the United States doubled the ton-miles of freight with an increase of car ownership of only 117,000 cars. The Federal Coordinator of Transportation had previously estimated that $100,000,000 could be saved annually by pooling of freight cars alone.[6]

Unification, furthermore, heightens concentration of traffic on major trunk lines, and immediately makes possible certain vital changes in types of rolling stock. Most important of these is the shift from steam to diesel and electric locomotion. In the early days of electrification and dieselization, decreasing costs with increasing traffic density were associated primarily with savings in fuel. These savings might be offset by diseconomies associated with underutilization of track capacities—costs which have led the Great Northern Railroad to plan abandonment of electric operation of its Cascade Tunnel, and the Milwaukee Railroad of much of its main western lines. (Cost of maintaining overhead wires seems to be important here.) In more recent years major economies have been effected in manpower.[7] These advantages are enhanced, furthermore, more or less in proportion as heavy loads are hauled at high, constant speeds over long distances. This means placing heavy emphasis upon full trainloads operating at high speeds between major terminals, and making no stops or only a very limited number of stops en route. Since there are other additional reasons which make it desirable to make changes over entire lines at one time,[8] it follows that the newer developments in rail traction point toward the concentration of traffic upon relatively few major trunk lines moving on "through" schedules between major terminals, and the handling of shipments in carload or trainload lots.

These and other technical changes cumulatively favor what *Fortune* calls "super-railroads." The full potentialities of "super-railroads" are dependent upon trunk-line unification, and the advantages of line unification are, in turn, heavily dependent upon simultaneous and thoroughgoing terminal unification (briefly considered below), and the specialization of traffic between railroad and other agencies, and the unification of management (both discussed in the next section).

As for *terminal unification* on railroads, at the low operating levels of the middle 1930's, the Federal Coordinator of Transportation estimated that at least $50,000,000 could be saved annually "by the unification of freight terminal facilities." [9]

Associated with both line and terminal unification is the problem of avoiding circuitous routing of traffic. In certain sample cases the Interstate Commerce Commission estimated that the average circuity of traffic was 12 per cent (i.e., the actual mileage hauled was 12 per cent longer than the most direct haul possible) for the United States as a whole.[10] In another sample, made at the height of the war shipping emergency, average circuity varied between 11.0 and 12.5 per cent, and 57.7 per cent of the traffic was found moving by circuitous routes.[11] Most of this was avoidable.

Not all circuitous routing would be avoidable—particularly during a period of peak freight movements—even in a unified system. Some of it, "because of differences in grades, terminals, volume of traffic and other operating characteristics" may even be economical.[12] Most circuitous routing, however, is due to the existence of competing rail systems operating over the same general territory, and, of course, the amounts of rolling stock, operating personnel, and the costs of operation increase approximately in proportion to the degree of additional avoidable haulage.

Terminal unification means not only the common use of passenger and freight terminal facilities by railroads, but also joint usage by railroads and other media, such as trucks, buses, and water transport. If joint usage is not possible, then transfer between terminals should be facilitated.

SPECIALIZATION AND UNIFICATION OF TRAFFIC BETWEEN RAILROADS
AND OTHER TRANSPORT MEDIA

There is an enormous and rapidly expanding literature on the subject of railroad and highway unification. In the British Transport Act of 1947 the two media are brought together in a single piece of basic legislation which views public-service railroad and highway facilities as suppliers of complementary services throughout. Administratively, public hauler services on highways are to be interlinked at most terminals with railroads, and traffic is to be differentiated between the two transport media according to their relative efficiencies in handling different types of passenger and freight traffic. Both are then supplemented, under the same administration, by internal canal and internal waterways networks, and all are to be managed with a view to unification with both harbor and dock development on the one hand, and the flow of traffic between internal transport media and overseas shipping facilities on the other.[13]

In western Europe, along with the development of economic unification, there has been an increasing demand for a complete recasting of the structure of internal transport as a whole. This means international unification of existing rail, highway, and internal waterways systems, to be followed by various extensions to round out each of the existing arteries on a regional or continental basis. Thus studies have been made for a vast road network to provide improved communications between the various countries, for a system of uniform contracts for all haulage by road and rail, and for standardization of railroad equipment in rolling stock, automatic couplings, over-all dimensions, etc.[14]

Precise statements of the circumstances under which one type of transport service is technically and economically superior to the others cannot be made except at particular places, for specific types of traffic, at given levels of technological development, and under standard accounting and pricing procedures. In general the cost of highways is joint between commercial and noncommercial traffic, more or less irrespective of traffic density, in such a way as to make possible the application of some workable formula for allocation of the proper share of the cost of road construction and maintenance to the various forms of commercial traffic. Controversy over cost allocation in the United States has been particularly bitter between the railroads on the one hand and the truck, bus, and Mississippi River barge lines on the other. The stakes, of course, are very large. Nevertheless, when all overhead and operating costs are accounted for, the economic superiority of truck and bus systems appears, in general, when one or a combination of the following is found: short hauls; many intermediate stops; thin traffic; less-than-carload lots; high-value and perishable freight; lightweight packaging; continuous point-to-point pickup; quick-delivery service; movement over difficult terrain (e.g., heavy and numerous grades). In 1949, trucks accounted for 75 per cent of the "tons hauled" but only 11 per cent of the "ton mileage." [15]

Such considerations would not, conversely, mean total exclusion of trucks from all classes of long-haul traffic. In general, however, over long distances the rail and air trunk-lines enjoy marked advantages. There are unquestionably some further offset advantages in favor of rails when overhead costs of highway construction and maintenance are fully added to public-service road-transport outlays, since recent investigations suggest that damage to highways from heavy trucks is definitely out of proportion to their mileage use of the road. (A study of the relative effects of four different axle-loads on a concrete pavement, conducted under the direction of the Highway Research Board of the National Research Council in 1950 and 1951, showed that, based on all types of subgrade, "the 22,400-lb. single-axle loads caused 6.4 times as much cracking . . . as the 18,000-lb. single-axle loads, . . . [and that] the 44,800-lb. tandem-axle loads caused 12.3 times as much cracking . . . as the 32,000-lb. tandem-axle loads." [16] And, although truck registration fees may vary with vehicle weights, damage to highways (which rises rapidly with higher axle-weights) may not be compensated through taxes on gasoline consumption. The miles-per-gallon ratio drops slowly from eight miles per gallon at 16,000 lbs. to five miles per gallon at 60,000 lbs.[17] An increase in tax payments, moreover, would not have much effect upon the allocation of traffic between rail and motor carriers since they are only a small percentage—about 10 per cent—of total truck-operating costs.[18]

With regard to passenger traffic in motor vehicles, where load-limits relative to types of roads are kept within reasonable bounds, buses make much more economical use of highways. Assuming an average of about 1.75 person occupancy in private automobiles (which may be high for peak hours), and making comparison with buses with an average of 45 seats, we find that buses if fully occupied, as they are during peak hours, can carry 31,500 to 40,500 passengers per lane-hour, or an average of approximately 13-fold the passenger-car average; if standees are added, the ratio is higher still.[19] (In addition, assuming 1.75 persons per car, approximately 170 square feet of parking space is required for each person in a private car, while as a bus passenger he requires no parking space at all.)[20]

While an integrated national highway system is still incomplete, nevertheless the lines of development are quite clear.[21] Unification of bus and commercial trucking systems has made rapid progress. The Greyhound bus system in the United States gives close to national coverage by a single integrated network. A series of mergers have come close to providing a number of other regional bus and truck systems which offer only slightly less comprehensive coverage.[22] Central municipal bus and truck terminals are becoming common. With the development of huge inland freight terminals[23] by the Port of New York Authority, a major pioneering step has been taken toward fairly complete highway and railroad freight-terminal unification.

Unification of waterways facilities and their integration with other forms of land transportation provide special problems. Before turning to these, brief mention should be made of economies arising from coördination of the more conventional types of land transport with pipelines, power grids, and certain other special types of transport media.

As for *coördination between land transport and pipelines,* we have in the latter an alternative form of freight shipment which has become of enormous importance in the United States. On January 1, 1945, the network of oil and gas pipelines was 358,637 miles in total length—nearly 50 per cent more than the total of first-line steam railroad track (226,696 miles).[24] By 1953, the gas pipeline network alone was some 425,000 miles in length[25] and was swiftly being rounded out as a series of regionally unified systems covering the country as a whole. The oil pipeline network was much smaller, but was growing along the same lines.

Similar, though nowhere nearly so extensive, networks are to be found in the Russian Transcaucasian area, in the Near East (connecting the Iranian, Mesopotamian, and Arabian oil fields with both the Persian Gulf and the eastern Mediterranean seaboard), in Venezuela, and in the West Coast area of the United States. In all cases, oil (but rarely gas) pipelines are closely interlinked with water, rail, and highway shipping facilities, where at the principal transshipment points rail takes over movement to secondary distribution points, ships handle oceanic movement, and where trucks handle movement from secondary shipping points to ultimate destinations. Cost factors heavily favor pipeline delivery *to* ports and water transportation *between* ports. For 1946 it was estimated that the cost of moving oil per ton-mile by pipeline was slightly more than four times the cost by water.[26] The case for specialization of oil shipment by water wherever possible is, accordingly, very strong. But given such specialization there is also a strong corollary case for integration between these two media on the one hand, and between them and the far more costly yet wholly indispensable rail and truck facilities standing ready to take over distribution to ultimate users at major terminal points.[27]

With respect to the rapidly mushrooming gas pipeline network, gas, of course, provides an alternative fuel to coal, petroleum products, and electrical energy. When it is gathered up by a complex system of feeder lines from natural gas fields to supply an interconnected web of regional trunk lines, we find systems developing which are capable of delivering massive quantities of heat energy which would otherwise have to be supplied by fuels moving by rail, water, or high transmission wires. If, contrariwise, the gas poured into the leading mains is largely or entirely manufactured gas—as is the case, for example, in both England and Germany—then the network is supplying an alternative way of shipping coal itself. How important a factor these two types of gas movement are can be judged from the fact that one-eighth of the freight revenue of all Class I American railroads in 1956 came from bituminous coal shipments,[28] and that natural gas supply alone increased more than six times between 1918 and 1947 (617 per cent), while coal increased scarcely at all (101 per cent of 1918).[29]

As for *electric transmission grids* they are, in a way quite similar to pipelines, basic components of the freight traffic system as far as fuel supply is concerned. When coal converted into electricity is transmitted over long distances by wires, these take the place of railroads, waterways, and highways, together with their various forms of rolling stock, barges, etc., and their storage and terminal facilities. The same issues of inter-media specialization and traffic differentiation which must be faced among other freight shipping media must be faced here as well. In addition, as will be pointed out more fully in the following chapter, electric power grids make possible significant and large-scale redistribution of industry, and this, in turn, greatly influences the pattern, flow, and volume of traffic in general. Accordingly, a plan for the future development of transportation media should include power transmission as well as oil and gas pipelines.

There are a number of other lines of development which should be included in the future planning of land transportation networks. Among these, two are of special interest. One is the proposal to substitute continuous belt transmission for intermediate and short distances, and for specialized types of freight, where the volume of traffic is very heavy. Such a belt, seven miles long, was used on the Bull Shoals Dam construction in Arkansas for hauling crushed rock. A belt 130 miles long is under consideration in the Ohio coalfields, for direct movement from the major coal-collecting points to leading metropolitan coal markets. The other, and possibly more promising, is the proposal to "suspend pulverized coal in a mudlike mixture, or slurry," pump it through a pipeline, and then deliver it to customers "dried and pulverized or pressed into blocks." [30] Pilot-plant operations indicate that costs might be considerably lower than movement by available rail facilities. An incidental advantage is the fact that such a system would make relatively inexpensive the mass movement of low-quality by-product steam fuels, ideal for steam power generating yet largely wasted because they are too costly to transport by the usual means. Also suitable for pipeline transportation are "all pulverized materials which do not stick, or form into lumps; cement, flour, dye, coal-dust, Thomas meal [and] plaster of paris." [31]

Inclusion of pipelines, electric transmission networks, and such mechanisms as the long-distance continuous belt, raises some extremely interesting questions in the over-all planning of land transport. For example, both natural and manufactured gas production are interlaced, partly through by-products and partly through main products (gas), with the entire heavy-chemicals industry. Wherever either is used as a source for the generation of electric power, then power generation is also technically integrated by direct mechanical linkage with these processing industries. This interlinking, furthermore, is of a special kind. Each step or process constitutes a link in a chain which cannot be broken without bringing an almost immediate stoppage to other operations. There tend to be few points where storage is possible (at reasonable cost). Thus, if mining of coal, or production and refining of petroleum, or the coking of coal in by-product coking ovens at steel mills, is linked with the public-utility network distribution, continuous or near-continuous operation becomes a practical necessity. Fuel-supply industries then become a coordinate and indispensable part of the transport system, and their development and operation need to be planned accordingly.

One final aspect of *land transport* unification should be mentioned, and relates to *unification of managements*. In 1954 there were still in the United States some 439 rail carriers, operating 234,342 miles of track. (There were once more than 6,000 separate companies.) They are divided into 126 Class I carriers, operating 224,838 miles of track; 155 Class II carriers, operating 7,353 miles; and 158 Class III carriers, operating 2,151 miles.[32] In addition there are a host of special switching and terminal companies; there are separate express, forwarding, brokerage, and financing companies. The pattern of owned, leased, and commonly operated lines and rolling stock is intricate and constantly changing. Yet within the individual (company) systems there are no effective or regional inter-media traffic allocations;[33] rail-owned bus and truck systems duplicate their own and others' rail and highway lines;[34] major and feeder lines crisscross each other in a bewildering fashion in many of the more important traffic areas.

In no other major industrial country is such overlapping and duplication in railroad managements still to be found. The smaller European countries and Italy, Germany, Russia, Japan, and France possess completely unified national rail systems under central coördinating managements. England had 120 separate major and many minor railroad managements prior to the Railways Act of 1921, at which time all lines were unified into four major networks—the London, Midland and Scottish; the London and North-Eastern; the Great Western; and the Southern. In the Transport Act of 1947 all railroads in Britain were unified in a single national system. In France a unified administration under government direction was established for all lines in 1938. In various other areas, such as Brazil, Argentina, South Africa, and China, where several administrations are to be found, either a high degree of regional consolidation has been effected, as in the case of England, or there are compacts which coördinate complementary networks on a unified basis.

Although it is impossible to estimate with any degree of accuracy what the duplication and overlapping costs, two American estimates, based upon different plans for unification, have indicated the general proportions of the avoidable waste. The Prince Plan,[35] calling for seven major regional systems, would have saved in the 1930's, its proponents believed, in the neighborhood of $743,489,000 per annum, "or about 30 per cent of total railway operating expenses for 1932." [36]

The Miller Plan, calling for a completely unified national railroad system, would result in savings, its author maintained, amounting to "a reduction of at least one-fifth of the total expenses, representing possibly from 3 percent to 4 percent on the $19,000,000,000 outstanding railroad securities. They might even reach a total of $1,000,000,000 per annum." [37]

There can be no doubt that the possible economies in manpower might be considerable. A confidential estimate by a member of the Interstate Commerce Commission suggests that the executive, management, and general office staffs of the railroad companies, and of the railroad associations and regulatory bodies, amount to probably double the number required to run an efficiently organized national system.[38] But this is not all; high costs associated with inefficiencies of over-all management arise also from the considerable duplication of rail and highway long-haul traffic—where the rails and airways have an inherent superiority, and much underutilized capacity—and the failure properly to integrate long-haul rail with short-haul bus and truck networks. The huge buses, for instance, take traffic away from the railroads which the latter need in order to operate a low-cost long-distance passenger service, and they do this primarily because the railroads have not succeeded in bringing their charges and services into line with the technical and cost superiority they could enjoy if they specialized in the traffic most appropriate to them.

Confusion in long-distance transport is paralleled by a similar confusion in feeder lines and short hauls to and from major terminals. The palleting and "piggyback" innovations of the postwar period have already gone a long way toward correcting this situation, particularly for the enormously important less-than-carload traffic.

Regardless, accordingly, of how central administration is co-ordinated with managerial decentralization by regions or functions, the case for unification of functionally specialized transportation facilities is clear. Such steps as have been taken to evolve "a coordinated industry, working as a common unit for a common end" in the American transport industry are mostly on the technological level;[39] the unification of management—whether involving a single, consolidated national network or a regional and presumably more flexible system—is long overdue.

SPECIAL PROBLEMS OF LOCAL AND METROPOLITAN TRANSPORT UNIFICATION

Local transport unification involves some unique problems which set it off from those of land transport, and it has long held a rather special interest for students of urban and regional planning. It has been relatively easy to visualize transport unification in all its ramifications in the relatively small, compact, and highly complex life of the urban community. Furthermore, the case for such unification on grounds of public convenience and necessity has been comparatively easy to make; the opposition to it has been scattered and weak. Finally, transport unification has increasingly been tied up with the over-all problems of urban, metropolitan, and regional planning as a whole.

This interdependence may be seen in plans encompassing both small and large urban units. Thus the plans for a "garden city" of the pioneering English type necessarily project highway arterials, streets, lanes, and sidewalks as composite elements of a mosaic that embraces location and intercommunication among residential, business, shopping, and industrial districts on the one hand, and playgrounds, schools, parks, and other public and recreational districts and facilities on the other.

In so doing they mirror on a smaller scale most of the problems that must be faced on the larger canvas of the metropolitan area. The concept of the metropolitan area itself reflects the changing view of the widening scope of regional and functional interdependence. Increasingly, it is coming to include—as, indeed, was already true with some early city-planning proposals, as in the case of Washington, D.C.[40]—not only the urban nucleus, but also the suburbs and various intermediate areas where city and town merge into the countryside. Wherever the significant area of planning is viewed in this manner, the case for a unified transport system is everywhere conceded. One of the most successful and comprehensive early programs was that of the London Passenger Transport Board, which comprehends under its jurisdiction the whole of subway and surface transport for Greater London, excluding only part of the rapid-transit suburban traffic from the major rail terminals. Somewhat less developed are surface arterial streets and highways, with the result that traffic tends to clog heavily during certain downtown peak hours.[41]

In some respects more nearly complete was the prewar passenger-transport unification of Greater Berlin, which united the *Ringbahn* (electric express-trains that ring and crisscross the city) and suburban traffic with subway, streetcar, and bus traffic. The metropolitan plans for Moscow, New York, Los Angeles, and San Francisco offer additional examples of a similar handling of the problem. It seems only a question of time until the underlying pattern will everywhere be adopted.[42]

When one turns to goods traffic, however, the situation is more complicated and more confused. Nevertheless, in broad outline the engineering and cost case for transport unification is equally strong for the bulk of the commercial movement. Part of this traffic moves in bulk to and from major railroad and water terminals to factories, warehouses, coal bunkers, lumberyards, milk stations, and the like. Part consists of movements from these centers to retail outlets, construction sites, and various types of bulk users. From retail outlets an additional series of movements flow as delivery services covering all or a large part of the metropolitan area. Finally, a considerable portion of commercial traffic—made up of vehicles for sales, repair, and miscellaneous services, moving vans, etc.—flows irregularly and follows no clear-cut pattern. These various types of freight movements cannot—as in the case of door-to-door delivery—be kept altogether distinct, but this fact does not detract from the observation that for all types except the last a high degree of traffic unification is not only possible but is imperatively necessary if urban transportation systems are not to become increasingly more costly and inefficient.

Much has been done toward a rational handling of commercial freight in a number of major seaports by the establishment of port authorities charged with both planning and regulatory functions. The need for such authorities is greatly enhanced wherever —as, for example, in the case of the Port of New York—there are many different state, county, and municipal jurisdictions involved. The New York–New Jersey Port District has power to unify railroad, water, and airport facilities, and suburban transit, and to construct and operate bridges, tunnels, canals, and terminal facilities required in the handling of freight for the entire New York port area. Similar authorities, though sometimes with less comprehensive power, are to be found in London, Hamburg, Amsterdam, San Francisco, Seattle, and many other great world ports.

With respect to the other principal types of urban freight movements, door-to-door pickup and delivery service for through traffic should, it appears on the basis of present evidence, be handled as a unified service. In retail distribution it seems probable that something like the United Parcel Service, which may pick up goods from retail establishments and make delivery anywhere in the metropolitan area, might be generalized to cover most goods shipments to customers from all retail outlets. For certain specialized deliveries of standard and uniform commodities, such as fluid milk, the advantages of unified delivery are found in elimination of the duplication of routes, facilities, and manpower. In some cases, the possible over-all savings are spectacular.

The possible economies from metropolitan traffic unification are substantial in all cases where careful studies have been made.

The Port of New York Authority estimated that its New York Union Motor Truck Terminal would save "1,830,000 truck miles a year";[43] that its Newark Union Motor Truck Terminal would save "over-the-road" truckers in northern New Jersey annually 1,365,-000 truck-miles, 294,000 gallons of gasoline, and 14,600,000 tire-miles; and that local truckmen (traveling in Newark) would realize annual savings of 760,000 truck-miles, 147,000 gallons of gasoline, and 4,550,000 tire-miles.[44] But such figures underestimate the significance of the change-over in terms of other economies: better utilization of truck capacity, lower handling costs, actual decrease—through traffic-interchange arrangements—in the volume of freight moved through the streets, reduction in city traffic congestion, more convenience and speed of movement, and other gains.

A great deal of the success of the major conurbation schemes, such as those for the New York metropolitan area and the British schemes for London, Birmingham, Glasgow, and the Merseyside, would depend upon a radical reconstruction of urban traffic—a reconstruction coming about in part from the alteration of direction and volume of flow from the congested areas as a result of decentralization of population and regrouping of spatial relationships of residential sections, recreational areas, and industrial and trade centers, and in part from the necessity of linking up the metropolitan transportation system with that of the region as a whole.

UNIFICATION OF LAND AND WATER TRANSPORT

The criteria for unification of land and water transport are essentially similar to those promoting coördination of rail and highway systems. They run the gamut from the elimination of duplication of routes and transport equipment on through to the interlacing of administrative and management staffs.

Here again, a preliminary consideration for intercoördination of water and land transport is that each major transport system—oceanic, coastal, and internal waterways—be internally unified on the widest possible footing. The history of water transport since the turn of the century indicates a general trend toward such unification. The trend is very strong in oceanic shipping.

It is even more pronounced in recent plans for the development of comprehensive internal river and canal systems. And these efforts to unify water transport systems have usually been accompanied by attempts to increase both the smooth interchange between, and the specialization of traffic among, water and other transport media on an ever-widening scale.

The case of internal waterways is especially interesting. In this field, of the six key variables of time, distance, accessibility, convenience, completeness of service, and costs, which determine the extent and nature of traffic specialization among the principal transport media, internal water transport commonly enjoys definite advantages only in the last. Under appropriate circumstances, the costs of water shipment may be so much lower than rail or highway that it is not possible for these latter to compete at all. The circumstances must, of course, be present in conjunction with other factors: shipment of large quantities of low-revenue, bulky, heavy, relatively nonperishable and easily storable raw materials or semimanufactures which do not require costly storage or stand-by terminal handling facilities.

With respect to *routes,* the general conditions are that they must not be unduly circuitous. Stream currents should be slow and seasonal variations in flow relatively small. Such variations as do occur in the capacity of waterways to carry traffic—due to icing over in winter or to unavoidable variations in stream flow—should be accompanied by similar natural seasonal variations in the flow of traffic. Silting up of river beds should not be a serious problem. There should be few falls or rapids, and by-pass canals should not require large and costly supplementary construction. Locks should be few, and natural channel depths of rivers and canals should be more or less uniform and not unduly costly to maintain.

Favorable examples are found in the Great Lakes–St. Lawrence system; the lower Rhine, Elbe, and Moldau and Baltic and North Sea system; the Volga-Don-Moscow river and canal system; and the Garonne-Languedoc canal and river network. Examples of unfavorable conditions which may be difficult to overcome are found in the rapid silting-up and wide seasonal variations in stream flow on the Missouri, Arkansas, and Plata rivers.

With respect to the *handling of freight,* the bulk of the ship or barge traffic should be ample for full loads which may move directly and without interruption from terminal to terminal. Freight should originate and be discharged without the need of transshipment, or where transshipment is required it should be for relatively short distances (i.e., the major haul should be by water). The widths of canals, the widths and lengths of locks, and the dimensions and equipment of tugs, barges, and terminal facilities should be standardized with a view to maximum economy in the handling of cargo.

As an instance of unfavorable circumstances, the general failure of the highly developed British internal waterways system to hold its own after the middle of the nineteenth century appears to have arisen from shortcomings in the respects mentioned above. "There has been," Fenelon writes,

practically no co-ordination and consolidation of the various local systems, which were planned piecemeal in the constructional period, almost without relation to each other. There is no uniformity of depth, width, general conditions, or in the dimensions of locks, tunnels or overbridges. . . . Canals built to suit one kind of boat are generally unsuitable for other types, and thus only the smallest barge can navigate over any distance. On the Continent and in the New World 600 ton barges are usual, whereas in Britain the maximum is often below 100 tons and may fall as low as 40 tons.[45]

The *volume of freight* should be adequate to tax terminal capacity on the one hand, and the carrying capacity of rivers, canals, locks, ports and harbor facilities on the other, to the limit. A corollary is that traffic should be distributed as nearly equally as possible over the daily (24-hour), weekly, and annual cycles, and a further corollary is that return loads should be available.

A favorable example is found again in the canal and river system of the lower Rhine, which interconnects the east-west and north-south traffic in coal, iron ore, chemicals, and heavy manufactured products of the whole North German, Belgian, French, Dutch, and Luxembourg industrial complex. For another, it has been largely the development of bulk shipments north from the Gulf ports up the Mississippi River which has accounted for the enormous expansion of traffic (nearly doubled between 1939 and

1948), where there has long been plenty of downstream traffic. An almost total lack of upstream traffic is the principal obstacle to the development of water transport on the Missouri and the Columbia.

Another condition for the expansion of internal water transport is *unified management* of the river and canal system. For central European waterways it has been necessary to set up international commissions to effect some degree of unity in the handling of river traffic crossing national boundaries. Two such commissions, for the Rhine and the maritime Danube, existed before the First World War. The Treaty of Versailles added three more commissions—for the Elbe, the Oder, and the fluvial Danube.[46]

The problems faced by the commissions included practically every phase and aspect of transport: rules and regulations governing shipments, rates, pilots and crews, port facilities and charges, customs, maintenance and repair of channels and canals, etc. The Transport Commission of UNESCO has been attempting to secure international uniformity for all the principal internal waterways networks. Only in the United States and the Soviet Union has it been possible to accomplish this for any major river system. As for carrying equipment, the need for unified direction of public haulers is not greatly different. As far back as 1869, 480 private shipping companies and 670 independent shippers were brought together in a central association for the purpose of effecting some degree of rationalization of freight handling equipment and operation on the Rhine. What can be accomplished has been demonstrated by the successes of the Federal Barge Lines on the Mississippi,[47] and the Russian fleets on the Volga-Don-Moscow system.

A further condition for the success of internal waterways shipping is the *coördination of water transport as a part or phase of multiple-purpose water resources development* on the leading rivers. This means handling problems of water navigation as part of a program which also includes flood control, watershed protection, sanitation, irrigation, power development, harbor improvements, defense and war objectives, fisheries protection, and provision for miscellaneous commercial and recreational uses, public and private. It is only in recent years that multiple-purpose development of river systems as a whole has been accepted in public policy. The Tennessee Valley Authority was the great pioneering development. Other examples now are the St. Lawrence waterway, the power and irrigation developments on the Volga, Dnieper, and Columbia, and the power developments on the fluvial Danube and the Rhone.

Wherever multiple-purpose possibilities exist, the watershed, rather than the river channel, becomes the primary unit of reckoning. Water transport is then promoted by river developments intended largely or primarily for other purposes. This is true, for example, of dam construction which regularizes stream flow and of dike construction to prevent floods. Possibly an even greater advantage is found in the fact that multiple-purpose development lowers the cost of river maintenance for navigation purposes. At times it may be this factor which gives water transport a decisive cost advantage over parallel rail and highway haulage.

A final factor is *integration with rail and truck facilities at loading and unloading terminals* to permit continuous flow, through-billing and through-rates, simplified forms, lower handling and management costs, etc. This raises, among other things, somewhat the same problems of terminal unification as those discussed above in connection with rail and highway transport. An interesting example is found in the proposal by the Inland Waterways Corporation, operating the Federal Barge Lines, for "A Modern Union Freight Terminal to Serve Barge-Rail-Highway for the Port of St. Louis" (title of brochure). The problem of inter-media transshipment on internal waterways is, to all intents and purposes, identical with that which led to the development of warehouse, dockage, and other central freight and passenger terminal facilities on a grand scale by the Port of New York Authority.

In summary, there will be relatively few cases where at any given time all these six conditions are fulfilled to the advantage of internal waterways transport. There are, however, several fairly close approximations. In general, the over-all combinations are favorable for bulk traffic on the Mississippi River and its leading tributaries of the lower Ohio and Tennessee, and possibly the Missouri as far as Omaha; on the lower Rhine and its interconnections with Belgium, Holland, France, and Poland; and on at least the lower parts of the Volga-Don system.

All comparative cost data are subject to considerable dispute. Some of the claimed economies have been debated by experts at length. Railroad authorities tend to hold that when all costs are included, there are few instances where internal water transport could justify itself.[48] Without going into the matter here, it may suffice to say that wherever the conditions cited above are found in more or less favorable combinations, and whenever transport facilities are planned for the future with a view to differentiation of types of traffic and utilization at or near capacity of the several specialized media, most cost evidence from European and American sources seems to favor considerable expansion of waterways.

The case for unification of coastal and maritime shipping facilities, and for unification of these systems with land, internal waterways, and air transport networks, is similar to, and in the long run, no less compelling than the case confronting internal waterways. In a discussion centering in the technological and the cost factors which promote farsighted and comprehensive unification of transport, these two fields might be dismissed with such a generalization but for one special problem. That is the extraordinarily difficult problem of the multiplicity of national and political jurisdictions. This can be best seen in connection with airways development, although there are no fields of transport in which it is not, to some extent, an important problem.

AIRWAYS AND THE PROBLEM OF INTERNATIONAL
TRANSPORT UNIFICATION

National frontiers play a role in international transportation and the flow of world trade similar to the multitudinous local restrictions which throttled the movement of goods and persons in the medieval world, and of which the Swedish historian Heckscher[49] has written at such length. Internal national unification swept those away, though there has been some tendency—most notably in the United States—for some recrudescence of efforts to Balkanize the internal economy.[50]

An investigation in the late thirties[51] showed that a truck

traveling from New York to the State of Washington, thence south
to California and returning via Washington, D.C., moving through
24 states and the District of Columbia, would face load limitations
differing in all but two states en route and ranging from a maximum of 60 tons (Washington, D.C.) to 12 tons (Tennessee).
Additional variations occur with respect to heights of trucks,
widths, loads per tire, types of goods that may move freely from
one state to another, license charges, and so on. There has been
some improvement in this situation since that time,[52] but the
handicaps placed before interstate trucking are still formidable.
A significant step toward uniformity in state legislation and regulation of taxes on commercial trucking was taken in 1955 with the
drafting by the Western Interstate Committee on Highway Policy
Problems, Council of State Governments, of a model "Vehicle
Registration Proration and Reciprocity Agreement." This plan
was then recommended to the western states. By January, 1956,
9 states had "signed agreements substantially in accord with the
model agreements."[53]

Far more serious are the impediments facing international
transport. The importance of this problem lies in the fact that
just as transportation served as a leading agent of national unification in its early days of technical infancy, so now it has become
the principal agent of world unification during the years of its
maturity. This fact has long been clear in the fields of railroading
and oceanic transport. In recent years it has been dramatically
emphasized by the swift rise of air transportation. Nowhere is the
need for eliminating the barriers of national frontiers so clear-cut
as in the frontierless air; in no other instance is the geographic
frame of reference so obviously international, so plainly coextensive with a global "one world."

This need has been felt to some degree almost from the beginning of modern modes of rapid transport. One of the earliest
international agreements was signed in 1846 between representatives of German railway associations and the representatives of
railroad companies in Austria and Hungary. It called for standardizing of rail gauges, equipment, rolling stock, methods of
handling and routing traffic, through rates, etc. This agreement
was subsequently extended to include Belgian, Dutch, Luxem-

bourg, Roumanian, and Russian railroads. It provided the pattern for the International Agreement on Freight Transportation, signed in Berne in 1890. The Berne agreement has been gradually expanded to include both freight and passenger service throughout Europe and the Near East. Paralleling this geographic extension there has also been a steady widening of the range of technical, economic, and administrative understanding which has served to keep continental rail unification only a few steps behind that taking place inside the several national compacting parties.

Similar compacts have served to unify international rail networks in North America among the United States, Canada, and Mexico, and in South America among the leading rail networks of Chile, Argentina, Brazil, Uruguay, and Paraguay. The same has been effected in North Africa by the French, and in eastern, central, and southern Africa along the Cape to Cairo railroad. A major technical obstacle—the difference in rail gauges, and hence in sizes, weights, and clearances of rolling stock—effectively prevents thoroughgoing interlinkage between the central European and the Russian and Spanish rail networks. Aside from this factor —which may, of course, also greatly complicate unification of railroad systems throughout the Asiatic mainland because the Chinese, Indian, Persian, Near Eastern, Korean, and Indo-Chinese rail systems are also different from the Russian gauge—a wideranging series of joint-traffic conferences have slowly been clearing the ground for international network interlinkage in this vast area.[54]

A like picture holds for international highway, internal and coastal waterways, and oceanic traffic unification. A series of conventions, culminating in the intercontinental coastal highways passing from northern North America to the southern regions of South America along both coasts, has carried international highway planning in the two Americas to an advanced stage of development.[55] In Europe the picture is much more complicated because of the enormous importance of the motor lorry in times of war. Yet, as pointed out above, the pattern for highway networks which has been laid out by internal developments of the type of the autobahnen in Germany and the *autostrade* in Italy need only be extended across national frontiers to bring about a continental highway unification. A series of international conventions (1926, 1931, 1949) have sought to unify European rules governing operations of all types of commercial and private traffic over all roads.

In oceanic shipping, unification has been brought about by a wide variety of international agreements covering the use of port facilities, the carrying of mails, safety, radio-maritime reporting and communication, customs inspection, schedules, and rates. These have been paralleled by a series of national consolidations of major shipping lines and a number of line conferences which call for the regulation of traffic and the formulation of rate policies among lines serving the same ports or regions and handling the same or similar kinds of traffic.[56] Shipping conferences are typically set up along regional lines, and they usually result in a high degree of traffic pooling which requires, in turn, increasing administrative coördination among the participating companies.[57]

The problem of unification of international river and canal transport is far more complicated, and is largely confined to the central European states. Efforts to unify have a long history tracing back to the Congress of Vienna, in 1815, which "formed the basis of several subsequent treaties concerning particular waterways, such as the Scheldt, Danube, Rhine and Congo." [58] Nevertheless, the only functioning commissions up to the time of the First World War were those of the Rhine and the Danube. Following the war a series of investigations were made which showed the urgent need for effective coördination of internal waterways cutting across international frontiers if conflicting rules, regulations, and administrations, mounting tolls, and the like were not to choke traffic to death. As previously mentioned, three new river commissions—for the Elbe, the Oder, and the fluvial Danube— were established in Europe shortly after the signing of the peace treaty, and some measure of coördination among these commissions was effected through the League of Nations Transit Organization. Despite nationalistic handicaps, the case for unification of internal waterways on both a river-system and a continental basis, is now reasonably clear.

All the problems of international transport unification, however, are thrown into sharpest relief in the case of air transport.

The international and regional machinery to handle these problems has mushroomed with the swift growth of airlines since the end of the First World War.[59]

In 1944 an effort was made to unify the work of all international aeronautical coördinating bodies in a conference called at Chicago. An International Civil Aviation Organization was established, by over fifty nations, and a series of technical annexes dealt with problems of international unification on such subjects as "rules of the air, airways systems, communications procedures, traffic control, airworthiness requirements, licensing of personnel, aircraft registration, weather reporting, maps and charts, log books, customs procedures, and investigation of accidents." [60]

A rational extension of the central ideas dominating the participants at the Chicago conference would develop a world air-transport network possessing the following characteristics. (1) A common set of uniform rules, standards, and practices would apply to layout, facilities, and operation of airdromes and airways, and would govern radio beacons, weather reporting, and other aeronautical flight aids and communications for all public-carrier lines throughout the world. (2) Standards for safety of construction, facilitation of repairs, and supply of fuels would be uniform. (3) A single international regulatory authority would coördinate the activities of the various national air-transport authorities, public, semipublic, and private, including the multifarious aspects of unification of air transport with other forms of transportation on land and sea.

Complete unification of all public-service air transport on a global basis has actually been proposed on several occasions. (Internationalization of civil aviation was first proposed by France in 1931. Subsequently several other nations supported the idea.)

The general lines along which detailed solution of the problem of integration with other media would be carried out appear to be determined by two main characteristics of aeronautical transport. In the first place, its superiority as a transport medium over other types rises in proportion as one finds, in combination, high-value cargo, long distances to be traversed, low weight, and low bulk. In the second place, a leading characteristic of air transport is that its routes are straight-line, or very nearly straight-line, connections between principal traffic centers. The first set of advantages means that air facilities are bound increasingly to dominate long-distance passenger transport, and that they will continue progressively to gain certain classes of high-value freight traffic moving long distances or by unduly circuitous routes. The second advantage means the establishment of many traffic routes which only to a very limited degree duplicate land or sea arteries. Stefansson, for instance, is of the opinion that the bulk of future international air-borne traffic in the Northern Hemisphere will move across the Arctic Circle.[61]

The speed and the revolutionary character of technological changes in almost every aspect of aeronautics are so great at the present time that it is impossible even to guess the extent to which air transport will supplant other forms in the future. Yet, its success rests upon the same basic principles of (a) network unification on an international basis and (b) traffic differentiation by close coöperation with the older sea facilities that have so long been characteristic of other types of transport. The planned unification of one is necessarily coördinate with the planned unification of the others. The principles, that is to say, which guide unification of the various forms of transport on a local and national basis are equally—and, in some respects, even more insistently —valid in the international sphere.

COÖRDINATION OF TRANSPORT NETWORKS
WITH RELATED INDUSTRIES AND INSTITUTIONS

As with the various communications services, so also with each of the various forms of transport, unification requires the closest possible coöperation on a continuous, permanent, and systematic basis with industries manufacturing transport supplies and providing supplementary transport services. This interdependence is a two-way affair. Cheap and efficient transport is the lifeblood of industry, and the condition of its being both cheap and efficient is low-cost and highly efficient equipment able to travel freely over the widest possible appropriate geographic area. This means a universal and all-embracing system of construction and operational standards covering every important aspect of transport, but so organized, adjusted, and kept flexible through continuous and active contact with research as to make possible major changes without seriously disrupting the flow of traffic.

In illustration we might say that it is as necessary for the railroad operative that brakes, rail gauges, couplers, and signal apparatus be uniform throughout the network as it is important for the musician that the material and quality of the strings on his violin be exactly determinate. Properly conceived, this is simultaneously the condition for both high-quality performance and the maximum variation in styles, techniques, tastes and interests. The key to successful standardization, more precisely, is not regimentation but *controlled variation*. And *controlled variation* in the fields of transport requires an ever more far-reaching, meticulous, and finely detailed coöperation on a functional basis between the several transport networks and their numerous supply industries and services. This requirement for long-range coöperative planning is as binding as that which unites the several conjoint phases of multiple-purpose projects, as in the case of river valley developments of the TVA type, and it operates in such a way as to make the planning of any one aspect conditional upon the simultaneous coördination of all the other aspects.

What this means in detail for various manufacturing industries and supply services we shall have occasion to examine in chapter xi. At this point it may suffice to say that as far as the technological factors and the problems of operation are concerned, in the general field of transport, there is no serious disagreement among experts. The situation faced by American manufacturers during the war, where differences between the British and American (Whitworth and Sellers) screw thread systems, requiring duplication of repair stocks throughout all theaters of war, cost American manufacturers an estimated $100,000,000[62] illustrates the principle. Multiply the figure by a hundred—or perhaps a thousand—and we have some picture of the economies that may be effected through unified and long-range planning in this vital area.

SUMMARY

In broad outline the chief principles underlying transport unification are easy to state and relatively easy to visualize.

1. Unification of each traffic system is complete within each

geographic frame of reference. For local transport, the frame of reference is the town or metropolitan area. For railroads, it is the continental or intercontinental land mass. For internal waterways, it is the major river system and its tributary, supplementary, and interconnecting river, canal, and lake systems. For oceanic traffic, it is the sea lanes of the world. For airplanes, it is the globe.

2. A precondition to specialization of traffic between modes of transport is the maximum degree of unification, on a weblike pattern, of each separate traffic medium—rail, highway, airway, etc. —consistent with the over-all pattern of transportation development as a whole.

3. The criterion of specialization of traffic calls for a system "with each mode of transport operating in its field of greatest economy and usefulness and functioning with a minimum of waste and duplication." [63] Unification, in short, assumes traffic differentiation by types of transport media, with each type operationally developed in its over-all cost advantage as a coördinate and complementary arm to all other types.[64]

4. Within each geographic frame of reference, unification means simultaneous and coördinate integration of the several transport media, including oil and gas pipelines, and it must be traced out with a view to close coöperation with power grid systems.

5. Most of the various types of transport have evolved as multiple-function media or as coördinate parts of multiple-purpose developments. Thus, highways and airways serve both commercial and private users; internal waterways are being planned on a watershed basis with a view to simultaneous development of facilities such as water transport, power, generation, flood control, and recreation; railways and highways provide the bulk of the right of way for wire telecommunications lines and some long-distance oil and gas mains; many transport terminals handle freight, mail, and passengers and constitute important telecommunications centers. The frame of reference for the planning of each transport medium should, accordingly, be coextensive with the coördinate functions or purposes with which each is interlaced.

6. All transport forms should be planned (*a*) with a capacity to

handle peak loads, and (*b*) with a view to keeping all facilities to a minimum consistent with optimum volume of business (i.e., volume which makes optimum use of optimum facilities), because the initial investment in most fields of transportation is very heavy and because the manpower, materials, and fuels required are in large part costs of an overhead character and are also quite high (e.g., about 28 per cent of all fuels used in the United States are absorbed in transportation). The costs of underutilization of facilities, that is to say, are almost as high as full utilization; costs are lowest when the capacity factor (ratio of actual use to rated capacity) is at or near 100 per cent. The general rule, then, is that—given the structure of demand and after making due allowance for future changes—transportation planning should provide not the most but the least supply of facilities and equipment.

In general these principles may be summarized by saying that a highly developed transportation system of the modern type consists of a fully coördinated series of complementary and closely interlaced webs, each of which is operationally coextensive with its appropriate geographic frame of reference. Within each frame of reference—the metropolitan area, the river valley, the continent, the oceans, the air—each web is laid out as an internally balanced and coherently preplanned operational network, and in actual practice is to some degree managed as such. Duplication and overlapping are reduced to the minimum, and each web as it is spun is governed by its present and prospective relationship to the over-all traffic system—comprising all modes of transport—with which it is functionally interlaced. And the over-all traffic system—governing and being governed by factors which determine resource utilization and industrial and population distribution—should then be viewed as coördinate parts of general economic development.

X

Evolution of the Universal
Energy Pool

A leading characteristic of the modern industrial system is that with each new technical advance the availability and the cost of power set the limits to output.[1] It is also characteristic that this power is increasingly supplied in the form of electricity which also serves, with the dawn of automation and electronics, as the most important single agent for the effective synchronization of the entire range of productive processes.

Power is key. The trend is toward supply and it is increasingly made available through networks which are technologically co-extensive with major economic regions, be these subdivisions such as the American Pacific Coast, or western Continental Europe. It is the essence of such a regional network that it has developed to supply electrical energy at all points of use, that it operates best as a single unified web, and that this web extends from all principal points of generation to all leading power transmission and distribution facilities. Power, that is to say, within each region of reference, should be planned as a whole.

This latter feature may be illustrated by thinking of the power system as a gigantic sponge which "soaks up" energy from a widely scattered series of generating stations and then "squeezes it out" through a seeming infinity of outlets to all types of users. Perhaps better analogy would be the water-supply system of a great urban center like New York City. Here water is gathered behind huge dams from the watersheds of the Catskills, the Adirondacks, and the Delaware River, transported over long distances to the major urban distribution points in giant conduits, and then parceled out through an intricate network of mains and smaller piping to all types of users. In a power system the impounded waters would be likened to the generating stations, the conduits to the transmission grids, and the city mains and detailed pipe and plumbing network to the unified distribution maze.

The key to ample, adequate, and low-cost electricity supply is found in the creation of the widest possible energy pool. The creation of such a pool in turn depends upon, first, the supply of current from as many different sources of power as possible; second, the generation of current wherever possible as a coördinate part of wider-ranging multiple-purpose developments; and, lastly, the unification of both energy supply and energy distribution by all-inclusive, interconnected, regional high-voltage transmission grids.

The implications of full development along each of these three lines are extraordinary. They call for a type of long-range development planning in both power supply and related industries. Experts sometimes hesitate to dwell upon the possibilities for good and bad inherent in this course of events. Yet the more dramatic of the successive steps taken in the past and forecast for the future are fairly well known to all. Furthermore, most of their end results are, in effect, generally accepted by experts of virtually all shades of opinion, advocates of public and private power alike.

Attention was first called to these matters in the United States under the head of "giant power," not long after the turn of the century. Abroad, the first and most successful effort at national planning in Great Britain was the evolution of the nationwide power system of the Central Electricity Board. The International grid system of Von Miller[2] and the continental grid pattern of Oliven[3] failed of support only because of an excessive nationalism combined with the opposition of powerful vested interests. The measure of the European disaster of the 1940's is the inverse of the well-being which such planning might have brought.

In Goelro (Commission for Elaborating the Plan for the Government's Electrification for Russia) the Soviet authorities developed not only an early scheme for a uniform national electrification,[4] but inadvertently launched the machinery for several Gosplan schemes. Goelro pioneered the way and largely set the pace for full and effective scientific mobilization of the economic resources of the country. Such mobilization is not, necessarily, a prelude to war and totalitarianism. Even the partial mobilization of economic resources within the United States during the war years showed that a vast increase in our capacity to produce is entirely consistent with the free enterprise system and with significant advances in democratic freedoms.

It is not the fact of power-development planning which distinguishes various countries, but rather the degree and thoroughness of development and the nature of the objectives pursued. Thus the largest of the completely integrated and privately owned regional power systems in the United States, that of the Pacific Gas & Electric Company in northern California, resembles at every important engineering point of power development the publicly owned grid system of the Tennessee Valley Authority. There is little to distinguish either system in these respects, except for comprehensiveness of national coverage, from that of the British Central Electricity Authority or the plans for electric power development for France under the original Monnet Plan.[5] Similar plans exist or are found under consideration in countries varying as widely in stages of industrial development and social organization as Mexico, India, and Ghana (Volta River Development).

Since the present period of human history has become the "power age," an understanding of the economic and other factors determining this type of development is of fundamental importance. The details of development are extremely technical and complex; the larger outlines and trends, however, are relatively easy to grasp.

HYDROELECTRIC GENERATION IN MULTIPLE-PURPOSE SYSTEMS

In contrast to the earlier type of isolated hydroelectric plant, located at a waterfall or remote dam installation, power is increasingly being generated by plants functioning as coördinate features of unified developments which affect nearly all phases of life of the given river valley system. At the same time, the current generated by such hydroelectric stations is supplemented by the addition of steam plants, some of which may be planned with a view to the simultaneous supply of steam, gas, or other types of by-products. As the transmission grids expand geographically, these two types of multiple-function generation plants are brought into direct interconnection with each other and with other contiguous networks in handling the over-all generation load. Simultaneously, each new step then favors use of additional types of by-product energy from a wide variety of industrial processes. The transmission grid may become—in addition to serving as a broad "highway" for the supply of primary power—also a sort of energy "scavenger," soaking up energy from sources such as low-grade and otherwise waste fuels and turning natural gas into electricity at locations where it would otherwise be allowed to escape into the air.

At the point of generation, to repeat, the general tendency is toward construction of the plant as a part of an integrated multiple-purpose development. This is most clearly seen in the case of hydroelectric power. For the United States the pioneering experience of the TVA has been decisive.

The idea of combining power utilization with flood control and navigation was not, of course, new. A *Report of the National Conservation Commission* in February, 1909, after noting that a "first requisite" was to reduce floods and a second the "development of terminals" for commerce, went on to urge that

Broad plans should be adopted providing for a system of waterway improvement extending to all uses of the waters and benefits to be derived from their control, including the clarification of the water and abatement of floods for the benefits of navigation; the extension of irrigation; the development and application of power; the prevention of soil wash; the purification of streams for water supply and the drainage and utilization of the waters of swamp and overflow lands.[6]

While all of these features of river valley development appeared in the consideration of TVA, three were primary: flood control, navigation, and power. With other projects the emphasis may be different. Thus in the MVA (Missouri Valley Authority) project, irrigation is primary, power is secondary, and navigation is unimportant. In the ARA (Arkansas River Authority) project, irrigation and flood control are of roughly equal importance, and power is secondary. In the Columbia River project, power is primary and irrigation is secondary. In the Central Valley (California), the roles are reversed. Similar differences are noted abroad. The Niger development is primarily for navigation and power. The Japanese river projects are jointly for power and irrigation. The Yangtse is for power and irrigation in its upper reaches, power and navigation from the gorges to the sea. The Danube is almost wholly for navigation. The Volga is jointly for power, navigation, and irrigation.

Whatever the variations in emphasis, power is almost always a prime consideration, but according to best current practice it is practically never—except during the early stages of development in such instances as the São Francisco River project in Brazil and the Pacific Gas & Electric system (northern California)—considered separately from the pattern of unified river system development. The reasons are partly engineering, partly economic, and partly social and cultural, and these reasons are so closely interlaced that it is difficult, if not at times wholly impossible, to make clear where one begins and the other ends.

A crucial case for unified hydroelectric development is presented by the need for extending control over the soil coverage of the watershed. Since the main purposes—current control for navigation purposes, water for irrigation, power generation—always call for large storage-basins, the virtually universal problem of silt accumulation behind dams is a vital issue. Obviously, the silt cuts the storage capacity, and the speed with which the accumulation takes place controls the useful life of the dam:

At Boulder Canyon silt is accumulating at the approximate rate of 125,000 acre-feet per year [and] would result in filling the space reserved for silt within 26 years from the first year of operation—1936. The siltage rate at the Fort Randall project in South Dakota is estimated to be about 65,300 acre-feet per year . . . and indicates that the space reserved for siltation would be filled within 21 years.[7]

The same serious problem is faced by all large dam constructions planned for developments of the TVA type on the Missouri, Arkansas, and Columbia rivers and for the Central Valley project in California.

From the point of view of current generation, decrease in storage-basin capacity also eventually curtails the total amount of power that can be generated since it thereby limits the capacity to even out power generation in keeping with the curves of demand for the system as a whole. But this destruction of the very purpose for which the dam was built in the first place is only the beginning of the damage:

When the silt space in a dam has become filled, the silt begins to pass through the water turbines, resulting in the clogging of downstream channels. The gritty silt tends to increase the wear on the sealing rings and accelerate erosion of turbine blades, both of which result in a reduction of efficiency. The finely divided silt, if spread on farm lands, tends to fill the voids in the soil and form an impervious surface. At times when there is plenty of water, attempts are made to flush this material into the drainage ditches which in turn results in filling the ditches rapidly with excess material.[8]

Furthermore, the actual size of the storage basin depends upon the speed of surface runoff. Thus for any given volume of precipitation, the more rapid the runoff, the larger the basin must be, the more expensive the dam installations, and also the speedier the silting-up process. Thus there is no choice but to exercise some type of control over land utilization on the watershed.

The nature of the best type of land-use planning on the watershed will depend on the character of the local hydrological cycle on the one hand, and the conditions of natural growth and cultivation on the other. As far as the hydrological cycle is concerned, it need only be remarked here that the more evenly distributed the precipitation over the year, the simpler is the problem of planning soil conservation on any given watershed. Conversely, the more highly concentrated the rainfall or the water from melting snows—as in the monsoon country of southern Asia, or in the American desert country of the upper reaches of the Colorado, Snake, Arkansas, and Missouri rivers—the greater the danger that soil erosion will tend quickly to become irreparable.

Lands unfit for cultivation should be left as forest or grassland. Utilization, however, needs in both cases to be kept under rather close control. Thus, on the Colorado watershed, the sheep and goat herds kept by the Navajo Indians crop grass and forage plants so closely that the effect is almost as bad as if the lands had been plowed up. This circumstance alone accounts for part of the rapid siltation of Lake Mead (Boulder Canyon). Forest lands badly handled will show similar results, as the evidence of the TVA and the Soil Conservation Service has demonstrated.

Even more important is the type of farming conducted on the watershed. According to the director of the TVA, "If the changed farming practices now in use on many tens of thousands of Tennessee Valley farms were applied to all the agricultural area of our watershed . . . , the soil might absorb as much as a quarter of the customary 23-inch surface run-off of rain each year." [9] The methods referred to are contour plowing, prevention of gullying, shift in type of crops on heavy slopes to forage grasses which hold the water, and the planting of various legumes and applying of artificial fertilizers which by enriching the soil restore or maintain its chemical capacity to sustain hardy plant growth. Interest in these methods has stimulated farm modernization, which in turn requires extensive use of rapid soil-building fertilizers on run-down land, grouping of uneconomic small holdings into large farms, purchase of power-driven agricultural equipment, new types of barns and houses, etc. Thus farm modernization is linked with hydro-power interests in the best use of watershed lands by many ties, and in turn,

The development of soil and its increased productivity are not simply problems of land, of farming, and of agricultural science, any more than the development of a river is only water control, dams and engineering techniques. The restoration of land fertility, the healing of gullies, the reforestation of hillsides, these are no more ends in themselves than are flood control, navigation, and power. As the river is not separable from the land, so the land is inseparable from the forests and minerals, from the factories and shops, from the people making their living from their resources. . . . The farm, too, is a "seamless web." [10]

As an interesting by-product, it is also true that as programs for watershed forest planning are added to dam construction for the creation of large storage-basins, there are immediately made available extensive recreational facilities for fishing, boating, hunting, and tourist travel. This represents a definite gain. Speaking of water impounded behind the TVA's great network of dams, Lilienthal writes that

. . . on these lakes are thousands of new pleasure craft of every kind—costly yachts, sailboats, homemade skiffs. Ten thousand miles of shoreline—more than the total of the seacoast line of the United States on the Atlantic, the Pacific, and the Gulf of Mexico—are available for the recreation of the people. Thousands of acres along the shore are devoted to public parks, operated by the states, by counties, and by cities. More than 225 boat docks serve the needs of fishermen from all parts of the United States. There is far more fishing in the new lakes than there was on these same rivers before the dams were built—one hundred times more on the storage reservoirs and thirty times as intensive on the main stream reservoirs. Careful studies showed that not more than 10 per cent of the available fish "crop" is being harvested annually, [yet] in 1952 sports fishermen alone are estimated to have taken some 8,000,000 pounds of fish and 10,000 tons of mussel shells.[11]

Thus, concern over problems of stream flow and silt control leads gradually to a whole series of related improvements "upstream" whose value to the community is in direct proportion to the extent to which the administration carries out the interlaced developments on a coördinated and planned basis.

Where irrigation plays an important role, as in the Central Valley project in California, the Columbia River, and most of the Central East Asia river development schemes,[12] there are other multiple uses. High dam construction makes possible correspondingly larger power generation from any given volume of water while providing high-gravity flow of irrigation waters.[13] In the Central Valley, a large percentage of the power generated at Shasta and Friant dams is used for pumping water from the Sacramento and San Joaquin rivers lower down, and for subsurface pumping where water tables are not falling. Here water tables, stream flow, irrigation water, pumping, power generation and consumption, and crops are bound together in a unified web of interdependencies which is as close and exacting for the two major valleys as is the cycle of plowing, fertilizing, planting, cultivation, and harvesting for the production of individual crops.

It is impossible to determine in any logical or precise manner the sum total of the economic gains from such multiple-use development, for they ramify endlessly throughout the economy, and are capable of being used to enrich the social and cultural as well as the economic life at myriad points of contact.

Experience and practice vary with conditions in river valley development, but in no case are there objectively valid criteria whereby the policies of cost allocation may be settled. On the whole, it seems probable that in most cases the cost of total plant installation for water power alone might be decreased by allocating costs to other conjoint aspects of such multiple-purpose schemes so as to compete—when due allowance is made for absence of fuel costs—with steam-condenser plants. Transmission costs are apt to be on the average somewhat higher because of the remoteness of generating stations from the principal consumption centers. Yet if these generating stations are united in a grid system, there are important reasons why multiple-purpose generation will invariably favor maximum utilization of whatever water power is available.

Such a pooling will also favor a mixed or "complex" system, uniting hydraulic with steam-generated power. Before considering the economics of this interlinkage, however, it will be worth indicating briefly the multiple-purpose features of steam and atomic-power generation.

STEAM-GENERATED CURRENT IN MULTIPLE-PURPOSE SYSTEMS

In a few countries, such as Switzerland, Japan, and Norway, and in various sections of the major industrial countries, such as the Pacific Northwest in the United States, and the Dnieper and central Siberian regions in the U.S.S.R., electric current comes mainly from water power. But in most industrial countries the bulk of the current is generated in steam plants. In England approximately 90 per cent comes from this source. In Germany and France the percentage is somewhat smaller, but steam dominates by a heavy margin. In the United States, with only 20 per cent of the estimated national hydroelectric resources developed by 1955, an estimated 78.1 per cent of total capacity was steam generated.[14] The reason for the relative importance of steam varies from one country to another. In the case of England, water power is available in negligible amounts and confined almost wholly to Wales and Scotland. In Germany, most water power comes from small sections of the Bavarian and Swiss Alps. In France and the United States the relatively low level of water power development may be the more important cause.

The fact remains that steam is the most important source of power, and much of steam-generated power is capable of becoming multiple-purpose in three principal ways: by the construction of plants designed to furnish both electric power and heat in the form of steam or hot water, by the construction of electrical generating stations to utilize low-grade local fuels and by-product industrial heat and gases, and by transformation of certain industrial plants so as to use publicly generated current instead of power produced by their own plants. (The last will be considered later in connection with the economies flowing from grid interconnection. The first two merit summary consideration here.)

In the first method, the plant is constructed so as to supply steam at high pressure to turbines from the generation of power, and then to "bleed" the steam as it leaves the turbines and feed it into heat mains at some uniform temperature as steam or hot water for supply to adjoining industrial and other types of consumers. The centralization of heat generation for public supply has become widespread. Between 1922 and 1930 the New York central heating network doubled in length (from 34 to 67 miles) and the heat supplied tripled (from 1,500,000 to 5,000,000 tons). The corresponding figures for Hamburg for the same interval show an eightfold increase in length of mains (from 1.2 to 10 miles) and a fourteenfold increase in steam supplied (from 25,000 to 355,000 tons).[15] Plans have been formulated and partially carried out for extending these heating networks so as to embrace the heat requirements for the central core of major urban areas. Russian engineers in the late thirties estimated the practicable limit of heat main extension from the steam plant, if the volume is sufficiently great, to run in the neighborhood of 10-12 kilometers (6.3-7.5 miles) when supplied in the form of hot water.[16] In the decade 1940-1950, 36.2 per cent of installed Russian electric power capacity was developed as "steam by-product." [17]

The net advantages of central heat supply are numerous, providing the demand in concentrated areas is sufficiently large to justify optimum-type stations and heat mains.[18] The question has naturally risen of the extent to which further economies in both plant construction and fuel utilization might be affected by combining electric-generation with steam-supply plants. Where the structure of demand for the two types of service is sufficiently alike, the saving in investment cost of combined steam-electric plants over separate plants appears to be quite significant.[19] Russian figures show estimated production costs per kilowatt-year to run from 100 rubles for large steam by-product plants to 250 rubles for medium-sized plants, with comparable figures for steam-condensing plants of 300 and 500 rubles respectively;[20] a thoroughgoing application of combined methods throughout an entire economy would, it was estimated, provide a threefold improvement in the average rate of fuel utilization over "best results obtained in condensing steam stations" alone.[21]

The last estimate, on the basis of other available data, seems very high,[22] yet it is made in a context which visualizes an eventual complete revamping of heat supply on a central-station basis for all major urban and industrial areas. It is also true that the net economies from combined heat and power stations for space-heating purposes would be much greater in countries with long winters, as in Russia or Canada. In more moderate climates by-product steam is used primarily for industrial purposes. Some of the newer steam-operating stations of the Pacific Gas & Electric Company, to give an example, are located so that by-product steam may be used on a continuous full-load basis by adjoining oil refinery plants. Under certain circumstances there may be, in addition to steam-power stations, supplies of steam or power from other sources to be poured into the appropriate distribution networks. (See, e.g., the discussion on atomic-power plants below.) Part of such power might be a by-product from other industries and processes, and part might come from plans for utilization of local low-grade fuels.

As reconstruction of steam plants of such a character is carried through, the planning of steam-generated current becomes necessarily coördinate with steam supply to public users and industrial processes in a fashion directly comparable to the role of hydraulically generated current in a multiple-purpose river valley development of the TVA type. If the primary purpose is to generate steam, and the configuration of demand over the daily and annual cycles is not too unfavorable,[23] then the plant will be constructed to produce by-product electricity. If the primary purpose is to generate power, the roles are reversed, but this reversal does not seriously affect the nature of the plant. Such steam-electric plants may be constructed either to take care of a particular industrial establishment or to supply a miscellany of urban, industrial, commercial, public, and ultimate-consumer needs.

For the individual industrial plant the savings in over-all investment charges and in operating expenses from combining power generation with heat supply were early shown to be very considerable, as several papers given before the World Power Conference in 1933 conclusively demonstrated.[24] Yet in order to realize these economies, the consumption needs of the industrial plant for both steam and power must be correspondingly large, and the distribution of its demand for both, over the daily and annual cycles, must be such as to promote a high-capacity factor (ratio of consumption to installed capacity). Since these requirements can practically never be met by the individual industrial user, supply from his own plant of either power or steam is bound to be in surplus at least part of the time. In this event, the surplus will be wasted unless there is a public-service network into which to discharge it. In the United States, the percentage of power supply from public-utility systems has steadily increased from 69 per cent in 1920 to 87 per cent in 1955.[25] Wherever such a power network exists near at hand, linking up with it results in converting the plant into a coördinate part of the power-supply system. The same might be true of by-product steam or hot water. The best alternative for the individual plant is then to buy all or part of its requirements from the public-service networks. In any event, the general effect of attempting to utilize the economies of combined heat and power plants in an individual industrial plant is almost certain to link it into one or both of the public-service webs.

If a plant is constructed to supply a miscellany of industrial, commercial, and other urban demands for steam or hot water, a number of possibilities are immediately opened up. In addition to the demand for volume, the resultant variety of demand tends, for one thing, to even out the load, and consequently to give a better load-factor (ratio of given rate of utilization to peak load) to the optimum-sized plant. More important, plants can be constructed primarily to meet the heat demand, and by-product surplus energy can be poured into the power grid, which can supply a far larger area than can the steam mains. This is because of heat loss with increase in distance in the one case, and line loss in the other. The first limits economical heat distribution to something less than 10 miles under favorable conditions; the corresponding figure for power is around 300 to 400 miles. In this general area of problems lie the reasons why the growing emphasis upon combined heat and power plants points toward making a public utility of both, and increasing the relative proportion of plant requirements purchased from such networks rather than produced for self-use.

Returning to the over-all picture, steam-electric networks have a further effect upon industrial and urban location because, for one thing, there is also a tendency for steam-electric installations to move the generating plant from the fuel base to the consumption center. (The limiting factors here are twofold. One is the cost of shipping coal by rail or water, or by pipe-line as dust or in a flux; the other is the relative advantage of moving the industrial plant to the fuel site.) A special illustration of the effect on plant location is provided by plans to utilize waste heat from processes requiring either or both heat and electricity to produce other materials or goods. A German engineer, F. Marguerre, has estimated that shifting the German coal-briquetting industry to a steam-electric basis would yield an additional 5,000,000,000 kilowatt-hours of electric power annually.[26] This would require concentration of electric station capacity, and it might supply very considerable quantities of by-product steam which would call for additional relocation of steam-consuming plants.

The mere presence of such dual heat and electricity grids provides pools into which may be "dumped," so to speak, any waste or surplus energy. In the case of a steel mill, for example, there may be large quantities of by-product heat, surplus stack gas (from blast furnaces), and by-product coke-oven gas. Given a heat main into which it may be poured, the first may be utilized as a source for generating steam or hot water. The second may be used as a substitute for the commercially more valuable coke-oven gas, or it may be employed as a low-grade fuel for the generation of hot water or electricity. Coke-oven gas may be used for either of the foregoing purposes, or it may be fed directly into gas mains for sale to the general public. In this last case, the coke ovens are linked directly into a public gas-supply system which serves even larger areas than the heat networks. Gas "grids," using by-product coke-oven gas in large part, have been developed quite extensively in England—currently constituting an interconnected web some 10,000 miles in length—and on a very large scale in pre-Nazi Germany. The case is not essentially different when natural gas may be substituted for manufactured gas.

In this latter case, there exist not two but actually three interdependent energy supply pools—electricity, steam (or hot water), and gas—stemming from unified energy development of a single type of fuel. These are to some extent alternative to each other at the point of supply, but the more carefully one examines the evidence, the heavier is the case for regarding them as functionally specialized networks—coördinate and supplementary to each other—which need to be planned on a unitary basis within each region. The general principle underlying utilization is that the total cost of installing the necessary additional plant for utilizing the waste, including any additional extension of the distribution networks, should supply energy at a price as low as or lower than that charged for the output of single-purpose plants.[27] If, however, the distribution networks already exist, and the scale of by-product energy to be utilized is high enough to justify the necessary additional plant of an optimum or near-optimum size, the allowance for distribution costs may be considered negligible and the case for utilization becomes stronger still.

In these circumstances, dual-purpose heat and power generating plants are interlinked with multiple-product industries which both use and supply heat and energy, and the whole is united in an interdependent complex where each and every unit comes to take on a public-utility character, and should, accordingly, be planned as such. Additional reasons for planning each with respect to the other is found in the facts that (*a*) the various uses for steam, hot water, electricity, and gas in the community are partly supplementary to each other and partly alternative—e.g., gas may be used as an alternative to electricity for many purposes,

(b) the generating and supply plants and the grids are very expensive and become more economical in proportion to the rise in the volume of demand and any smoothing out of the curves of usage, and (c) the expansion or contraction of one type of service (or product) automatically carries definite implications for expansion or contraction of other types of service with which it is interlinked. Steam-generated current, under advanced technological methods, in short, raises problems very closely analogous to those of hydraulic generation in multiple-purpose river valley developments.

MULTIPLE-PURPOSE ATOMIC ENERGY

It no longer seems visionary to count on the probable massive addition of atomic energy to the power pools of the relatively near future. The by-product central heating plant opened at Harwell, England, in connection with the Atomic Energy Research Establishment, demonstrated that the critical problem of the "heat exchanger" has been solved, at least on a pilot-plant basis. A further step was taken at the Arco (Idaho) plant, where electric power was generated from steam derived, via heat exchange, from atomic energy. By the summer of 1956, Britain and the Soviet Union each claimed to have such a plant operating on a fully commercial basis. On April 7, 1955, the Atomic Energy Commission announced plans by four private and public groups to build a total of 455,000 kilowatts of atomic generating plants.[28] As the early study of the Cowles Commission[29] made clear, the central problem from here on is primarily one of economics, not of engineering—that is, the problem of reducing plant costs.

With two major exceptions—"breeder" fuel and the disposal of radioactive wastes—such engineering problems as remain are primarily those having a direct bearing on over-all economy of operation. Basic materials appear to be adequate for large-scale development for the indefinite future. The cost of supplying the refined raw material at the power source is comparatively low relative to that of the fossil fuels of coal, gas, and oil. Thus the critical problems appear to center on the investment cost, and this in turn depends in large part—possibly primarily—upon the possibilities of multiple-purpose development.

With respect to the basic raw materials, the primary "fuels" are, of course, uranium and thorium. Uranium is not a rare element. "Its abundance in the earth's crust is about the same as copper, tungsten and zinc, metals which have been extensively mined and are now key components in our industry." Thorium is only a little less abundant. The problem, however, is not one of quantity, but of availability:

The highest grade deposits of uranium are in the form of pitchblende, the highest grade thorium ores in the form of monazite sands. The largest known concentrations of both these materials occur outside the United States: pitchblende mainly in Canada and the Belgian Congo, and monazite mainly in India and Brazil.[30]

Far more extensive, however, are small concentrations of these two ores found in connection with other mining operations—principally for gold and other metals found in rocks of igneous origin, such as granites and oil shales. The mining of uranium and thorium, that is, may come to be a joint process with the production of scarce nonferrous metals and oil. This might mean, as the Cowles Commission surmises, the production in the future of atomic fuels and these scarce metals in circumstances where the costs of production would be prohibitive for any of them taken alone.

Estimates of the cost of uranium processed to the necessary fineness range upwards from twenty dollars per pound. The Cowles Commission, however, has found that even if the price were multiplied a hundredfold to $2,000 per pound, the kilowatt-hour cost "would still be only 0.8 mills," and, in view of the fact that a pound of uranium is the energy equivalent of between 1,250 and 1,500 tons of standard-grade bituminous coal, at $2,000 per pound uranium would be "no more costly in terms of its energy content than coal at about $1.60 per ton (at the same thermal efficiency)."[31] This, however, is on the assumption that the breeder operation will be successfully solved. The problem here is that of turning the pure uranium, which appears when refined as "heavy uranium" and is nonfissionable, into "light uranium," which is the source of atomic energy. Only one part in 140 of the pure uranium is "light uranium"; the "breeder reactor" is the hoped-for answer to the transmutation into "light uranium" of the other 139 parts. This breeder process is now theoretically possible; when it becomes practically feasible the "atomic age" will have fully arrived.

Meanwhile, other developments may help it along. By 1950 atomic bombs had already become something like six times as efficient as the ones exploded at Hiroshima and Nagasaki. This means that scientific advance has made possible the release of a larger percentage of atomic energy, and there is reason for believing that this percentage may continue to rise with new theoretical insights and engineering techniques. As long as it remains a possibility—and scientific opinion holds increasingly to this view—that what is exploded in a bomb may ultimately be made available as usable industrial energy, every step in that direction holds out at least the hope of further multiplication of the effective total supply of atomic fuel. There is even a dim possibility that the reverse process, atomic fusion instead of atomic fission, which underlies the development of the hydrogen bomb, might in turn find its appropriate industrial application at some time in the future. If so, then to uranium and thorium might be added lithium, helium, hydrogen, heavy water (deuterium), and possibly still other elements used in effecting "fusion," and with these additions all problems of scarcity of fuel supplies would disappear.

The problem of supply does not, however, appear to be the critical limiting factor. Far more important seems to be the scale and cost of plant investment. Estimates of total cost, including piles and reactors as well as heat-transfer and power-generating plants, vary between plants which would cost as much as or somewhat more than the typical hydroelectric plant—when dam construction, transmission lines, and the like are added in—and plants costing ten to twelve times more.

There are, however, some extremely interesting possibilities in this connection. Since the cost of the raw material is, relatively speaking, low, and the weight involved is infinitesimal, power-generating plants may be built almost anywhere. The industrialization of areas relatively poorly endowed with water power and fossil fuels becomes possible on a large scale.[32] Two further possibilities present themselves: (1) location near, or in connection with, large industrial users, and (2) location in, or near, large metropolitan centers.

With respect to the first, the Cowles Commission examined eight industries "in which the cost of energy is an important element in total production cost," ranging from phosphate fertilizers where energy cost represented 33 per cent of cost of production to railroads and the chlorine–caustic soda industry where the corresponding figure was 8 per cent.[33] With respect to both industry and, second, metropolitan-area energy supply, attention was paid to the possibility of joint production of electric energy and direct heat. In industry, the problem is to supply *both* electric power and space heating on a basis almost precisely similar to that discussed above in connection with the operation of steam heat-and-power plants.

In either case, some extremely interesting questions immediately arise. For one thing, virtual elimination of transport and transmission cost by locating generating stations at industrial or metropolitan sites radically alters the whole fuel-transport system for both fuels and basic raw materials to be processed. Thus, shifting aluminum refining from northern sites far distant from the sources of bauxite and alumina, but where low-cost hydroelectric power was available in large quantities, would reduce the cost of aluminum some 8 cents per pound if local power-generating plants made possible refining in Alabama at tidewater of shipments of bauxite from Dutch Guiana, and some 14 cents if refining were done in Dutch Guiana at the bauxite source. Somewhat the same might be true of other industries using large quantities of electric power for processing purposes. But it might also be true of industries, such as iron and steel, requiring vast quantities of direct heat or process steam. Atomic energy, that is to say, might become a major factor at once in the planning of transport and in the location or relocation of a wide variety of heavy industries consuming power and process heat.

Again, every power-generating unit based upon atomic energy would exist as a coördinate part of a two-way system. On the one hand, it would typically be a producer of electric current where some, or all, of the power generated from this source would be pooled, via a unified transmission and distribution grid, along with steam, hydroelectric, gas, and other types of power-generating stations. As will be pointed out below, no matter how large the available supply of, or the demand for, electric current at any one consumption point (industrial or public service), the advantages of power-plant interconnection are so great as to be absolutely decisive in all except the exceptional case (e.g., a processing plant far removed from civilization).

On the other hand, all atomic-energy plants would be producers of several products, and the nature of this process is one which has encouraged, virtually from the very beginning, almost complete vertical integration. This integration reaches back to the original mining operations and all the way through piles, reactors, and allied plants up to top-policy formation. The reasons for this, of course, are only in part technological. They are in part scientific, in part matters of public policy.

Given a vast peacetime use in the form of a component source for the generation of electric power, national and international planning then would come to embrace—on its technical and economic merits—the bulk of the power and fuel-supply networks of the world. It would, in effect, be a multiple-purpose system from basic raw materials, through all processing, and at the point of power generation.

TRANSMISSION BY HIGH-VOLTAGE AND REGIONALLY UNIFIED GRIDS

The central and dominating feature of modern power development is the evolution of the regionally unified grid transmission system. It is the grid which defines the scale, the geographic extent, and the effectiveness of the "power pool," which gives power its unique public-service and public-utility role, and which expresses in most readily understandable form the values of long-range planning along scientific and engineering lines.

The general pattern has long been clear. The British Central Electricity Board early planned a completely unified national grid transmission network. By the middle thirties the broad outlines of the original scheme had been filled out and the grid system "comprised approximately 4,075 miles of transmission lines, about 2,880 of which operate at 132,000 volts and the remainder at 66,000 and lower voltages." [34] Subsequent development, both before and after nationalization in 1947, has consisted essentially of a process of filling in details and further rationalization of the general scheme originated in 1926. Begun and carried through its first stages of development by a Conservative government, the system was carried toward completion by a Labour government. In its projected final form, it resembles the German scheme outlined by Von Miller in the late twenties, which began by adding both current generation and distribution to a much larger national grid. The heart of the Von Miller scheme provided for a national grid that would ring the Reich with 220,000-volt double transmission lines, convertible at will into 380,000 volts, from which would branch off, as secondary and smaller strands from the unified power web, lines of 110,000, 60,000, and 40,000 volts. All generation, steam and water alike (except power exchanged across international frontiers—e.g., with Switzerland), and all distribution networks (even when separately owned by municipalities or by private interests) would be coördinated in a unified engineering and tariff system.

The Oliven scheme extended the same principles under a plan whereby Europe would have been crisscrossed with about 10,000 miles of 380-400 kilovolt transmission lines which would have unified the whole of the major power-systems of Europe: one line from Paris to Warsaw, 1,200 kilometers in length; a second from Lyons to Rostov, of 3,000 kilometers; a third from Norway to Rome, of 3,000 kilometers; a fourth from Calais to Lisbon, of 2,100 kilometers; and a fifth from Upper Silesia to Albania, of 1,500 kilometers. A series of schemes have been under discussion since World War II looking forward to at least partial revival of the Oliven plan for western Europe.[35] The fundamental pattern of Goelro in the U.S.S.R., as pointed out above, visualized a parallel extension of a high-voltage transmission grid over the continental area of central Eurasia.

The underlying engineering-economic factors favoring unified grid transmission networks are everywhere the same. Avoiding unnecessary detail as far possible, they may be summarized as follows:

1. All power-generating stations—except, possibly certain highly specialized or geographically remote plants requiring un-

usually large supplies of electric current—would pour current into the common pool for simultaneous transmission, distribution, and consumption on the closest possible approximation to full capacity. Full capacity means rated capacity of generators multiplied by 24 hours a day and 365 days a year (8,760 hours per annum), minus allowance for breakdowns and repairs.

In technical parlance, what is involved here is the problem of *off-peak load*. Since electricity is by its very nature nonstorable and must accordingly be used as it is produced,[36] the total capacity of generating stations and of transmission and distribution networks must be at least as high as the maximum demand which may occur at any hour of the day, on any day of the year. Plant investment must be high enough to meet not the average but the highest, or *peak*, demand. Since investment constitutes a major— and aside from fuel costs in steam stations the dominant—cost, anything that tends either to reduce peak demand or to increase off-peak demand, substantially lowers the price at which current may be supplied, and hence increases the volume and variety of current usage. Generally speaking, in hydraulic generation, and in all transmission and distribution, it costs nearly as much to produce at any fraction of capacity as it does to produce at capacity. Hence, the higher the degree of capacity utilization, the lower the cost per kilowatt-hour.

The principal criteria of degree of plant utilization are known as the capacity factor, the load factor, and the diversity factor. To illustrate, if a plant with a rated generating capacity of 100,000 kilowatts operated 24 hours a day, it would produce 100,000 x 24, or 2,400,000 kilowatt-hours per day. If it operated at this level for every day in the year, it would produce 100,000 x 24 x 365, or 876,000,000 kilowatt-hours per annum. If, however, the total annual production were but 438,000,000, or half the amount of which the plant was capable, the station would have an annual *capacity factor* of 50 per cent.[37] If, again, the highest level of current generation for any interval during the year—peak production—were not at the rate of 100,000 kilowatt-hours but 90,000 kilowatt-hours, then production at the rate of 60,000 kilowatt-hours at any other time would mean that the plant at that time had a *load factor* of 66⅔ per cent.[38]

Any increase in usage which would increase the off-peak load would improve the load factor, and any averaging-out of the interval of usage which would raise the total consumed during any time-interval would improve the capacity factor. The principal means of improving off-peak business is by increasing the number and variety of off-peak users, the *diversity factor*.[39]

Generally speaking it follows that (a) the more extensive the transmission grid geographically, (b) the heavier the use of current per customer, (c) the larger the number of customers, and (d) the more varied the types of usage, the better the three factors are, and the lower the unit cost of generation becomes. Conversely, the lower the cost of current, the more rapid is the rate of electrification, the greater the encouragement of off-peak usage, and the steadier the distribution of demand for current over diurnal, weekly, and seasonal cycles.[40] The key to all this, as may be grasped upon a moment's reflection, is steady widening of the grid pattern.

2. All generation stations and their generating equipment would (a) be built or installed to optimum size or as close to optimum size as the available current flow (in hydraulic generation) or fuels (in thermal plants) makes possible, (b) be constructed wherever possible as coördinate parts of multiple-purpose projects, (c) be constructed with a view to investment and other economies arising from planning in advance of future demand, and (d) be differentiated in such a way that hydroelectric, steam-and-heat, and atomic-energy plants would carry the basic (non-peak) load while condensing plants and old plants would provide peak-load, stand-by, and reserve capacity.

In general, as long as capacity, load and diversity factors are favorable, the advantage of large-sized generating units grows with every increase in the volume of demand. Up to a certain rather indeterminate point, the larger the generators and generating plant, the higher is the mechanical efficiency and the lower are the investment and operating costs per kilowatt of installed capacity. For both hydraulic and steam plants, costs decline with increase in plant size. According to the Federal Power Commission, at 1947 prices, American steam-plants of 5,000 kilowatt capacity had an investment cost of $120 per kilowatt; of 25,000 kilowatts, a cost of $100 per kilowatt; and of 100,000 kilowatts, a cost of $95 per kilowatt. Production costs at 60 per cent annual plant factor were respectively 6.4, 4.8, and 4.0 mills per kilowatt. For hydroelectric plants investment costs were $200, $135, and $115 for plants respectively of 1,000 kilowatt, 25,000 kilowatt, and 100,000 kilowatt capacity; production costs per kilowatt-year were respectively of $6.10, $2.70, and $1.80 for plants of 5,000 kilowatts, 25,000 kilowatts, and 100,000 kilowatts.[41]

Furthermore, typically, the larger the plant, the more it is apt to be linked into big transmission-systems, and hence the better are the load, capacity, and diversity factors. That is, in addition to the economies flowing per kilowatt-hour from increase in size for any given capacity factor, there are those which arise from increasing the capacity factor of the several sizes of plants. "For each successive doubling of the plant factor," the Federal Power Commission found, "thermal efficiency improves, on an average, at a generally constant rate of about 23 percent." [42]

If, in addition, the generating plant is constructed as part of multiple-purpose developments, both overhead and operating costs can be still further reduced. This comes partly, as pointed out above, from spreading costs over two or more coördinate functions. But there are further economies. If, for example, hydraulic and steam generating stations exist in the same system, the over-all costs of generating current can be decreased by shifting the basic load (that part of the load in continuous demand) to plants where costs per kilowatt-hour decrease most rapidly with improvement in the capacity factor. In most complex systems this means that hydraulic power—where practically all costs are of an overhead character (i.e., varying inversely with output) —carries the basic load and other power sources the peak load.[43] The advantages of having hydraulic power carry basic load are enhanced, as is illustrated notably in the case of power from the St. Lawrence project, where stream flow is relatively even over the year.[44] Where some of the generating stations combine heat and power, fuel costs tend to take on an overhead character, and these stations, accordingly, should share in the basic load. This would leave ordinary condensing and technically obsolete stations to handle peak demand.

It is difficult to sum up all the factors in such a way as to present a clear picture of the potential over-all economies resulting from complete integration. They are, however, very great. In the case of the Oliven plan it was estimated that interlinkage would make possible, from existing generation capacity, the production of an additional 20 billion kilowatt-hours, or a 25 per cent increase over the 80 billion kilowatt-hours produced in 1930 in all Europe, without any additional cost except that involved in transmission-line interconnection.[45] This figure makes no allowance for future economies arising from differentiation of load between hydraulic and steam-generated power, from multiple-purpose projects with either type of generating station, from planning ahead for economies associated with the improvement of load and other factors, or from a host of further closely related changes which an effective rationalization of the power industry on such a basis would involve. The importance of some of the possibilities can be seen in the case of improvement in the load factor. A British estimate (made in 1955) has it that an increase in the British national load-factor average from just under 50 per cent to 66 per cent (compared with an estimated American average of 75 per cent) would make it possible to "do the same amount of work" with three-quarters of the existing generating capacity, and that "this would mean that by 1975 about £1,000 millions could be saved and diverted to productive purposes." [46]

3. Transmission should be by high-voltage alternating current, with all primary, secondary, and tertiary lines uniform and standard with respect to voltages, types of current, and frequencies. Generally speaking, the larger the system and the heavier the demand, the higher is the voltage of primary lines. As voltage rises under favorable factor conditions, the greater is the volume of current which may be conveyed along the wires per unit of transmission investment. This relationship holds now up to 280,000 volts (Hoover Dam), and it may shortly be true up to 330,000 and possibly even to 440,000 volts. In 1947 an American company began experimenting with a 500,000-volt line. Such a line would be able to "do the work of two at lower standard voltages" of around 220,000 each.[47] The cost problems in this area are quite complicated, but it may readily be seen that, since

with every shift in voltage special installation, transformer facilities, and other equipment must be provided, the case is overwhelmingly strong for seeing that all stations pour current into the system at the same voltage level, and that all "stepping-up" of voltages at the generating station and all "stepping-down" at consumption centers employ uniform, standard equipment.

The same holds for types of current and frequencies. Clearly, widespread use in the same area of both alternating and direct current means double transmission and distribution lines, not to mention the financial burden laid on consumers arising from the necessity of purchasing new industrial or household electrical equipment when moving from one current district to another.[48] The same is true for frequencies, of which a single but quite typical case must suffice. Early in the history of the British Central Electricity Board it was found that the standardization of frequencies throughout England would cost from £18 to £20 millions ($87 to $90 million) and yet was well worth the expense because of the decreased cost of converter equipment, transmission lines, and generating facilities—in the original purchase price, and in all costs of maintenance and upkeep—quite aside from the convenience to the general public.[49]

4. The transmission grid should be nucleated in such a fashion as to be coextensive with each major industrial and metropolitan area, and all nucleated networks should be interconnected by high-voltage lines for every economically homogeneous territory, whether it be national or continental in scope.

It is easy to see the first part of this proposition, but not the second. For a wide variety of technical and cost-accounting reasons, referred to above, the case for complete unification of the transmission web within each major industrial and metropolitan area is so strong as to require no elaboration. It is distinctly analogous to the case for unification of telephonic connections, and extends all the way from costs of generation to the servicing of the distribution network. Equally noteworthy, but not quite so obvious, are the advantages of system interconnection.

As for the second proposition, that nucleated networks should be interconnected by high-voltage transmission lines, the case is not essentially different, provided, of course, that the areas of heavy usage are not too far removed from each other. Wherever fuel used for generating power is located at or very near the point of heavy industrial or urban consumption, or wherever the cost of shipping fuel by water, pipeline, or other means is very low— an especially important point for the future of atomic power—the generating station is bound to be located at the point of consumption. This tendency is further enhanced by the fact that most power generation from steam, gas, and atomic energy is, or may be, associated with the multiple-purpose plant where the "purposes" other than power are steam, hot water, or other by-products which require massive industrial or general-user markets.

But it is still true that, just as heavy industrial users gain by tying in with a public-service line because it is able to take current from the larger pool in periods of high industrial use and pour into the system current generated in attached power plants in periods of low industrial use, so the same holds for the interconnections between nucleated areas themselves, even where generating plants are constructed primarily for serving local needs. Not all current, however, is generated to serve massed local demand. Wherever hydroelectric current is a significant component in the power pool, and wherever the costs of shipping fuel energy by high-voltage wires from fuel source to consumption centers is as low as or lower than the corresponding cost of shipping the fuels themselves, either generating plants will tend to be removed from such consumption centers or specialized uses will be found for much of the current at the generation site. The outstanding case here is that of hydroelectric power where cost is associated with multiple-purpose river valley development projects. Some heavy industrial users, such as aluminum and magnesium processing plants, may actually move to the generating sites. But in most cases the bulk of the current will be moved considerable distances from the generating station by high-voltage lines.

Furthermore, interconnection always makes possible specialization of generating plants within the grid system of hydroelectric and multiple-purpose steam plants for the basic load, and the use of condensing plants and old plants for stand-by and reserve purposes. Even where this point does not weigh heavily, it is also true that two of the major nucleated areas will rarely have precisely the same peak-load distribution, daily or seasonally, and hence the two interregional current demands may be dovetailed to mutual advantage. An outstanding case is the heavy industrial and metropolitan use for current in the San Francisco Bay region during the winter, when power required for pumping water in the intensively cultivated agricultural regions in the Central Valley is light. In the summer months this structure of demand is almost exactly reversed, and for this reason (dovetailing of seasonal peak-loads) generating plants required for one will supply both. Finally, a further advantage of interregional grid hookups is that all plants and generating equipment can be built to optimum size with less chance of experiencing long periods of high excess- and reserve-capacity. Considerations such as these demonstrate that system interconnection has all the advantages of regional unification.

5. The terminal distribution networks should be laid out as completely unified webs designed to serve the maximum number and variety of consumers. This principle is now generally accepted, and the reasons for it are consistent with those favoring unification of transmission lines within nucleated areas, and interconnection between regional systems. The early British Central Electricity Board was able only gradually and by piecemeal action to bring about unification within villages, towns, and major metropolitan areas. In the United States, the U.S.S.R., Germany, and many smaller countries the situation is more favorable. It is interesting to note that in the United States the bulk of the lower rates are found, in the main, in areas supplied by grid transmission and unified distribution networks, and that, while consumption rates are high per capita, these are areas of relatively low population density which are not very heavily industrialized. They are areas, that is to say, where the economies of comprehensive power planning have been able to overcompensate for the relatively unfavorable consumption demand.

SUMMARY: FROM UNIFICATION OF REGIONAL POWER POOLS TO THE
COÖRDINATE UTILIZATION OF RELATED NATURAL RESOURCES

The unification of power generation, transmission, and distribution upon the widest possible regional and interregional basis carries with it growing emphasis upon the coördinated utilization of an extraordinarily wide range of natural resources. Involved, directly or indirectly, are activities ranging all the way from modernization through the electrification of household utilities and appliances, on the one hand, and reconstruction of machine and chemical production processes, on the other, to reconsideration of practically all phases of community life, city growth, and industrial and commercial development.

Wholly independently of social philosophies and theories of social organization, and because of engineering developments and the economies of operation alone, the unification of power has taught the lessons, provided the facilities, and supplied the incentives for resource and development planning on a comprehensive regional basis. The TVA, the Central Valley project, the British Electric Authority, the power development plans of France, Germany, Italy, and many others are all essentially alike on this score.

The planning of a power grid, as pointed out above, immediately promotes reconsideration of the entire transportation problem. In a typical case, that of the Columbia River basin, the provision of a deepwater channel for the lower reaches of the river system supplies a competitive medium for heavy cargo shipments by rail. The problem of traffic specialization among water, rail, and highway facilities, where expansion of each involves immense investments over long periods, encourages comprehensive planning. The possibility of electrification, encouraged by the dual influences of low costs of shipment by water on the one hand and low costs of electric power on the other, means additional railroad investments which can be borne only under circumstances favoring heavy trunk-line and "through" shipments. And this is accomplished to best advantage only when railroad networks are developed on a regional basis and as coördinate parts of a unified traffic system which includes water, highway, and air networks.

Power is also a substitute "fuel." Where energy supplies—as in England, the north-central United States, and the Rhineland industrial areas—rest largely on coal, the grid system may radically alter the entire pattern of fuel shipments. In some cases, generating stations will move to coal sites. In others, coal will move in bulk from the mine mouth directly to generating plants. Here the combination of steam and electric supplies, or power generation and gas, have the general effect of gradually tapering off the demand for coal for domestic and most industrial purposes. It is no accident, accordingly, that the Central Electricity Scheme has been paralleled by proposals for complete rail unification in England, for the latter is viewed as merely a first step in that overhauling of the rail network which has been promoted, to a considerable extent, by the two complementary changes in the heat and energy supply system of the country.

Similarly, the grid pattern, as pointed out above, revolutionizes regional water utilization by unifying the need of water for urban and industrial purposes with transportation, watershed control, and agriculture. Where irrigation plays an important role, as in the Central Valley project in California, it becomes necessary to plan the irrigation network for the agricultural land on a unified basis which closely resembles, and is closely tied in with, the pattern of the principal power-transmission lines. In the California project, the reservoirs, canal systems, generating and transmission facilities, and pumping stations are functionally interconnected and planned as facets of a single integrated network. Power, in short, becomes a coördinate part of a national (or international) water resources scheme which, as in the United States and England, places all water utilization throughout the nation on a multiple-purpose development basis.[50]

But planned power exercises a still more subtle and far-reaching influence upon the functioning of a modern industrial system. It splits every mechanical and chemical process down the middle, separating power generation and energy transmission from the power-utilizing operations. With respect to the individual power-consuming plant or firm, the "prime movers" of industry are on the one hand "collectivized" and progressively removed from the locale of use. And in usage, on the other hand, the energy is introduced immediately into the operating machine by direct gearing of motors to working parts in mechanical operations, by resort to electrolytic, electrothermal, and electrochemical action in chemical operations.

In brief, it is clear from the wealth of engineering, cost, and

statistical data lying behind the summary outlined above, that
the pooling of the "prime-mover" capacity of industry—along
with the other uses of electric power—requires unified planning
on the largest possible regional or interregional units of reference
of energy generation, transmission, and distribution.

This is only the beginning of the technical imperatives. In
planning, both the volume and the structure of all power uses,
and the location and the power requirements of the massive
chemical and other power-consuming industries become matters
of prime importance. The more completely the latter are reorganized on an automation basis, the more will the structure of their
requirements affect power consumption. Simultaneous, coördinate, and long-range planning of the principal classes of power
consumption, that is to say, becomes an ironclad technical requirement for the maximum efficiency of each.

XI

The Possible Impact on Goods Distribution

Although goods distribution might seem to be the area of the economy least affected by the scientific revolution in industry, it may well be the one where the new methods might, if given free rein, introduce the most drastic changes in organization and structure, and make possible the most significant savings in the use of resources. Whether the United States and other industrially advanced countries can really effect large-scale savings in distribution remains to be seen, but the existence and the scale of our built-in inefficiencies may show the underdeveloped areas—compelled as they are by the remorseless logic of lean resources and overwhelming need—how to make the best use of what they have.

At least potentially, distribution would seem to be affected most directly by any rapid spread of the standards and specifications revolution referred to in chapters i and iv; it is, however, also affected by all the other components of the scientific revolution in industry. The chemical revolution throws into distribution channels an enormous variety of new and substitute materials, greatly complicating the problems of product differentiation and the handling and vending of nearly every type of consumers' goods. The automation revolution introduces many new standards of design, methods of materials handling, and problems of quality control over consumers' goods. The energy revolution opens up new possibilities of population location, which favor further changes in distribution methods, and certain of its more direct by-products introduce new changes in food preparation, preservation, and nutrient qualities, and similar allied innovations, which affect the flow of consumers' goods. Furthermore, the distribution of goods cannot clearly be separated from their production. Nearly every step in the direction of the scientific revolution in industry tends to make them still more interdependent.

In attempting to define the meaning of distribution, the Research Division of the Organization for European Economic Cooperation (OEEC) has come up with the following:

... distribution or the distribution process is taken to include all activities connected with the transfer of goods to the consumer once the production process has been completed. Such activities include those often undertaken by producers, such as market research, advertising, employment of sales representatives, transport, packaging, as well as the activities of distributors as such, that is importers, wholesalers, retailers, and similar groups. Further, the distribution process is taken to include the provision of services as well as goods. It is almost impossible to distinguish the provision of services from the provision of goods, but the term services is taken to cover all distributive activities that accompany the supply of the physical goods to the consumer. The term therefore includes, for example, the fittings and layout of the shop, the advertising and display of the goods, delivery of the goods, the choice of goods provided for the consumer, the advice given regarding selection and so on.[1]

So defined, they continue:

Productivity in distribution is seen to concern producers and manufacturers, transport undertakings, wholesalers, importers, agents and other intermediaries, retailers of all types and finally the consumers themselves. Further, governments and those responsible for the policies of governments are equally concerned with productivity in distribution in so far as they help to determine the character of the economic and legal framework within which the enterprises and the consumer operate.[2]

In effect, as far as distribution may be considered a physical process,[3] it comprises a series of traffic arteries and warehouses filled with producers' and consumers' goods. Transport media connect these warehouses with production plants, wholesale warehouses with retail warehouses, and the latter—where home-delivery systems still exist—with homes and institutions serving consumers. Both wholesale and retail warehouses are variously specialized by the types or classes of products and the clienteles served.

So considered, distribution is an inextricable part of production, being simply a collective noun to include all stages and aspects of goods movement, storage, and final disposition to the consumer, once they leave the factory in finished form. The impact of the industrial changes dealt with in this study may, then, affect and give rise to problems in (1) the types and varieties of goods entering the arteries from production plants; (2) the directions of movement, the scale and product mix of shipments, and the type and interlacing of the media used for handling this traffic from plant to warehouse; (3) the number, location, size, types, and degree of specialization of warehouses, wholesale and retail; and (4) the means of communication used to keep goods moving through successive storage places until, finally, they come into the hands of consumers.

The first problem may, in this context, be regarded as that of appropriate product-differentiation, or, in the main, of adequate standards and specifications for goods. The second is a special aspect of the problem of transport (chap. ix). The third is the problem of regional and urban distribution of wholesale and retail establishments, and their size, specialization, location, and number. The fourth might be considered as the problem of advertising and sales promotion, or of communications and supply of information required to equip buyers at various steps within the distribution line (business sellers and buyers) and at the end of the line (consumers)[4] for making particular decisions.

With no undue stretch of the imagination, we can view the distribution system as such a unified whole. On the technical side, this is precisely what distribution is. Large sections of it are already organized in such a way as to embrace all, or nearly all of these steps in a single organization, and their managements have come, within the normal functioning of business enterprise, so to view the problem of distribution. Good examples are the great American mail-order houses such as Sears, Roebuck and Montgomery Ward, parts of the operations of grocery chains such as the Great Atlantic and Pacific Tea Company and Safeway, and a few of the leading coöperatives abroad—perhaps most notably the system in Great Britain which links production with the Coöperative Wholesale Society, and in turn with a nationwide system of retail outlets.

Other examples where all or most of the several steps in distribution have been brought under unified management include automobiles, various lines of durable goods, gasoline and oil, and certain lines of clothing. In these instances, whether the move toward formal business integration is from manufacturer to consumer, or from retailer or wholesaler toward the manufacturer, the entire distribution process is viewed as a continuous flow of goods under unified direction from producer to ultimate user. Were this picture then extended so as to embrace all distribution, one would find in principle virtually nothing new in its technical reorganization along lines similar to those discussed in the previous chapters except, possibly, the sheer scale of the potential economies that might be realized. This is not to suggest that individual manufacturers can or should try so to organize the distribution of their own products. Nor should it be taken to imply that certain functions, such as those of independent middlemen, do not need to be performed. It is, rather, to suggest that all aspects of goods distribution must be considered together in the problem of rationalization in this area.

Consider first the implications of the substitution of scientific for ordinary commercial specifications for the flow of goods from factory down into distribution channels.

LIMITING PRODUCT DIFFERENTIATION TO MEANINGFUL VARIETY

Any successful attempt to re-specify the properties of goods entering into distribution channels so as to direct attention solely, or even primarily, to meaningful varieties—even with the fullest latitude allowed to genuine differentiation to suit any and all consumer tastes, preferences, and whims—would immediately make possible enormous economies in goods distribution.

Part of the story may be clarified by citing a couple of startling, and hence possibly somewhat extreme, examples. A semiautomatic West Coast wholesale warehouse, stocking by rough estimate about half of all available drug items, keeps on hand around 75,000 items. About 95 per cent of these are duplicative. That is to say, about 95 per cent represent merely different brand designations for identical products. In short, instead of stocking all the estimated 150,000 items, a warehouse could have supplied any retailer need with a nonduplicative total of between 5,000 and 10,000 items.[5] Again, the average American grocery supermarket in 1940 carried about 1,200 food items. By 1956 this had increased to about 5,400 items. Even in 1940 part of the total stock represented meaningless product variation. The bulk of the increase to 1956 represented similar meaningless brand duplication.

Limiting discussion for the moment to the facts cited here, it is easy to see that multiplication of such meaningless variety (1) confuses the consumer, making choice difficult between varieties in general, between meaningful varieties, and between meaningful and meaningless varieties; (2) vastly increases retail and wholesale inventories, expands requirements for storage and store space, and complicates problems and manpower requirements for handling and maintaining stocks; (3) tends to multiply for any given volume of sales the frequency and number of supply orders from retailer to wholesaler, and from wholesaler to manufacturer, and to reduce to the minimum the size of all such orders; (4) increases thereby the number and frequency of transport movements between successive supply-points, and accordingly the volume of transport equipment and manpower required to manage supply flows for any given volume; and (5) tends generally to neglect mileage and other transport cost differences incurred in all such flows by directing the flow from each manufacturer to all warehouses in the country, regardless of location, rather than to relatively few and near-by warehouses, reduces the sizes of shipments, and multiplies indefinitely the extent of cross-hauling of identical commodities at all steps in the movement from the factory to the ultimate consumer.

But this is only the beginning of the diseconomies associated with neglect of meaningful product-differentiation. Promotion of pseudo differences is costly for many reasons, and when one manufacturer begins such promotion all others are forced, on survival grounds, to follow suit. Among the methods employed which add to costs, and hence to wastage of resources, are the attempts to supplant familiar and technically accurate product- and quality-identifying terminology and descriptions with brand names and meaningless claims, and the multiplication of different package sizes and colors. One of the by-products of such promotion is a sort of Gresham's law in the competition among products of varying qualities, whereby poor and functionally low-quality goods tend to drive out the better. A startling illustration of this is the wholesale resort to the placing of all goods—however simply utilitarian—on a style or "model" footing, and the promoting of what is now widely referred to as "accelerated" or even "creative" obsolescence. In both cases, it is deliberate policy to substitute relatively short-life and low-durability products—notably in such cases as women's clothing, automobiles, household appliances, and, more recently, furniture, rugs, and draperies—so that social style or fashion pressure combines with repair and maintenance costs to force the consumer prematurely to discard the goods or to turn them in on the purchase of new models.

The problems of distribution begin with production engineering. In the field of style goods a pair of wartime examples will illustrate the point. In one instance it was found that substitution of fast for non-fast dyes for cotton textile fabrics would have increased the usability of clothes made out of these textiles (mostly women's and children's clothes) by cutting down the "throw-away" rate by around 20 per cent. The cost of fast dyes was virtually identical with non-fast. However, non-fast dyes tended to increase the turnover of consumer wardrobes; to increase the amount of consumer expenditures on clothes; to add to the costs of weaving, cleaning, and keeping in stock the affected lines of clothing; to increase costs of marketing through—among other things—handling "returns"; to require more cotton acreage, more cotton textile spinning, weaving, and dyeing plant-capacity, more inventory and warehouse space, and more manpower—from field workers to store clerks. In the specific instance cited, it was estimated that at the time (1942) the increased throw-away rate absorbed an amount of cotton in excess of the entire Allied demand upon the United States for cotton textiles for military purposes.[6]

A second example relates to shoes, and is taken from data supplied by the Standards Division of Office of Price Administration (OPA) to the Kilgore Committee:

During 1943 about 250 million pairs of shoes with cattle leather soles were produced. The cost of these to consumers approximated one billion dollars. 180 million pairs of shoes with oil- or wax-treated soles will give approximately the same wear as 250 million untreated pairs. The cost to consumers would be about $715 million instead of $1 billion, a saving of $285 million. This is equivalent to a 28½ per cent decrease in the cost of shoes to consumers or a decrease of $1 for every pair. From the conservation and rationing viewpoint this increased wear would be equivalent to making available an additional 100 million pairs of shoes to civilians. . . . Shoes with oil-treated soles subjected to actual wear tests have given from 25-50 per cent increase in wear. Hot wax impregnation has increased wear by 40 per cent.[7]

In neither of these two cases would the proposed changes have reduced in the least the style or consumer-preference factors; but costs to the consumer would have been reduced in terms of original purchase price, frequency of necessary shopping trips, and returns and adjustments or repair. For the given need, resources would have been conserved—in fields and animals, in plant investment, and in manpower. As a further by-product, the entire rationing program for shoes would have been wholly unnecessary.

There is now scarcely a branch of highly style-conscious consumer purchase where this story is not repeated, and where the possible economies are not on a similar scale. But the scale of possible economies grows larger with the effort to heighten "obsolescence" factors in the construction of automobiles, furniture, household supplies, and other equipment. A wartime technical committee of automotive experts estimated that it was feasible to design an automobile which would, while costing a little more in original manufacturing expense (although not necessarily in price paid by the consumer), yet have a usable life of from 15 to 20 years; consume from two-thirds to one-half the normal amount of gasoline per mile; run at least 400,000 miles before requiring a major overhaul, such as for new piston rings; be designed so that repair or even total removal of the engine would take half the time required for most servicing on conventional American cars. Costs of effective operation through the life of the car could be cut by as much as one-third to one-half.[8]

While it may be objected that such high durability and efficiency might well prove incompatible with consumer style preferences and desire for change, the point is at least debatable for the vast bulk of automobile owners faced with private car transportation costs running between 10 and 12 cents per mile (when all capital and operating costs are included). Furthermore, the desire for change itself is largely induced by high-pressure sales methods and probably could not be sustained in their absence. Strong evidence along this line is given by the rising sales of small cars, particularly the Volkswagen—which is sold with little or no sales promotion, without inducements of special "turn-in" and other offers, and has relatively little "style appeal."

At any rate, most of the components of automobiles and other durable and semidurable consumers' goods do not have style features. Examples are batteries and tires. Here, federal tests of eleven makes of a given size of flashlight battery showed that the lowest had a life of 130 per cent of the minimum required by federal specifications, while the highest was 157 per cent; of No. 6 dry cell batteries, the lowest was 104 per cent and the highest was 163 per cent; of radio B.N.-size batteries the lowest was 132 per cent and the highest 185 per cent.[9] There was no significant rank correlation between qualities (durability, performance, etc.) and prices charged. Yet, it is very important to note, a 50 per cent increase in performance means, for any given structure of use, a curtailment by one-third of the needed raw materials, productive plant, and manpower—all the way from first processing, through transport and on to wholesale and retail outlets.

These are not isolated examples. Further evidence, over virtually the entire range of consumers' goods and services, is supplied in the monthly *Consumers Reports* of the consumer-product testing agency, Consumers Union. There are few cases of any statistically meaningful correlation between the general structure of quality ratings and prices. On numerous occasions, the highest performance was found to be associated with the lowest price.

Solution of this problem has great significance for distribution. It begins with the acceptance, in actual design and processing or

construction, of meaningful standards of performance, and the
drafting of physical-material specifications using these standards
for guidance at each step of production and distribution—and
the provision of full information for the consumer. This step
would amount to applying to consumers' goods what is becoming
general practice in the durable-goods field and in the purchase
procedures of the federal government as well as of many state
governments,[10] municipalities, hospitals,[11] and other institutions.

CONSUMER STANDARDS FOR STRAIGHT "UTILITY" AND INDIVIDUAL-PREFERENCE GOODS

Quite aside from the vested interests, the principal objection to
this procedure seems to center upon a rather vague fear that
such standards and grades for consumers' goods would result in
the flooding of markets with a deadening uniformity of narrowly
utilitarian products. However, as was pointed out in chapter iv,
this argument misstates the problem, and misconceives the potentialities of the procedure.

Suppose all consumers' goods and services were to be classified
by type and volume in such a way as to divide consumer expenditure into three main groups. About half would be strictly of a
utility[12] character and hence wholly subject to standards procedures; about one-quarter would have important consumer-preference components, but of such a character that demand could
be satisfied almost entirely from standard products; the remaining
quarter, though subject to highly individual preference, would
still have one or more features to which standards could be applied. While there are no statistically adequate data to justify
such a division, it is the writer's opinion, based upon nearly thirty
years of research having to do with standards,[13] that the market
for consumers' goods is divided roughly in the above proportions.

Examples of the straight "utility" group are cement, steel, wood,
and other materials going into foundations and basic housing construction; lime and plaster, laths used in wall construction; bolts,
nuts, screws, and similar construction components of such durable
commodities as automobiles, dishwashers, washing and drying
machines, ranges, vacuum cleaners, radio and television sets,
furnaces, furniture, and the like; basic food components such as

salt, spices, herbs, edible fats, yeasts, culinary chemicals, flour, and fresh fruits and vegetables; drugs, medicinals, and medical supplies of all sorts.

The list could be extended. It would also include many commodities and services related to consumers' goods, such as the packaging of all straight-utility items; repair and maintenance of houses, furniture, and durable goods; public-utility services of gas, water, electricity, and garbage collection. In all these, and in many more classes of consumer purchase and service expenditures, utility (in the above sense of the term) is the sole criterion. In all such cases, buyers stand to gain by standards of quality, performance, identification, terminology, grading, labeling, and information; and they would stand to benefit in exactly the same way, and for the identical reasons, as do manufacturers who employ similar standards in their own purchasing.

Standards in this area would not mean the absence of choice. Some may want durability, and some may prefer short-lived products. Some may want larger or more powerful radio sets or automobiles, some less, and bigger furnaces or smaller ones. But in each individual case, the establishment of high functional standards would provide a basis, simultaneously, for making the best use of materials and for effecting some clear correlation between price and quality for the consumer.

The second class of consumers' goods mentioned above, where variety is desirable but a rational system of standards, specifications, or grades is applicable, includes stationery, pens, blotters, inks, paper for magazine and newspapers; book sizes and print types; qualities and weaves of natural and synthetic fibers; metallic-alloy and plastic surfaces; floor surfaces and finishes; bedsteads and mattress sizes and construction; pots and pans; household dishes, glasses, crockery, and miscellaneous utensils; soaps, cleansers, and detergents; windows and doors; "modules" in exterior and interior construction;[14] most graded and rated foods such as fish, poultry, meats, eggs, processed foods, frozen foods, canned fruits and vegetables.

In all these cases the introduction of rigorous quantity, quality, packaging, and other standards and identifications would still give the buyer all the range of choice desired, and in terms of all usual or daily needs. The reasons why this is so are threefold. First, the variety which might be made possible via standards is very great. Second, with respect to a very large percentage of such goods, the consumer emphasis is precisely upon the existence of such standards as a condition to obtaining the satisfactions anticipated from use. And third, where differentiation is deemed important, standards may introduce variation which is below the threshold of discrimination.

The meaning of the first and second is obvious. The third may be illustrated by modular construction in residential housing. The module is defined to mean variation of sizes of brick, lumber, windows, doors, wall panels, and other building components by some basic unit differences, most commonly 4 inches. This permits the precutting and prefabrication of all such components "off site," and hence the direct application of mass-production techniques. It has been estimated that the savings in residential construction costs from modular construction would cut costs 20 per cent or more.[15] At the same time, the house as a whole, all the rooms, and the layout can be of individual architectural design, with all features subject to individual homeowner preference in design and appearance. The point is simply that the eye of the technically unskilled—and in most cases even of the engineer or architect—cannot catch the differences in heights, widths, and lengths which are less than 4 inches. Such lesser differences, in other words, are *below the threshold of discrimination.* The consumer, accordingly, stands to lose nothing by way of freedom of preference, while gaining materially in lower costs. At the same time, the lower costs are reflected in the need for less manpower both on and off the site; in smaller investment and plant requirements; and in very considerable savings in materials, distributor inventories, etc.

Finally, with respect to the last quarter of consumers' goods mentioned above, we come to the range of goods and services where style, personal taste, and similar idiosyncrasies of choice are clearly involved. Yet here also, standards may be drawn relating to components which are consistent with the further widening of range and variety of choice. Examples are color, or chromatic, scales for paints, pigments, and dyes; color fastness and fidelity specifications for artists' paints, pigments, canvases, brushes, and other equipment; nomenclature standards for colors, drugs, and dress goods; construction and workmanship standards for style dress goods, draperies, rugs and carpets, furniture and upholstery, and decorative fabrics; construction, materials, finishes, and performance of musical instruments; fidelity of recordings and of both sound and visual reproduction equipment.

Similar illustrations might be indefinitely extended, of areas where highly individual tastes, aesthetic and otherwise, dominate, and yet where standards are of very great importance both for cost reduction and for the facilitation of artistic control over variables. Benefits from some standards which have been set in the past are so general, so pervasive, and so well accepted that most people are unaware of their existence—e.g., numerical notation systems; the alphabet, words, and language rules; scientific systems of classification and notation; musical notation; the convention of driving on one side of the road. Most of these increase the range of choice, or enlarge the area of freedom of selection and self-expression. They simplify the unimportant details, as in human communications, the better to enhance control and experimentation *over* the medium, and over ideas and expression *through* the medium. Further expansion of standards in the goods and services referred to above would have a similar effect.

At one time 300,000 or more synthetic textile dyes were produced. An instance of the absence of color standards, and of standard nomenclature for colors in the field of durable goods is given by a writer for *Retailing Daily* (June 7, 1956):

For pink we have—shell pink, Mayfair pink, petal pink, coral pink, Bermuda pink, desert pink, frosting pink—where is pretty pink? For green we have—sea mist, Sherwood, turquoise, meadow, spring, vintage, arbor, willow—where is gorgeous green? For blue we have cadet, seafoam, lagoon, startone, alpine—where is Bali blue?

Not only do buyers not know what these words mean, but when, for example, kitchens and bathrooms are fitted out in single colors, shades cannot readily be made to match even if presumably of the same color, nor be combined easily if of different colors. (In a Los Angeles building exhibit, a bathroom was fitted out in what was intended to be a uniform color-scheme, but the 11 pieces of equipment were of 11 different shades—some of them clashing violently.)

This same problem with respect to the nomenclature and the qualities of products or their components is found in the case of drugs and medical supplies, household supplies such as soaps and detergents, practically all the new synthetic textile fibers and plastics. The entire medical profession and the general public are faced with a virtual babble of trade and trade-marked names applying to compounds such as aspirin, antibiotics, laxatives, vitamin pills, and the like. It is entirely possible to employ scientifically and technically valid standards which accommodate materials, and some or all components of assembled consumers' goods, to functional use. A few organizations have begun extensive work in this field. The General Services Administration has drawn up such standards and specifications for the guidance of federal purchases.[16] Both the Army and the Navy have similar purchase guides.[17] A certain amount of protection to the public has been provided by government standards for containers for fruits, vegetables, and other foods, and by federal and state controls over weights and measures.[18] The Food and Drug Administration exercises control over drug identification and potency,[19] and the Federal Trade Commission over advertising claims made for drugs, foods, and other consumer products.[20]

A few private or semipublic institutions and some business enterprises have done important pioneering work along similar lines. Examples of the first are the American Hospital Association, the American Laundry Association, the Edison Electrical Laboratories, and the Underwriters Laboratories. Examples of the second are the standards work of various engineering societies in the consumers' goods field, the American Society for Testing Materials, and the American Standards Association.[21] Examples of the third are Sears, Roebuck & Company, Montgomery Ward, R. H. Macy, and the Great Atlantic and Pacific Tea Company.[22]

Yet it is also true that the surface has barely been scratched. The possible economies in resource conservation, and in both industrial and consumer investment as a result of the application of standards procedures to consumers' goods are enormous. If conservative business estimates of economies from the introduction of standards ranging from 5 or 10 upwards to occasionally 20 and 30 per cent, can be relied upon—and they are frequently very carefully estimated—then the parallel economies from standards in consumers' goods must, on the available evidence, be considerably higher. Modular construction, as indicated above, has been estimated to make possible savings in residential construction costs of 20 per cent or more. If standards were applied to drugs on a strictly therapeutic basis, nine out of ten items could be eliminated, both wholesale and retail, from inventory, and prices could be lowered to the point where they would bear some meaningful relationship to production and distribution costs. In some cases therapeutically valuable drugs could be provided at a half to a hundredth part of the price charged ultimate consumers.[23]

But this is only the beginning of the economies which might be effected in distribution by the extension into this field of the same processes of internal technical rationalization which have been introduced into the more technologically progressive manufacturing plants of the country.

REORGANIZING GOODS SHIPMENTS FROM PLANT TO WHOLESALE OR RETAIL WAREHOUSES

Goods leave the manufacturing plant to move by rail, water, truck, or air to wholesale and retail warehouses; next, move by similar means, although mostly by truck, from wholesale to retail establishments; and, then, move from retail establishments to the homes of ultimate consumers or to establishments serving ultimate consumers directly. What can be said about possible economies in these movements?

First, as far as brand multiplication gives rise not to real but only to pseudo product-differentiation, it tends to destroy significant relationships between plant location and markets. Producers located anywhere in the country may sell in national markets not because they offer lower prices for identical products, or because they enjoy economies of scale or lower shipping costs, but because they are able to force distributors to stock their items through high-pressure advertising. How much of duplicates or excess plant capacity and of crosshauling is due to this factor alone is impossible to say in any given line of distribution. Some examples, however, will illustrate the point.

During the Second World War it was found that two types of wood were in general use for most ordinary heavily coated furniture—northern birch and southern gum. To all intents and purposes the two were interchangeable. Yet northern furniture plants relied heavily on southern gum, and southern furniture plants on northern birch. Possibly half of the ton-mileage of these shipments was completely unnecessary, and hence could be eliminated. But the same was also true of the finished product. While the data were not conclusive, it appeared to be true that the finished goods were also so-called "standard lines," and that the amount of unnecessary crosshauling from plant to customers, of what in the trade were regarded as identical products, was certainly very high.

The food chains, some of the larger department stores, the mail-order houses, and increasingly the automobile and some of the appliance companies have attempted to eliminate such crosshauling by placing contracts, or locating their own plants, close to major marketing centers. But the percentage remaining is still very high. In processed foods and in drug lines. crosshauling is general, if not well-nigh universal. An example more restricted in area is the cross-hauling from farms or plants to retailing centers of milk which is graded in such a way as to make the differences from brand to brand virtually indistinguishable. Crosshauling occurs with most brand-name breads shipped from central bakeries; most canned fruits and vegetables; much if not most refrigerated or frozen eggs, meat and fish products, butter, margarine, fruit juices, and the like. The same may be true of many containers, particularly glass containers.

Wholesaling and jobbing costs appear to be unnecessarily high in the distribution of fresh foods, both in the United States and Europe. Speaking of wholesale markets in England, Elliott writes that

. . . these have changed but little since governmental committees condemned Covent Garden, London's fruit and vegetable depot, as "a confused and unorganised anachronism" and placed on record the story that it costs as much to distribute and retail a side of beef in the course of three days as it does to rear, feed and tend the animal for three years, transport its carcass, perhaps over thousands of miles of ocean, and pay a fair profit to those concerned, including the primary producer. Two years after the Linlithgow Committee administered its castigations, the "spread" between wholesale and retail prices of British Columbia box apples was 124 per cent, Nova Scotia barrel apples, 100 to 200 per cent, and Jaffa oranges 50 to 290 per cent. In milk, meat, bacon and potatoes, the same story repeats itself; middlemen are too thick on the ground.[24]

While these costs are high, many attempts which appear at first blush to bring order out of chaos sometimes actually operate to freeze these practices and diseconomies still more firmly into the distribution system. Such, for example, are the Agricultural Adjustment Acts in the United States, the various state marketing control acts, and the network of interstate trade barriers operating in the same direction. This is planning in reverse gear.

To what extent does this picture hold for other lines of goods? Data on jobbing and wholesaling of soft goods, such as textile fabrics and both women's and men's clothing, do not show a much better picture. In mass-produced goods, intermediate costs are frequently even higher, as in the case of many drugs. Experimentation indicates, even on the individual-firm basis, enormous potential savings in wholesale operations. The Kraft Food Company, found that the "Zonor" system—involving a complete reorganization of its warehouse handling, selling, and warehouse-to-retail-distributor handling and routing—saved 25 per cent of all its distribution costs. Warehouse operations were almost completely mechanized on a "push-button" basis by the use of standardized pallets and chain-conveyer systems. Sales and deliveries were zoned; significant economies were found available at every point.[25] Many similar examples might be cited.

REORGANIZATION OF CONSUMER DELIVERY

Two aspects of this problem are of special interest in this connection. First, the possibilities contained in unification of delivery systems, and, second, those associated with the amount of travel required by the average buyer to obtain the goods sought.

The first can be illustrated with a few examples of economies

associated with the pooling of delivery services. A Department of
Commerce publication summarizes the early history:

> For many years central delivery systems have been operating suc-
> cessfully in cities throughout the United States. Even before World
> War I a large number were doing a flourishing business. With Amer-
> ica's entry into the conflict in 1917 the Commercial Economy Board,
> a Government agency operating under the Council of National De-
> fense, instituted a program designed to encourage the organization
> of cooperative delivery companies, especially among retail grocers.
> The program suggested by the Commercial Economy Board was
> based upon a study of 22 central delivery concerns then in operation.
> Where 659 men were needed before consolidation, the cooperative
> delivery systems required a total of only 207—a saving of 452 men, or
> 69 per cent—and service to customers was practically as good as it
> was before and in some places better.
> The Commercial Economy Board further stated that a conservative
> estimate of the average savings in the systems that were well managed
> was 50 per cent. The saving in manpower for the 22 systems was 69
> per cent. Money savings were proportionally large. For the nation as
> a whole it was estimated that 150,000 workers could be released
> throughout the country at that time by the restriction of delivery to
> once a day over each route and the establishment of central delivery
> systems.[26]

Subsequent experimentation has confirmed this picture for both
peacetime[27] and war experience. A wholesaler's delivery pool in
Winnipeg, Manitoba, consisting of "18 merchants making wholesale delivery of automotive parts . . . resulted in estimated savings of 65.5 per cent in mileage, 68.8 per cent in gasoline, and
from 30 per cent to 75 per cent in cost to each participant, depending on his previous type of operation and volume of business." [28] Comparable economies were achieved in an experimental
retail delivery pool organized under the auspices of the Canadian
Wartime Prices and Trade Board.[29] The Department of Commerce estimated that comparable savings could be achieved from
generalizing pooled delivery systems throughout the United
States, and that economies might eliminate half the route miles,
half the required trucks, manpower, etc., and might at the same
time result in considerable improvement in the quality of delivery service.[30]

Studies of milk delivery systems have borne out this conclusion.

A report of the Connecticut Dairy Conservation Committee[31] made during the war showed that significant economies could be effected throughout all phases of the milk distribution system. Beginning at the farm pickup end, it found widespread overlapping of collection routes and territories. "Studies have indicated," the report goes on to say,

that individual producers and commercial truckers travel about 18,000 miles daily to assemble milk from Connecticut farms and deliver it to the major markets. With exclusive territories and large trucks, this assembly could be performed by traveling about 10,000 miles daily.

The possibilities of increased efficiency in the handling of delivery services take on added importance when it is realized that they are symptomatic of the need for overhauling retail distribution as a whole, and that they are largely unrealizable unless supported by modernization in other sectors.

By "modernization," it is important to reëmphasize, is meant only such technical reorganization of distribution facilities as (a) may properly be said to constitute consistent and valid application of criteria of economical use of resources in the sense now commonly recognized in many well-run manufacturing processes with respect to the use of the plant, equipment, manpower, investment, etc., and which (b) still promotes the widest possible convenience of shoppers and the greatest freedom of expression of choice between meaningfully differentiated products. In such a context the failure to develop adequate and economical consumer delivery-services must be related to many other, and equally important, failures in the organization of distribution.

It is, for example, linked with the inability of consumers to discriminate between meaningful and meaningless product differentiation. A consumer cannot glean adequate product information from sales representation in the newspaper, or over the radio or television system. Ordering by telephone then becomes difficult. Quality-price comparisons cannot be made without seeing the goods—if then. Exaggerated sales and advertising claims further aggravate the difficulty.

Again, deterioration of public-transport systems compels increasing resort to the family automobile in order to "shop around" for better bargains. In many lines of goods, the location, size, differentiation, and grouping of retail facilities tend to bear little or no relation to residence of buyers, or to shopper convenience in buying. [32]

Consequent distribution costs to the buyer may be very great. For example, if the average over-all cost of the family automobile may be estimated to run around 12 cents per mile—which seems quite reasonable—in slow urban traffic, mileage cost to and from the market may, when parking charges are added, run close to double this figure. In addition, resort to the family automobile, carrying typically only one person, puts thousands of extra automobiles on the street, clogging traffic arteries, and slowing traffic movement to a snail's pace, while the amount of time and energy spent in shopping—even for daily necessities—is further increased. This means further addition of overhead costs to be borne by the community in the form of parking space, street carrying-capacity, policemen, and traffic controls.

Distribution facilities, growing helter-skelter, result in unnecessarily high investment costs to the community, the consumer, and the retail establishments themselves. It is difficult, if not impossible, to appraise the scale of the excessive and wasteful investment which results. But miscellaneous data crop up from time to time which permit some intelligent guesswork. The parallel, and to some extent consequent, multiplication of retail outlets is a case in point.

EXCESSIVE MULTIPLICATION OF RETAIL OUTLETS

An especially striking example of excessive duplication of retail outlets is provided by the distribution of gasoline service stations. During the war a study conducted by the Consumers Division of the Office of Price Administration[33] estimated that even for normal times approximately two out of every three gasoline service stations in the United States were undersized, uneconomically operated, and in most cases superfluous. "Optimum size" was estimated, from data supplied by experts in the industry, at the extremely conservative figure of $49,000 worth of sales per month, including 21,700 gallons of gasoline. Confidential estimates in the trade typically called for a much higher figure of around 80,000 to 100,000 gallons of gasoline a month, with other sales of oil, tires, batteries, etc., in proportion. Yet even on the much lower and more conservative figure used, and with a sample drawn from 17,045 stations selling an annual aggregate of $279,500,000 worth of products, it seemed clear that some 5,700 properly placed and properly equipped stations could have handled this business. At the same time, with the smaller number of stations the service could have been better, the locations more conveniently distributed, and the over-all costs for dispensing gasoline could have been cut by 1 cent per gallon, or by 25 per cent of the distributor's margin.

Personal inquiries to industrial and trade sources, made over several years, indicate that careful study would show such excess in many other lines as well. It is, for example, probably roughly the same picture in the vending of automobile tires and accessories, domestic appliances, furniture, and house furnishings; in men's and women's clothing and shoe stores; in "five-and-ten" stores, notion stores, and drugstores. It may also be true in many areas of grocery stores and fruit stands. In all or most of these lines, that is to say, half or more of all the retail outlets may be unnecessary in terms of consumer needs and the capacity to satisfy demand with the lines of products offered at the present time. In addition, there has been a vast increase in the social overhead in the rise of such practices as door-to-door and time payment selling.

Trade estimates for door-to-door selling suggest that the number of persons in the United States engaged for part or full time in this traffic may be around 3 million—or nearly one-twentieth of the gainfully employed population. The true figure is more probably around 1 million, but even so, there seems to be no clear case for more than a fractional part, if any, of this activity. Typically, the prices of goods thus sold appear to run markedly above ordinary store prices.

Most, if not all, of door-to-door selling might be eliminated and a great deal of the needed retail-store capacity might be reduced, if stock carried on the shelves were further reduced by the elimination of meaningless product-differentiation. This would reduce also the necessary wholesale and retail inventories, the frequency of ordering, and, consequently, the number of part-truckload freight movements and the store investment and manpower required to handle the traffic at all points along the line. It would, moreover, enhance certain economies of scale which, under present circumstances, are very difficult to realize.

Superficially, at least, the possible economies of scale are in many lines quite striking. The rise of the supermarket offers a good example. Between 1934 and 1937 the Great Atlantic and Pacific Tea Company (A. & P.), the operator of the largest chain of grocery stores in the United States, "closed 21.7 per cent or 933 of its 4,306 units in 38 cities. At the same time, however, it replaced them with 204 super markets." [34] The over-all reduction in cost amounted to 37 per cent. Another investigation in the thirties reported that chain-store turnover of stock in the United States ran as high as 40 times a year as against a national average for all retail groceries of four to nine times a year.[35] Few data of such a precise character are available, but it seems clear that economies of such proportions are possible in most lines of retailing.

Since the war the spread of supermarkets has been phenomenal. Yet this expansion has also been accompanied by two practices which have largely deprived them of otherwise achievable economies of scale. First, though vending what are to all intents and purposes identical products, they have duplicated facilities almost as badly as did their smaller predecessors. Giant stores frequently duplicate giant stores as previously small duplicated small. Second, as pointed out above, they have vastly increased their stocks of meaninglessly differentiated goods, thereby greatly increasing the scale of needed plant investment, inventories, etc., required to handle any given volume of trade.

There are notable exceptions to the first, particularly in connection with some of the new suburban shopping-centers. There are no exceptions to the second in the grocery field. In those fields of distribution where the product line has been simplified and specialized by outlets, it has typically been concentrated on trade-marked items sold under exclusive-dealer contracts or franchise from the manufacturer, with the result that there are, for example, almost as many local retail outlets for automobiles and household appliances as there are makes in each product line. In terms of the volume of business handled in automobiles and household appliances, the floor space, inventories kept on hand, over-all investment, and manpower must be twice as much as is required for efficient handling of customer demands.

In short, the number and size of distribution outlets in most lines, and their location with respect to public-transportation facilities and general consumer convenience, have little resemblance to a rational structure of marketing outlets designed to handle retail trade at lowest over-all cost. Further, such irrationalities as exist tend further to be enhanced—or at least consolidated—by prevalent methods of promoting sales.

THE NEED FOR ELIMINATING CHAOS IN ADVERTISING AND SELLING

Functionally, advertising should be regarded as a means of informing buyers about qualities and prices of goods or services. How well does it, or can it, perform? The total of expenditures currently spent on American advertising is astounding. Table 7 gives the dollar volume of advertising outlays in the United States by media for five-year intervals.[36] Spectacular as these

TABLE 7

ANNUAL VOLUME OF ADVERTISING IN UNITED STATES
BY MEDIUM, 1935-1954
(In millions of dollars)

Medium	1935	1940	1945	1950	1954
Newspapers	762.1	815.4	921.4	2,075.6	2,695.3
Magazines	136.3	197.7	364.5	514.9	667.9
Television	...	...	...	170.8	803.6
Radio	112.6	215.6	423.9	605.4	564.9
Farm publications	3.5	6.8	11.8	21.2	31.8
Direct mail	281.6	333.7	290.2	803.2	1,202.4
Business papers	51.0	76.0	204.1	251.1	407.5
Outdoor	31.3	44.7	71.7	142.5	186.9
Miscellaneous	311.8	397.7	586.9	1,125.3	1,603.8
Total	1,690.0	2,087.6	2,874.5	5,710.0	8,164.1

SOURCE: *Printers' Ink*, Advertisers' Guide to Marketing for 1956, October 21, 1955, pp. 68-69.

figures seem, they do not include all outlays on advertising and sales promotion. Other sales expenses—such as are involved in premium and stamp plans, traveling salesmen selling to wholesalers and retailers, manufacturers' gifts and emoluments to retailers in such promotional schemes as are involved in the "battle for shelf space" in the grocery field (as, for placing trade-marked goods on special shelves or in preferred store locations), etc.— are generally believed in some promotion circles to equal roughly the amounts paid out to the media as listed in the table.

Without going into the very complex question of how much of this outlay actually serves a functionally useful purpose in supplying to consumers reliable, accurate, and useful information upon the basis of which to exercise full freedom of choice, a few illustrations, taken more or less at random, will serve to illustrate the need for a radical reëxamination of this distribution expense.

1. *Specific instances:*

Item: The number of salesmen in sales promotion to other manufacturers, to wholesalers and retailers, and to doctors and other groups of professionals has been estimated to be (1956) around one million. Informed trade opinion finds this total to be at least fifty per cent too high for handling the needs of buyers. Some 15,000 "detail men," at a cost between $4.62 and $9.23 per call, and involving an annual industry expenditure of $100,000,-000, made the rounds of doctors' offices in 1955, calling on "trade-name-weary individuals" who longed for reduction of the pressure and a simplification of the problem.[37]

Item: Salesmen who travel from door to door in sales promotion to ultimate consumers are variously estimated, as indicated earlier, to run from 1 to 3 million. With possibly minor exceptions, almost the whole of this labor force is promoting a type of selling which is excessively costly, which takes sales away from under-utilized retail outlets (usually able to give more reliable information along with the supply of better-quality and lower-priced goods), and which absorbs the time and energy of housewives, who are frequently as "tradename-weary" as the beleaguered doctors.

Item: Direct-mail advertising increased from $281.6 million in 1933 to $1,270 million in 1955, or by more than fourfold in 20 years. This mail is carried at a huge annual loss to the Post Office Department, and hence adds a further cost to the consumer through his taxes. Most of it is thrown away by the recipients without being read or even scanned. In the medical field, for example, "busy general practitioners" in 1954 were estimated as receiving an average of some 3,959 pieces of mail, of which 3,534 were sent out by pharmaceutical manufacturers, while the "not-so-busy G.P.'s" (who make up 75 per cent of the total number) would receive slightly more than 3,000 mailings from the industry, and various specialists would receive from 2,000 to 2,500.[38]

Resistance among doctors to this tidal wave of sales promotion is strong. A sample taken in 1956 for one month showed, of the total number of doctors reporting, that "9% see *no* detail men, 26% read *no* journal ads, and 40% read *no* direct mail advertising." To the drug industry, however, this posed not the alternative of letting up on the pressure, but the problem of how to effect a "scientific breakthrough in medical communications" to the "communications-saturated individual" with "disposable professional time [amounting to] only 32 minutes per day."[39] Of a rather large number of doctors personally interviewed by the writer, general practitioners and specialists alike, most reported that if time were available to them they could obtain far better and more reliable medical and drug information from their professional journals. Meanwhile, a welter of confusion has been created by pseudo-scientific drug trade-names and the swift multiplication of brands for identifical products.[40]

Item: Outdoor and billboard advertising is generally condemned as ruinous to the appearance of cities and rural highways by all interests concerned with civic appearance and the preservation and improvement of scenic attractions. The bulk of it is wholly uninformative. Yet despite this functional meaningless-ness, and in the face of widespread and growing condemnation by the public and campaigns undertaken against it by city and regional public-improvement groups of virtually all shades of opinion, "outdoor" advertising expenditures increased more than six-fold between 1935 and 1955, or from $31.1 million to $186.9 million.

Item: Radio and television advertising is generally tolerated as a public nuisance on the mistaken grounds that consumers thereby get their entertainment over these media "free." The bits and pieces of valuable information provided to the public are very few and far between; they are accompanied frequently by irritating ditties, and splattered with even more irritating repetition of trite and irrelevant claims and phrases; they break up program continuities, more or less irrespective of the nature or content of the program, including football games, dance music, and symphonic broadcastings. Yet in the same period this form of sales promotion over the radio and over television grew from $215 million in 1940 to over $1 billion by 1955.

Item: The vast expanse of newspaper and journal advertising is, in the main, little more informative than that of most other media promotion. At the same time, it absorbs enormous quantities of paper, directly and indirectly. A leading New York Sunday newspaper was weighed on a pair of household scales at 8½ pounds. Advertising must absorb a minimum of five pounds. To put out this Sunday edition requires some 16,000 Canadian trees. Indirectly, this type of pressure promotes in more and more fields —groceries, dry goods, hardware, etc.—unnecessarily expensive packaging and wrapping.

2. In general, the unnecessary use of resources involved in the methods of sales promotion just referred to is much greater than any such listing might indicate. Bound up with, and heavily promoted by, such methods are certain larger consequences. Among these the following are illustrative.

Item: By common agreement, advertising creates brand monopoly and tends to promote monopoly power. This means that it tends generally to deprive the public of the advantages and economies of competition. It is also a component in the promotion of the size of corporations without respect to comparative real manufacturing efficiencies; it shifts such competition as remains away from price and quality and over to factual irrelevancies and pseudo differences; it generally promotes such market restrictions as are involved in fair-trade pricing (which means manufacturer's price fixing) and unfair trade legislation (which means minimum price fixing, irrespective of costs). To cite a single example, in 1952 it was found that fair-trade pricing forced up the prices of branded goods between Washington, D.C., where fair-trade pricing does not exist, and outside Washington, D.C., where it is general, as follows:[41]

Brand-name item	Price in fair-trade states	Price in Washington, D.C.
Colgate tooth paste	$ .47	$ .39
Johnson's Glo Coat	.59	.49
Mentholatum	.39	.29
Bayer aspirin	.59	.49
Stuart's Formula	2.60	2.29
Uni Caps (vitamins)	6.96	5.47
Old English paste wax	.65	.49
Williams shaving cream	.53	.39
Insulin	1.26	.98

A housewife buying all these items would pay $11.28 in Washington, D.C., and $14.04, or 24 per cent more, in an adjoining state. With some larger items the ratio was even higher. Thus in the same comparison "fair trading" increased the price by 34 per cent on a Sunbeam Mixmaster (from $34.79 to $46.50), and on a G.E. heating pad by 50 per cent (from $3.99 to $5.95).

Item: High-pressure selling tends to inhibit the introduction of standards, grades, quality-identifying labeling, and, in general, all efforts to design, define, and describe products in terms of meaningful variation. High-pressure advertising companies are typically and strongly opposed to such efforts, and give such organizations as the government's Food and Drug Administration and the American Standards Association little or no support. Enough has been said above about this point to require no further elaboration here.[42]

Item: High-pressure sales promotion is known in trade circles as a "dealer-loader" device. The dealer is forced to stock the highly promoted goods, irrespective of relative quality or price, and irrespective of his capacity to supply customers with any part, or the entire range, of real product variety. Where manufacturer-imposed franchise and licensing systems are added, the pressure operates (*a*) to multiply the number of retail outlets to the maximum (the experience of the liquor industry following repeal of Prohibition being an early example of high success for this technique), (*b*) to load the inventories of the retailer to the maximum by putting him on a quota system and then edging up the size of quotas irrespective of demand for the product, as in the case of automobiles and household appliances, and (*c*) to keep the retailer's margins sufficiently low to reduce him to a state of continual disorganized dependence upon the manufacturer. In all cases, the tendency is to keep the store unit smaller than it otherwise would be; to increase the ratio of inventories to sales; to multiply the number and frequency of small-lot orders —increasing thereby the volume of transport equipment involved and advancing the ratio of underutilized equipment and manpower; and generally to keep the retailers small, in a financially precarious position, and dependent upon manufacturers. Yet, paradoxically, they are willing to support manufacturer-imposed fair-trade legislation with its "price-hiking" and market-curtailing effects as indicated above.

Item: High pressure tends generally not to increase the total volume of sales, but to redistribute them. There is no evidence to support the conclusion that curtailment of advertising and sales promotion even to 10 per cent of its current volume would seriously affect the expenditure-savings ratio of consumers as a whole. Nor is there evidence that high pressure generally transfers sales (*a*) to the more technically efficient, or (*b*) to the regionally better-located plant, or (*c*) to the better-quality or lower-priced products. Further, sales pressures are extremely high, whereas demand as a whole is relatively inelastic. For example, among the million-dollar advertisers of 1955, the largest total ($292,304,306) was spent on soaps and cleansers, drugs, and toilet goods, and the second largest ($279,258,504) on food, food beverages, and confectionery.[43] In some of the subclassifications under both of these heads, such as cosmetics and "television dinner" preparations, advertising did unquestionably increase sales. But most of the advertising under both headings was for staple items, the volume of consumption of which is a function of general income levels and cultural habits, not of current sales-pressures. For most of the items under the two headings, where the demand is relatively inelastic, advertising shifts sales from brand to brand, or from manufacturer to manufacturer, and has the effect of adding costs which, if anything, curtail expenditure on these very items by curtailing real income. Accompanying it, and promoted by it, furthermore, are meaningless multiplication of sizes and shapes of packages and containers; excessive amounts of wrapping; confusing multiplication of and meaningless change in terms which are supposed to be descriptive of qualities but in reality are mere trade-marked identification; increased resort to expensive methods of financing; and so on.

High-pressure selling also more or less dominate the media of public information. The radio and television, the journals and newspapers, and even now to a very considerable extent the schools, are flooded with its material; its bias colors, when it does not dominate, editorial content, the slant of the news, and, above all, any critical appraisal of this very line of activity itself. Judgments of the Food and Drug Administration, for example, are rarely reported in the newspapers; criticism of advertising is never reported. In this sense, high pressure is in a unique position. On the one hand, it tends to raise itself above, or render itself immune to, critical appraisal. And on the other, it meets all opposition—as with the "tradename-weary" doctors—not by relaxation of pressure but by steady increase of pressure and search for "break-through" methods to destroy any consumer or distributor resistance. Simultaneously, as the trade press makes clear, it helps to consolidate price fixing; promote "fair-trade" and similar legislation for controlling entry to business, price-raising, and the setting of prices at levels which tolerate and reward the inefficient producer, the inefficient wholesaler, and even the inefficient retailer.

The purpose here, however, is not to indict, but rather to see what alternatively might be done to promote efficient and low-cost distribution of consumer goods. Here it is a matter of what is technically possible, not of what is immediately feasible. It may, of course, very well be the case that "high pressures" are so firmly consolidated in the American distribution system that they cannot be either effectively curtailed, or redesigned in the foreseeable future. But for underdeveloped countries, the important point is that their own industrial advance need not be encumbered with misuse of resources in such a fashion and on such a scale. The alternatives seem reasonably clear; they are all entirely consistent with both free entry to business and freedom of consumer choice.

SUMMARY OF POTENTIAL DISTRIBUTION ECONOMIES

Whether, in the United States or elsewhere, distribution as a whole is relatively backward technologically, may be debatable. The belief among experts that this is the case is very widespread. For example, as late as 1942 an expert could state that

While enormous sums have been expended to promote efficiency in manufacturing, little has been done to promote efficiency in distribution. If productive techniques in 1942 may be taken as a base, then our distributive system is of the Model T vintage. The widespread adoption of the most efficient techniques in distribution would result in enormous savings in labor, time and materials.[44]

On the eve of the great depression of the nineteen-thirties the wholly preventable wastage in trade approximated at least $8 to $10 billion annually, something like one-tenth of the national income, or a sum equal to the whole of American foreign trade in the banner year of 1928.[45]

Twenty years later a Standard Oil Company executive quoted data from the United States Census showing that "between 1870 and 1940 the number of people employed in the production of raw materials and manufacturing increased threefold, while in the same period workers in the field of marketing and distribution increased ninefold—three times as much." [46] In the case of foods, data cited by the National Industrial Conference Board showed that farmers' prices between 1913 and 1938 dropped by 10 per cent "while the cost of distributing food rose 70 per cent." [47] Other estimates showed that 59 cents of each consumer's dollar in the United States goes for distribution (marketing) and only 31 cents goes to the production of the needed raw materials and its manufacture. While the statistical data are unclear,[48] the ratio of distribution costs seems to be slowly but steadily rising throughout the country. The reason most generally given is that distribution fails to effect possible economies.

This view of distribution, justified or not, is not confined to the United States. An Australian study has itemized a similar story in detail. It found that:

(1) The proportion of the working population engaged in distribution is too large relative to that engaged in production, and it is still increasing. (2) The relative proportion of the cost of distribution in the consumer's price is too large. (3) The number of so called "middlemen" is very great, and their activities do not advance anybody's prosperity, except their own, while society as a whole has to foot the bill. (4) Retailing outlets are too numerous and too specialized, and are still increasing disproportionately to the growth of the population. Thus the excess capacity existing in distribution is more serious than in industry. (5) The variety of brands and designs are unnecessarily great, the cost of advertising too high, and the inefficiency of the system finds its ultimate expression in the high rate of mortality of shops. (7) Because of the restrictive practices and monopolies the consumer is denied the benefits of technical advancement.[49]

In Britain, three specialists find that "No part of our present industrial organization has received more severe criticism than the distributive system."[50] A Fabian Society publication[51] estimated that in 1931 the total number of all persons engaged in distribution was 5,375,000, or more than 25 per cent of the total labor force of 21,075,000, and inferred from its data that the percentage in distribution was far too high. Since the war the categories of persons engaged in British distributive trades, despite the enormous and persistent emphasis upon increase of production, has steadily risen as a percentage of the entire labor force.

When one turns from Britain to the Continent, the situation is commonly held to be, if anything, worse. Outside of Germany and the Scandinavian countries, one might suppose—quite unjustifiably—that practically nothing significant had been done in the last hundred years to rationalize goods distribution. Despite its very great interest in technical rationalization, the Soviet Union has almost entirely neglected the field of distribution.

The scientific organization of distribution involves no principles basically different from those which have already brought such spectacular economies in manufacturing, transportation, power supply, agricultural production, and elsewhere. Such full technical and organizational rationalization may for a number of reasons never be fully carried through in any system at any time. Certainly, as indicated at some length in the preceding chapters, we find very few cases where the existing, available potentials have been fully realized. But it is still the economist's scientific task to point out these potentials.

The main difference between the general field of commodity distribution and the developments in other economic processes is that distribution may be more archaic, more confused. At certain points it even seems to be going backwards. A fairly good case could be made for arguing that distribution is building inefficiencies into our economic system almost as rapidly as other production processes attaining new efficiencies. Certainly, to many experts, distribution seems to be the problem child of the economist par excellence.

Fully to rationalize distribution would involve taking the following steps:

First, the simple and fundamental rule of consumers' freedom of choice would require a vast toning-down of high-pressure selling methods and the substitution of a residue, comparatively small, of informative fact-telling. The motto of high-pressure advertising and selling, Sombart once remarked, might well be "search out your customer and attack him." A recent issue of *Fortune* has a hardened old sales hand remind his listener that he will never amount to anything as a salesman until he realizes that "the customer is the enemy." Veblen in one of his more savagely satirical moods has suggested that advertising lives by the motto, *suppressio veri, suggestio falsi.* However that may be, there can be no question that high-pressure selling is a kind of misplaced tribalism—a tribalism of the type which anthropologists associate with regressive cultures. Its successes narrow the possibilities of true "freedom of choice" because it confuses judgment, diverts channels of public information such as newspapers and the radio from their proper function, and biases the media of entertainment.

But more relevant in the current context, it helps to freeze large, and in some instances growing, inefficiencies into the system—inefficiencies which are scattered all the way from raw materials supply (where, for example, immense amounts of paper pulp, paper-mill capacity, freight-haulage capacity, etc., are diverted from useful purposes to advertising copy) on through all phases of manufacturing and distribution, and down to the ultimate consumer.

Advertising which is truly informational has a very important role to perform, particularly when it is kept entirely separate from media where it has little more than nuisance value, such as newspapers, magazines, and journals, and particularly the radio. So constituted and confined, it is possible that as much as five— possibly even ten—per cent of the advertising bill of America might find some economic or cultural justification. Most of even this remainder would, however, need to be rewritten to be of much use to the consumer.

Second, wherever the goods themselves, or the uses to which they will be put, are below the objectively determinable "threshold" of taste, fashion, aesthetic preference, or individual idiosyncrasy, then they should be manufactured and prepared for shipment and use in terms of standard specifications as to sizes, shapes, packaging, physical and chemical properties, instructions for guiding the user, etc., and all such standards should be scientifically drawn in terms of the functions the commodities are to perform. This would hold for practically all building materials, the "insides" of almost all durable goods, hardware, fixtures, and basic household supplies, and practically all staple food, drug, and clothing supplies. Over this range of goods, the functional aspect would dominate, and all goods would be graded, rated, inspected, sized, and so forth in terms of the range of uses to which they would severally be put, and changes would be introduced only as the pattern of use was altered with changing standards of living, or as new technical developments made possible improvements, or alternative or new uses.

Above this threshold, scientifically drawn specifications would apply to certain basic properties such as chemical components, color fidelity, workmanship, etc. As was pointed out before, these standards are both reconcilable with maintenance—indeed, with indefinite widening—of the range of consumer freedom of choice, and with the fullest artistic and creative expression. Everything is to be said, for example, for rigorous standards of color purity and chemical fidelity in artists' pigments, fabric dyes, and interior-decorating finishes.

So to reorganize the supply of goods to be moved through distribution channels makes possible the placing of most manufacturing and supply industries—even those catering to the arts, the fashion industries, handicrafts—upon a mass-output basis. At the same time it makes possible the reduction of a wide range of distribution costs in transportation, warehousing, costs of handling, turnover, and so forth.

Third, wholesaling and jobbing would be unified and fused for each major line or class of goods—textiles, clothing, food products, drugs—in such a way that jobbing would appear as a mere aspect of wholesaling, and the wholesaling function would be kept as small as possible. With the growth, for example, of supermarkets and department stores, increasing percentages of goods move directly from processing sheds (as with vegetables) or manufacturing establishments to retail outlets. Where supply depots—as with building supplies and farm machinery—or warehouses must be interposed between the supply source and retail outlets, these should be specialized by the principal line and regionally spaced so as to supply a unified territory from a single centrally located source. This source—depot or warehouse— should be of optimum size or as near to it as circumstances permit, and both supply to it and haulage service from it should be completely unified.

Fourth, unification of transportation from raw-materials source or manufacturing plants to (a) warehouses and depots, or (b) direct to retail outlets, should be paralleled by coördinate efforts regionally to scatter consumer industries and services which may advantageously be localized. For any given pattern of unified transport, that is to say, the total cost of freight will be lowest when supply sources and manufacturing plants have been spaced within the locality and the major region with respect to present and prospective population growth, patterns of consumer usage, balanced employment schedules, etc.[52] The transport plant, the local and regional community plans, and the distribution network are, in other words, caught up in a balanced set of relationships wherein the success of each is largely dependent upon the performance of the others.

As a complementary principle, all supplies should move from the source to warehouses, or from the latter to retail outlets, by the most direct route possible—i.e., with the minimum of crosshauling or indirect routing—and so far as possible in full truck-load or carload amounts.

Fifth, retail outlets should be (*a*) of optimum size for each specialized class of goods—groceries, hardware, clothing, etc., and (*b*) regionally distributed in rough proportion to population and the structure of demand, and with the degree of specialization decreasing as population becomes sparser and more widely scattered. Specialized outlets (*c*) should be grouped in combinations, including services, most appropriate for the leading classes of consumer needs. Foodstuffs, drugs, current household supplies, etc., might make up one such group; shoes, clothing, children's toys and specialties, cleaning and dyeing, tailoring and repair, etc., might make up another; automobiles and durable goods and their supplies, hardware, repair facilities, might make up a third; and so on. Several other combinations are possible. These combinations might be brought together under a single roof as in supermarkets and department stores, or in nucleated groups as in some of the newer and more carefully planned suburban shopping-centers. Finally, (*d*) all small and lightweight packages, bought on the premises, might be carried away by the customer, but the goods to be delivered—small and light, or bulky—should be funneled through a unified delivery pool which is coextensive with each major shopping area.

Taken by themselves, each of the foregoing propositions may seem commonplace enough. Particularly in the present context, where we are concerned with the technically most rational and economical way of getting the goods from the source of supply to the ultimate consumer and not with the problem of incentives, motives, drives, or the infiltration of such things as bureaucratic red-tape which might come as a partial by-product of failure along these lines in such planning. Other similar questions, such as competition versus monopoly, private ownership versus public ownership or resort to coöperatives, and the maintenance of individual initiative and efficiency versus indifference and regimentation, raise highly important problems, but there is little or no reliable evidence that they are quantitatively more significant or qualitatively more distinctive in the field of distribution than in any of the other industrial fields we have examined. Since these questions, vitally important as they may be in determining the most economical prices, would require a separate study, they may be omitted from this discussion.

Suffice it to say, in summary, that it is wholly impossible to isolate the inefficiences in any contemporary distributive system with any great degree of clarity and precision, and hence, it is completely impossible to add up the possible economies. Careful study over a number of years, however, would seem to indicate that it might be possible in some important lines to cut the costs of distribution in half. Or, to put the matter somewhat differently, it might very well be the case that—in some parts and possibly the whole of the American system, at least—efficient organization would, for any given level of production, dispense with nearly half of all the manpower, the bookkeeping and accounting, and the retail and wholesale establishments and facilities of the country. It would dispense with very much of the warehousing, possibly half or more than half of all the shipping expenses from production centers to retail outlets, and possibly as much as eighty to ninety-five per cent of all the advertising and sales expense. Needless to say, these economies could be effected in such a way that they would only mean a redistribution of manpower and material resources for the performance of other duties and functions. The case of economies all along the line is here no different from what it is elsewhere: "make-work" through wastage of resources (i.e., employment of less than the most efficient means) is almost always a loss to society, and rarely a gain.

XII

Integration of Telecommunications Networks

THE ROLE OF COMMUNICATIONS
IN THE SCIENTIFIC REVOLUTION IN INDUSTRY

Electronics and communications are to the scientific revolution in industry what steam-powered machinery was to the early Industrial Revolution, that is, its most characteristic identifying feature. This feature, currently known as communications engineering, distinguishes the new productive order from the earlier as sharply as it was, in its turn, different from the antecedent handicraft world.

In the microcosm of the factory, as has been pointed out before, communications engineering has synchronized successive individual machine and allied production-processes to the level where the automatic plant has become prototypal for the leading industrial operations of the future. At the same time, in the macrocosm of society it has been engaged in perfecting the "nerve systems" for the instantaneous synchronization of an indefinite number of interplant and service schedules.

The revolutionary changes under way in the factory have recently attracted a disproportionate amount of attention. "Automation," at the factory level, has the ring of magic. But, in the larger sphere, a series of similar technological changes are rapidly being introduced whose combined effects upon the conduct of affairs, industrial and cultural alike, are certainly no less revolutionary. These changes in the larger sphere, accordingly, merit some detailed attention before we bring this preliminary survey of the scientific revolution in industry to a close.

The superficial facts, of course, are familiar to all. "Everything wears the face of dispatch," wrote Henry Hosmer in 1776, observing the widespread and spectacular speeding-up of life in early industrial England. Since then, the techniques and instruments of "dispatch" have crisscrossed the major industrial countries and girdled the world with vast and meticulously spun networks of communications. Space has become a variable of time.

For travel and the movement of goods, the earth has shrunk to the time-size of the state of Rhode Island as it appeared in the days of George Washington. But for the interchange of information and ideas, the globe has shriveled to the proportions of the smallest island in tiny Rhode Island's meandering Narragansett Bay. In 1937 it was already possible to write that "there is hardly a place on the surface of the globe which is not within almost immediate hailing distance, when we consider the hailing to be done by one of our many modern communication methods." [1] The bold prediction of Alexander Graham Bell, made in 1878, just two years after the invention of the telephone, that the future would see a grand system produced which "would enable anyone anywhere to talk by telephone to anyone else, anywhere, regardless of distance," was within sight of fulfillment when it could be reported that from any telephone in the United States it was possible to be connected with approximately 96 per cent of all the world's telephones. [2]

The telephone network which makes this possible, however, is only part of a much larger and more complicated system of telecommunications. It is important to see how that "nerve system" for the newly emerging world industrial society is put together.

UNIFICATION OF THE WIRE LINES

Historically, much of the organizational pattern subsequently used by the wire communications systems was set by the postal system. While postal services are very old in human history, [3] the pattern as we know it today dates from the efforts of Sir Rowland Hill who, in the 1830's, introduced a British nationwide postal service on the basis of the penny post, prepayment, and national pickup and delivery of mail on regularly scheduled routes. Other countries quickly followed suit. In 1863 delegates from most of the countries in the world met in Paris and launched a movement which consummated in 1874 at Berne with the establishment of the International Postal Union. The treaty was signed by representatives of 22 countries having an aggregate population of 350 million people. The Berne convention, in effect, universalized the principles of postal service along the lines laid down for domestic service by Sir Rowland Hill.

When the telegraph came along, the principle of low-cost, fixed-rate, uniform service and nationwide coverage was generally accepted as the ideal. After a short interval of experimentation, during which the feasibility of regional hookups was demonstrated, a process of consolidation began. Similar steps were taken shortly afterwards in the field of telephonic communication.

Abroad, unification of telegraph and telephone networks on a national basis has been generally paralleled by coördination of the two as functional segments of a single wire-communication system, under the administration of the postal service. Thus British postal authorities in 1870 took over and united the three leading telegraph agencies in one national network. Telephone networks were added in 1892. In Germany, by a somewhat different series of steps—beginning first with the interlinkage of postal and telegraph services on a municipal, then state, and finally on a nationwide footing—a similar result was achieved when consolidation of wire systems was rounded out by the government's taking over all telephones on the eve of the First World War. This pattern is general in all leading European countries at the present time, and has been copied in most of the underdeveloped areas.

In the United States, technical unification is very nearly complete for the wire services and for the postal system, but inter-facility integration is still partial and incomplete. The postal system has been a government monopoly since before the Revolution, and has been modeled on the British pattern since 1863. It is, however, entirely separated from the leading privately owned telephone and telegraph networks. Since the fusion of Western Union and Postal Telegraph in 1943, there has been a single national telegraph system. This is not the case with the telephone, for despite the growth of the Bell System on a national footing since the turn of the century, there were, in 1955, still some 4,800 independent telephone companies serving customers scattered over most of the states of the union, mainly in rural areas.[4] One of the independents, the General Telephone Corporation, has become a corporate giant in its own right.[5] Bell Telephone operates a fairly extensive telegraph service. Quite clearly, the telephone and the telegraph are not managed as coördinate parts of a fully integrated system.

The United States represents the exception and not the rule. But even here the degree of actual technical unification effected in day-to-day operations is much farther advanced than the facts of corporate ownership would seem to indicate; in fact, in most respects the unification appears to be as complete as any to be found in the European countries.[6] The engineering facts tend to promote the management of all the facilities as though they were coördinate operating parts of a single system.

Regarded from this point of view, four principles may be said to dominate the current expansion of the telephone and telegraph facilities: universal interconnection; automatic operation; multiple function and multiple use; and media integration. Each of these closely related principles tends in application to encourage further advance of the others; collectively, they call for comprehensive and long-range planning.

1. *Universal interconnection* means the direct physical interconnection of lines for continuous passage of messages over the circuits of all companies, at home and abroad, as though they were operated by a single company. This requires the development of a universally valid system of standards for telephone sending, receiving, and transmission equipment, standard operating rules, and standard systems of rates and charges. Since the last are set either by public policy, where the state owns and operates the wire services, as in most European countries, or by negotiation with state and federal regulatory agencies, as in the United States, they may be ignored in this context. In all cases, rates are based in part upon performance, and engineering is a major factor in performance.

The role played by standards in preparing and smoothing the way for all line and service interconnections is critical. The Bell System, whose procedures are more or less representative of the industry as a whole, describes them as threefold: "research and fundamental development, systems engineering, and specific development and design of new systems and facilities."[6] A large staff of scientists and engineers is engaged continuously in pure and applied research. New knowledge obtained through research and development is used in the systems engineering programs to create facilities for new telephone services and to improve and lower the cost of existing ones. Through engineering studies, specific projects are determined, objectives established, and broad technical plans laid out. Once a new design is adopted, the resulting standards then remain everywhere valid within the system until changes are once again introduced. "Every item whether it is produced in tens or millions, must be made so that it will fit precisely into place in the telephone network." [7]

Between the Bell System and other communications networks, all levels in the development programs are in more or less close and continuous contact with work being done by other companies along similar lines, at home or abroad. Actual equipment and operating standards of different operating companies are kept in some sort of concordance—largely through direct association and negotiation, supplemented by coöperation on various committees, domestic[8] and international, of member bodies of the International Telecommunications Union. Telephonic interconnections abroad, while frequently adding complications, present no basically different engineering problems. Connections within continents, as between Bell and the Canadian and Mexican networks, are made in the same way as among the several private systems within the United States. This holds for both telephone and telegraph.

Intercontinental cable and wireless connections present a more difficult problem. In some countries they are already closely interlaced; in others not. In Britain, for example, the Post Office, which owns and operates the national telephone and telegraph networks, is also closely linked with the government-owned Cable and Wireless Ltd. (nationalized in 1949) and the Commonwealth Telecommunications Board. Among the three there exists a functional division of labor[9] so that they operate as a single unified world communications system.

In the United States, overseas cable and wireless networks are divided among several independent companies. Yet in this instance, again, the separate networks generally operate as though they were parts of a single engineering system. With minor exceptions, messages originating anywhere may pass from one set of lines to the other in continuous transit. A similar picture can be drawn for every country in the world which possesses the economic resources to round out its network. Continental networks, then, apply the same principles of interconnection in the larger area. Finally, intercontinental networks link continental systems together on a global basis. In 1954, there were 336,090 nautical miles of cable, over half of which was owned and operated by the British Cable and Wireless Corporation as a single unified system.[10] Although filling-in remains to be done, the outlines of a single technically unified, global telecommunications system are already visible.

2. With respect to the second principle, *automatic operation,* a much greater amount of filling-in remains to be done, but it is now possible to anticipate the time when virtually the entirety of the telecommunications networks will be operated on a completely automatic basis. (The device of the teletypewriter is prototypal—information may be fed continuously into the lines by "hand" or from recorded tapes or facsimile equipment and be taken out from the other end by electromechanically self-loading devices.)

The operating-line requirements for high-quality continuous service become more exacting with the extension of the communications web. Thus mechanization at the automatic level is a necessity. Two developments of the automatic kind have already made it possible to combine extensive interconnection with high-capacity utilization of lines. One is the use of feed-back amplifiers for maintaining the strength of signals at the level required for clear reception. The second is the automatic dialing and switching system.

By means of amplifiers, spaced at appropriate distances along the line and using a number of different frequency bands separated by electrical filters, several messages may be sent simultaneously along the same set of wires. These are known as *carrier* systems. The development here has been extraordinary. Beginning with "open-wire carrier systems permitting from one to fifteen telephone channels above the frequency band of the voice channel,"[11] there has been expanded a further network of long-distance coaxial cable transmission lines which now span the continent.

A cable comprised of four pairs of coaxials is able to carry 2,400 simultaneous two-way telephone connections. Recent improvements in amplifiers, when placed at four-mile intervals, make it possible to increase the frequency band to 8,000,000 cycles, allowing up to 1,800 simultaneous telephone connections per pair of coaxials, or 7,200 for a cable comprised of four pairs of coaxial tubes. Improvements in construction and in amplifiers have made it possible to place in the depths of the ocean solid dielectric coaxial cables incorporating amplifiers. The first pair of cables of this sort was laid between Key West, Florida, and Havana, Cuba, in 1950 with a capacity for 24 telephone channels. A similar pair of cables, but with a capacity for 36 telephone channels, was laid between Nova Scotia and Scotland during the summers of 1955 and 1956, the inauguration of public service taking place in September, 1956.[12]

Alternative to the coaxial cables, microwave radio relay systems employing similar principles have been constructed and are being extended. Thus the microwave transcontinental line "is capable of transmitting six broadband channels in each direction." Since each channel, in turn, is able to handle up to 600 simultaneous telephone connections, the system may provide 3,600 telephone channels in all.

The second line of development, manual dialing (soon possibly to be supplanted by voice signals), coupled with automatic switching, makes it theoretically possible instantaneously to connect any two points within the system, however far removed. All the details of connection, including irregular situations arising from traffic congestion, and recording and billing charges, will be self-programmed by this "giant robot with limbs stretching over the continent."[13]

The routing, it is perhaps needless to add, may be entirely by wire, or principally by microwave relay, or by any combination of the two. There is no fundamental technical reason why the same automatic operation cannot be further extended to include links with deep-sea repeatered cables and overseas radiotelephone circuits. As a matter of fact, operator-to-subscriber dialing

over radio from the United States to Hawaii and to Puerto Rico
has been conducted on an experimental basis, a final design of the
necessary equipment determined, and a limited amount of the
equipment units put into manufacture. While the long-distance
dialing system in actual practice is still far short of even national
coverage, it may well become continental in scope. There is no
theoretical reason why the same principles might not eventually
be applied on a global basis to provide what would then become
literally universal and virtually instantaneous automatic interconnection among all individuals and all parts of the world.[14]

3. With respect to the third principle, that of *multiple function*,
quite obviously these lines stand available 24 hours a day, and
365 days a year, and they may be used simultaneously in varying
sorts of communications mix, or different uses may be dovetailed
over the diurnal cycle. Thus the same techniques which make it
possible to run from 600 to 1,800 two-way voice connections for
every voice circuit also make it possible alternatively to carry 18
telegraph messages for each voice channel. A coaxial cable of
four pairs of tubes, when used entirely for telephone messages,
can supply 7,200 voice channels. Used entirely for telegraph, it
would make possible the sending of 129,600 simultaneous messages. Used half-and-half, the cable could handle at once 3,600
voice and 64,800 telegraph messages.

At the other extreme, one television connection absorbs the
capacity equivalent of 600 voice channels. Each pair of coaxial
tubes in a coaxial system of the newer type (8 megacycle band
width) might provide, on the television channel, 600 voice channels and 10,800 telegraphic channels, all operating in two directions. The possible combinations, of course, are almost endless.
The same types of combinations would hold for microwave transmission. Line loading and connection routing can be handled by
the same robot switching apparatus used for long-distance telephone channels, and regardless of the type of message fed into
the system.

The wave guide, now only a laboratory means of communication, will provide communication over a hollow tube utilizing
transmission frequencies far higher than those of the coaxial cable.
Thus its over-all capacity will be many times that of a coaxial

cable. To obtain efficient use of such great capacity, large groups of all types of communication services will have to be channelled through the wave guide. Economic pressure will tend to promote the multiple function of facilities and the amalgamation of communication enterprises.

To maintain at all times the highest capacity-utilization—a prime consideration for low-cost operation[15]—all messages that could be delayed (as, much of facsimile and possibly a great deal of telegraphic transmission) might then be sent during off-peak hours. They could either be delayed, or be stored on tape or drums to be fed into the system automatically whenever under-utilization, over any circuit or combination of circuits, became evident. "Reperforator" switching permits complete automaticity of the entire operation.[16]

4. It would follow, from the above, that the fourth principle of *media integration* is in practice technically feasible and economically desirable. There would seem, accordingly, no longer to be a case on these grounds for separate wire systems of common-carrier telegraph and telephone communications, nor for separately operated common-carrier wire and wireless networks.[17] By 1950, more than a third of Western Union's wires were leased from the telephone companies. Meanwhile, Bell, largely as a result of the development of its automatic TWX teletypewriter service, was making heavy inroads on the telegraph business. Eventual complete fusion of all wire and wireless would seem to be in the cards. Abroad, formal separation by ownership or management groups has to all intents and purposes long since disappeared.

The case for integration of land wire- and cable-systems with underseas cables is, as yet, far stronger for telegraphic messages than for oral communication, although the new British-American North Atlantic telephone cable opens the way for applying the principles of multiple-use of the newer land coaxial cables to those at sea. At the same time the case for interlinkage of (*a*) wire and wireless, and (*b*) domestic and overseas wireless common-carrier systems has by this time received universal acceptance in principle. A multifunction world-wide telecommunications network of automatically operated wire, cable, and radio common-carriers is now technically feasible.

At all levels of innovation, from the research laboratory on through to the minutiae of construction and operation, and along the four lines of development outlined above, the need for careful, long-range, and comprehensive planning has been universally accepted. As the need for unification extends outwards from corporate networks to embrace successive national, continental, and global telecommunications networks, the requirement of such long-range planning becomes ever more imperative. On the technical side, planning must first be coextensive with each of the specialized services—telephone, telegraph, cable, radio transmission—and must then weave them together as separate functional strands in a balanced and interdependent system at all levels, from the local area to the global universe. But such an eventual result cannot be reached without further expanding technical planning in two directions: use of the radio spectrum, and the production of the necessary equipment.

PLANNING THE RADIO SPECTRUM

Three sets of facts have rendered the comprehensive planning of the uses of the radio spectrum on both a national and an international scale a matter of growing concern. First are the physical characteristics of the spectrum itself which, at any given level of scientific knowledge, set definite limits to the total number and the types of simultaneous uses.

Second is the perplexing fact that in the face of mounting pressure for radio-spectrum space, the full technical possibilities may not readily be exploited because it continues to be true that "administrative and political considerations, theories of economics, and the inflexibility of statutes, rather than engineering factors, govern the allocation to a great extent." [18]

Finally, there remains the fact that "the demand for radio service has always outgrown the useful spectrum space very soon after the technical means for using a given frequency range were known." [19] Throughout the history of radio transmission, demand has increased more rapidly than new frequency channels have been opened up, with the result that the problem of shortage has grown relatively more severe with the passage of time.

Any one of these facts taken by itself would require the comprehensive planning of spectrum use. Taken in combination, as they must be, the need for such programming is overwhelming and inescapable.

The characteristics of the spectrum are so complex that they defy summary description.[20] Two peculiarities of the electromagnetic spectrum as a whole, however, may be singled out because of their special importance in this connection. The first is the fact that not only is "most of the spectrum . . . unsuitable for communication," [21] but, also, the available evidence indicates that, in the main, in order to make better use of the parts now taken up, and to find economically feasible ways of utilizing the unused portions of the theoretically available frequencies, there will be required more intensive research, and more expensive sending and receiving equipment.

The unexplored and underutilized resources of the spectrum, in other words, have characteristics somewhat similar to those found by the Paley Commission (chap. i) for resources in general. Here science and engineering are once again seen to be running a "handicap race with nature" in which resources for future discovery and use are generally leaner, of lower quality, or more costly to use. The penalty for failure to overcome this handicap is mounting real costs. In this case it is also true that at some indeterminate point (i.e., the limits of the radio spectrum) no future additional resources exist at all. From this consideration it follows that at any given time it is probably true that more uses can be wrung from the spectrum by better planning of the currently available frequencies than can be gained by opening up new portions of the spectrum, and that this advantage will increase as successive portions of the theoretically available frequencies are turned to human account.

A second peculiarity is that since the characteristics of the spectrum for purposes of communication vary radically as one moves from the lower to the higher frequencies, and with the correspondingly appropriate modes of transmission, each range of frequencies may, in the face of the mounting demand, have its economic best use. To be sure, scientific and engineering developments may, as directional beaming and high-fidelity reception did in the past, greatly alter the total number, the possible geographic spacing, and the band suitability for different broadcasting services. The problem, however, remains, and from this it follows that purely on its technical merits alone there is no practicable way of handling frequency use except to plan allocations within the spectrum as a whole, and within each of its frequency ranges. For short-distance transmission, this is a domestic problem; but for long-distance broadcasting, where propagation crosses national frontiers, it is clearly an international problem.

The need for planning allocation is enhanced by the fact that numerous claims for space are made which are not in accord with the best technical practices and which, if granted or allowed to continue, tend to cut down the uses to which the total spectrum may be put. The Joint Technical Advisory Committee, in its report on *Radio Spectrum Conservation,* identified a number of such examples for most of the frequency bands. An obvious example is an excessive number of stations for a given volume of traffic. Federal Communications Commissioner E. M. Webster has stated that the total volume of traffic between San Francisco and Hawaii could be handled with less than half of the 19 circuits operated by private carriers and government agencies.[22]

An interesting case is the use of radiation for industrial, scientific, and medical purposes. Instead of being confined to a limited number of bands, with shielding devices required to prevent radiation from escaping into the atmosphere, the frequencies used are scattered throughout the spectrum, and shielding is only indifferently applied. In one instance, an improperly shielded diathermy machine in a doctor's office in Miami, Florida, created disruptive interference to radio-communications all up and down the Pacific Coast states. "If bands were provided for all these uses," the Committee concludes, "there would be nothing left for the communication and radio location services." [23]

The sheer pressure of demand also makes planning imperative. The problem is faced on both the domestic and international levels, and for all types of radio transmission. Internally, the case of the United States is to some extent typical of the problem all countries must eventually face. In 1955 there were 311,000 radio stations in the United States under authorization by the Federal Communications Commission. Compared to the total authorizations in all previous years of 1,635 in the common-carrier class, there were requests for nearly 5,000 new stations in the year 1955 alone. The comparable figures for the broadcast class were 7,700 applications and 5,720 extant authorizations; for all special and safety stations, 151,000 applications and 19,353 extant authorizations. For this last class, for every new authorization granted in 1945 (30,006), there were nearly five applications. The time is not far distant when the United States may well be equipped with a million or more transmitting stations and bands will have to be fitted together as tightly as in a jigsaw puzzle.

To cite another example, the British need for more domestic stations was stated clearly at the time of the Washington conference in 1927, when the first attempt was made to work out a comprehensive international allocation plan. According to the British delegate,

"All of those who have taken the floor, up to now, have spoken in favor of a single service (aeronautic, maritime or broadcasting). I would like to speak as the delegate of Great Britain which is equally interested in all three categories.

"We have almost five million licensed broadcast listeners, and the B.B.C., supported by public opinion, is asking for an enlargement of its frequency band; in the same manner, the maritime navigation service is asking for the enlargement of the band allocated to radio-beacon stations; the aircraft navigation interests, in their turn, are asking for new wave lengths because of the rapid expansion of the aircraft services. The British amateurs are asking for an extension of their frequency band; the commercial communications services complain of frequent interference; the police are asking for a wave length.

"We understand very well the reasons for all of these requests but it is impossible to satisfy them." [24]

Almost every country participating in telecommunications conferences has expressed similar needs for more radio-spectrum space. The problem, accordingly, is universal. It is also important to note that the underdeveloped areas are just beginning to make their needs and demands felt. As they develop, each will face the same domestic frequency-allocation problems which have long confronted the more technically advanced countries.

For practically all countries, the more important planning, furthermore, must take place at the very top level of global allocation, precisely where the most numerous and complex conflicts of interest render any type of planning the most difficult. These conflicts, however, against the background of irreducible facts of a technical character, have tended to promote interest in international allocation planning rather than hold it back. Small countries, such as Switzerland and the Central American countries, can have very few transmitting stations whose propagations will not cross national frontiers and create interference problems for other countries. Furthermore, they are bound to want most the very type of stations which create the greatest difficulties, i.e., the preferred lower-frequency mass-communication broadcasting bands. Here costs of transmission are lower,[25] the distance of propagation is longer, the consequent interference problem is greater, and the number of possible stations is smaller. Only with ultra and very high frequencies might they be amply supplied without incurring difficulties over interference.

There is no possible way out of this dilemma for the small countries except the international planning of spectrum use. For underdeveloped countries the problem is largely one of latecomers at the feast; the bulk of the good long-distance channels have already been preëmpted. There also exists a tendency to increase the power of transmitting stations, with the further result that the number of stations possible on any given frequency declines. Politically, it is impossible for the more highly developed countries to refuse to share the spectrum with the latecomers.

The net result is that all parties have come to have a large and growing stake in the international planning of spectrum use. The history of the steps by which it has evolved does not concern us at length in this place.[26] The groundwork was prepared long before the advent of wireless transmission with the establishment, in 1868, of the International Telegraph Union, with a secretariat to regulate international telegraphic communication. In the course of time this union took over parallel functions in telephone communications (1885) and radiotelegraphy (1906). In 1932, at a conference held in Madrid, the Bureau of the Union became the Bureau of the International Telecommunication Union (ITU).

The purpose of the Madrid conference was to unify international organization of telegraph, telephone, and radio communication on a world-wide basis. Frequency allocation was immediately placed in the much larger frame of reference where its problems are of concern for all types of communications media. To this end the ITU became a coördinating body for a wide variety of specialized international and regional associations, technical committees, and coöperative research bodies.[27] The three principal committees deal respectively with telephones, telegraphs, and radio communications.[28] In 1947 the ITU was established as one of the specialized agencies of the U.N. and was equipped with a permanent secretariat located in Geneva.

The United States has paid little attention to the telephone and telegraph work of the ITU, but it coöperates quite closely in radio communications. Coöperation among the United States, Canada, and the Latin American states has favored regional over world agreements. With respect to radio, prior to 1927 a gentleman's agreement governed use of broadcast channels between the United States and Canada. In 1937 an Inter-American Radio Office was created to administer the terms of the two Inter-American and North American Regional Agreements drawn up at a conference held in Cuba that year.

In Europe a complex series of international agreements has long since effected technical unification of the wire services. The International Broadcasting Union, established in 1939, sets standards and allocates frequencies to stations in Europe in very much the way that the Federal Communications Commission does in the United States.

The British have at the same time tended to favor Empire over other international agreements. Since the nationalization of cable and wireless in 1947, a Commonwealth Telecommunications Board has handled technical and policy problems for communications networks connecting the Commonwealth countries and the scattered colonial possessions. Accordingly, it cuts across both national and continental boundaries.

Somewhat the same picture holds for the elaborate overseas radiotelephone and radiotelegraph networks of the American government, operated by or for the Army, the Navy, the Air Force, the Voice of America, and the Civil Aeronautics Administration. These are truly global systems of communications under purely

American direction. At many points they are closely interlaced with private and commercial radio, telephone, and telegraph networks.

Within the United States, where most of the facilities are privately owned and operated, technical unification is effected partly via an elaborate medley of intercorporate agreements. The government, however, exercises an overriding control throughout. It does this partly as owner of the spectrum—declared to be official policy by the Radio Act of 1927—and partly as owner and operator of communications facilities. In the field of radio transmission, the government occupied in 1951 nearly half of the total spectrum assigned to this country between 4 and 20 megacycles, and 28 per cent of the available useful channels between 30 and 30,000 megacycles.[29] In addition it shared small percentages of the first and 18.5 per cent of the second with private users. At the same time it had under lease some 326,000 miles of teletype land-line circuits.

Government power to unify communications networks in the United States rests, however, primarily on its authority to regulate. While government ownership and operation of communications networks in general has been rejected,[30] since the passage of the Communications Act of 1934, the Federal Communications Commission (FCC) has possessed regulatory authority over the entire field of domestic and American-owned foreign communications networks. Despite the complexity of its organization, and notwithstanding its official acceptance of private ownership and a limited degree of competition in this field, the Commission is notable for the fact that it is the only federal regulatory agency which has become a real national planning body for a major American industry.

In this role the FCC has favored technical integration of the wire and cable systems of the country, and in some instances corporate consolidations of competing networks. (The outstanding example of the latter is the merger of Postal Telegraph and Western Union.) It serves as the coördinating body for public-service facilities in air and sea transportation and for meteorological reporting. It has the power to determine all domestic radio-spectrum allocations and the conditions and terms of equipment use and operation. And it is the ultimate negotiating authority in the making of all international agreements affecting American communications services.

While there is room, no doubt, for endless debate over this American way of combining private enterprise with government regulation—whether industry and the public are getting the best or the worst of both worlds—there can be no question but that under the aegis of the FCC, technical unification of communications networks is advancing along lines that are scarcely distinguishable from those usual abroad where the state owns and operates all common-carrier and broadcasting networks.

This coördination and planning do not stop with the unification of networks. It reaches back to the engineering side of the production of equipment used by the networks, and forward to the equipment for and conditions governing customer usage. This is true not only for the specialized networks, such as American Telephone & Telegraph for telephone, Western Union for telegraph, and Columbia Broadcasting System or National Broadcasting Company for broadcasting, but also for all efforts at interlinkage of networks, domestically and internationally, and for all problems of effective and economical use of radio-spectrum space throughout the globe.

PLANNING EQUIPMENT SPECIFICATIONS

The production equipment for the Bell System, as has been noted above, is so planned that "Every item, whether it is produced in tens or millions, must be made so that it will fit precisely into place in the telephone network." This would be the ideal situation for all communications systems, whether national, regional, or global in scope. There are three general problems: (1) the establishment of an internally consistent system of exact standards and specifications which is universally valid for each communications medium, and for all inter-media connections; (2) such a method of drafting these standards and specifications that they may be removed or altered, if outmoded or rendered obsolete, without at the same time disrupting the system; and (3) securing compliance with the corollary specifications for making the best and most economical use of the system.

The initial problem of evolving adequate systems of standards and specifications grows in importance as the interconnection of wire or wireless networks spreads out on a national, regional, or global scale. Almost every one of the special-function organizations drawn into the International Telecommunications Union faced this problem at the outset. Thus regulations of the International Telegraph Union in 1865, 1903, and 1925 specified the types of sending apparatus which might be used. Uniformity in the technical apparatus for telephone networks became the special task of an international consultative committee of the International Telegraph Union after the turn of the century. Its European Fundamental System of Reference for Telephone Transmission, a master reference system for telephone transmission designed, constructed, and installed by the Bell System, has given the United States and Europe a common set of primary standards.

As the national and international networks expanded, the need for more rigorous standards extended from sending, receiving, and line equipment to include materials and components, and, hence, equipment manufacture. This work, during the early period, was promoted by a number of standards-coördinating societies, including the standards-research institutions of the National Bureau of Standards, the British National Physical Laboratory, and the German Imperial Physical-Technical Institute. From its foundation in 1906, the International Electrotechnical Commission was concerned with technical standards in this field.

Radio transmission introduced a host of new standards problems. To illustrate, the central problem of band allocation might be viewed as one of avoidance of radio interference. The widths, and accordingly the feasible number of usable bands, then depend upon the qualities and types of sending and receiving equipment, and these in turn upon equipment specifications and tolerances. Implicit in any design of radio transmitting and receiving equipment it is a capability for operating in a certain band width. At the margins of the band the amount of carrier tolerance "varies from a thousandth of a per cent of the carrier frequency to about 1 per cent, depending on the frequency and the state of equipment development. Space so reserved serves only to avoid interference," and while the loss is not great, yet it "is one which can be reduced by purely technical means." [31]

"The limited available spectrum space," the FCC has pointed out, "makes it mandatory that many services prepare to employ much stricter engineering standards in future operations, such as improved frequency tolerances, reduced harmonic and other spurious emissions, better receiving equipment, etc." With respect to the latter,

Improvement in receiver performance is particularly important. For example, if the advantages of frequency modulation are to be obtained such as to warrant the required spectrum space, it is essential that well-designed frequency modulation receivers be provided. Such receivers must have proper selectivity, limiter and discriminator characteristics. Further, it is urged that no receivers for any service be manufactured which radiate an appreciable signal. A radiating receiver is in effect a low power transmitter often capable of causing serious interference to other receivers of the same or other services. The slight difference in cost between a well-designed receiver and one of poor design is more than offset by the gain to all services. It is expected that post-war receivers will be designed and manufactured so as to minimize the effects of image frequency response, radiation from best frequency oscillators and other effects that may be directly attributed to equipments of inferior design and performance. [32]

Although direct control of the FCC does not extend to the manufacture of equipment, it has been intimated that unless self-regulation by the industry corrects prevalent defects in receiver manufacture, federal action to enforce engineering standards for receivers will be taken. [33]

In the older wire services, the problem has been handled in several different ways. The simplest is that of the Bell Telephone System, which purchases the bulk of its equipment from its wholly owned subsidiary, Western Electric Company. With most other wire networks the problem is solved by negotiations between wire services and manufacturers for supply of standardized equipment, the standards then being worked out in detail through intermediation of special standing technical committees.

Every aspect of this problem has multiplied in importance with the addition of radio transmission, owing to such factors as the extraordinary variety of sending and receiving equipment, the large number of manufacturers, the rapidity of technical development, the large public stake in the form of both receiving and sending equipment,[34] and the needs associated with the interlacing of radio with common-carrier wire and cable systems. In 1943, largely on the initiative of the FCC, a Radio Technical Planning Board was established which included representatives from 19 trade associations and operated through some 13 technical panels.[35] It supplied data and participated in the 1944 Frequency Allocation Hearings. In 1948, it was succeeded by a permanent organization, set up jointly by the Institute of Radio Engineers and the Radio Manufacturers' Association (subsequently renamed Radio-Television Manufacturers' Association), known as the Joint Technical Advisory Committee (JTAC).

The JTAC is a joint business-government technical planning agency for the entire range of industries producing and using radio or receiving equipment.

At the international level this unified technical planning is even more evident. The three main sections of the ITU—the advisory committees on telegraphs, telephones, and radio communications —engage (*a*) in technical work which generally parallels that of the JTAC, and (*b*) in the negotiating of agreements and general overseeing of operations, more or less parallel to the FCC.

To be sure, at both levels the work of the multifarious technical committees is, at least formally, purely advisory. Yet it is also true that the technical facts are of such a compelling nature that, in the main, what these committees advise is apt to be carried into practice.

This brings us to the second general problem of planning the equipment specifications for telecommunications systems, that of so drafting and using standards that they may be altered or removed without disrupting the system. Between the scientific facts as developed by research and engineering on the one hand, and detailed problems of application on the other, is sandwiched what the Bell people refer to as "systems engineering." The work of the technical committees of the JTAC and the ITU shows that the systems-engineering stage is recognized in some form as a preliminary to the setting of standards for equipment and operation, and that by benefit of its reëxamination of the technical problems involved in each instance it is possible to redraft specifications for the system in such a way that change-over to them is relatively easy in production and operation—but not, however, without incurring at times some very high costs. This is a particularly difficult problem in radio transmission, where (*a*) it is closely linked with common-carrier wire and cable networks, and where (*b*) broadcasting changes in any of the three variables—channels, sending equipment, and receiving equipment—are apt suddenly to make obsolete the equipment of much of the industry. The difficulty of innovation-obsolescence in the radio field lies, that is to say, in the fact that all uses of radio must be so completely standardized as a mere prerequisite for effective communication that partial innovation is hard to accomplish.[36] Innovation is a condition for making the best use of the spectrum as the structure of demand for space changes and as research opens up new possibilities, yet at the same time, innovation imposes obsolescence on *all* of a certain class of use or a certain band of frequencies.

In contemplating a change of the above sort, it is the policy of the FCC to give

. . . careful consideration to the number of transmitters and receivers already in use, the investment of the industry and the public in equipment, and the cost and feasibility of converting the equipment for operation on different frequencies, as well as to the time required for an orderly change to the new frequencies.[37]

How difficult in actual practice this may be is indicated by the suggestion of the JTAC that, "As knowledge of propagation and equipment improves and becomes stabilized, it should be possible to establish in advance the basis for such transfers over periods as long as 25 years, although shorter periods should suffice in most cases." [38]

This amounts to saying that not only must the allocations in each period accord with the best and most recent advances in research and engineering, but also that the planning must, inescapably, project over a relatively long time-span. Pressure to lengthen the time may come from several factors, such as increase in the number of users, advance in the scale of public investment in both transmission and reception, increase in the variety of interests desiring to use band frequencies, widening of the geographic scope of reference, and more durable equipment.

In summary, it then appears that the time dimension of the necessary technical planning is paired in a general way with the space dimension. The latter moves outward steadily, to the ultimate of global interconnection; the former, to extending the temporal depth of planning in terms of years, if not decades. The heavier the demands made upon the telecommunications networks, the more powerful is the interaction. And the more powerful the interaction, the greater is the interest in extending technical planning to include equipment, design, and operating standards.

Turning finally to the third general problem, that of securing compliance of operators and users with the corollary specifications for making the best and most economical use of the system, we are faced not only with a fantastically swelling volume of traffic, but also with significant changes in the qualitative character of demand—in the form of the need for continuous industrial interconnection.

The source of the change in industrial demand arises in part from the continuous interlinkage of spatially removed but successive-step or confluent (e.g., assembly) processes which are being placed on a continuous, automatically self-correcting flow basis. With the direct interlinkage of the production schedules of individual plants, together with the cumulative realignment of transport and energy-supply systems along similar lines, ideally the entire concert of operations should approach as closely as possible to performance for 24 hours a day and 365 days a year. The interplant communications circuits required to maintain and coördinate these flows then come to be viewed in much the same terms as those of intraplant operations which converge on a single central control-panel. A good deal of the interoffice business traffic has already been reorganized in a similar fashion.

This new type of demand, for continuous and high-volume use, is one which fits perfectly into the telecommunications need for full-capacity utilization. In actual practice, the bulk of such industrial and business traffic is handled by leased circuits. There has been, accordingly, a very great expansion of this type of service.

Revamping the media to handle this traffic with the high-fidelity controls required for high-level, or eventually complete, automation of the plants and processes thus coupled together vastly increases the need for complete standardization of all communications equipment and operations as a condition to obtaining constancy, reliability, and economy of service. At the level of full automation on the part of interconnected plant schedules, and of the intermediating wire or wireless circuits, this need reaches its ultimate urgency.

To be sure, we are far from this point as yet, but it is not utterly fanciful to contemplate. Practically all the separate steps and the appropriate techniques can now be found in workaday routines. The pieces of the jigsaw puzzle may never be put together in a technologically thoroughly rational pattern. But to the extent that pattern is developed, such an automated communications web would become a technical component of series of interrelated plant schedules (themselves more or less fully automated internally), fed at both ends of the production lines by energy and transport facilities whose flows are also arranged, timed, and governed by the same or parallel intelligence systems. The technical replanning would then be compelled to embrace the entirety of the production of the electronics equipment used in intraplant as well as interplant processes, and the maintenance, operation, and rules for usage of the telecommunications system as a whole. Much, and perhaps eventually all, routine office and interoffice traffic might be transformed on the same pattern.

THE SHIFTING OF TRAFFIC WITHIN THE TELECOMMUNICATIONS
NETWORKS

Where the distances are long and the traffic load is light, radio transmission generally has advantages over wire and cable.[39] But where the reverse conditions prevail, there is no feasible alternative to forcing the growing traffic onto either the wire or postal services. In the United States, a prime principle in screening requests for radio frequencies is that they must show why wire lines will not serve instead of radio. Unless, as in the instance of international fixed public common-carriers, contravening considerations of public policy dictate the use of radio where wires would technically serve instead, the service for which the request is made will be rejected.

On the assumption, which seems to be fully justified by past history, that more space will not be available for common-carrier and broadcasting systems up the spectrum (higher frequencies) because of the growing demand for frequencies for purposes not readily transferred to wire, the pressure down the spectrum from increasing demand will force more and more traffic onto the wire services. Furthermore, any service up or down the spectrum that may be moved over onto the wires—television is a striking example—probably will be transferred there when the pressure becomes high enough. It is reasonable, accordingly, to suppose that coaxial cable systems will continue to be expanded in the future.[40]

At the same time, the rapid advances being made both in high-speed air transport, and in the handling of mail at terminals, is already siphoning off very large percentages of record traffic from the wires—telegraph in particular. When this is combined with the facts noted above, that telephone wires may alternatively be used for many different kinds of transmission in almost instantaneously varying load-combinations, and that the volume of wire traffic devoted to demand for continuous services throughout the diurnal cycles is on the rapid increase, there is a further reason for the complete technical unification of all wire services as a condition for retaining any of this traffic. It also, however, encourages closer working liaison with, and consequently higher levels of common technical planning between, the wire and wireless systems and the postal and air traffic services in the overlapping field of record transmission.

SUMMARY

As far as the purely technological facts are concerned, the over-all picture of the telecommunications system in the future is relatively easy to foresee.

In this prospect, common-carrier and broadcasting communications share use of the spectrum with other services according to unified national, regional, and international plans. Common-carrier and broadcasting are to a major extent complementary or supplementary to each other, and the facilities or propagation channels of each, wireless and wire alike, are capable of being used in whole or in part by the other. As a corollary fact, wire and wireless are also complementary and supplementary to each other. They are, accordingly, planned at the highest levels as merely different aspects of a common, interdependent system. The same is true of the wire and cable services themselves; they are multiple-function networks for simultaneous use, in varying traffic mixes, of intermittent public and continuous private messages, and of aural, visual, and control (radar, loran, etc.) communications of various sorts. Consequently, the pressure of demand which tends to push traffic off the air and onto the wires, and to spill over onto the postal services and airplanes, also promotes further planning for such inter-service coördination.

Universal interconnection among common-carrier systems promotes and is dependent upon over-all technical planning on a global basis; sharing of the spectrum with all other radio uses and services begins at the same level. Regional plans may then be fitted into the global; national and local plans into the regional. Because of the high costs and general resistance to change-over, plant investment in the wire and cable services, and sender and receiver investment in the wireless services, lengthen the time span of the forward planning at each level.

Interconnection per se requires standardization of sending and receiving equipment; of the frequencies, intensities, and regeneration of impulses; and of the rules, regulations, and tariff systems governing message transmission. Every move toward more intensive use of wires or frequency bands heightens the need for more exacting and universally (i.e., throughout the relevant system) valid standards. So, likewise, does every effort to place sending and receiving on an automatic basis. And so, once again, does any demand—particularly when arising from industries using such networks to integrate production and business schedules on an automated or near-automated basis—for continuous and unbroken service.

The related technical planning then moves backwards to include design and standards incorporated in the equipment. At this point the technical problems are virtually coextensive with those of electronics engineering as a whole. The theories of communication applicable to an automated plant are akin, when not coextensive, with wire and wireless systems. Scientific work behind each is in large part, if not ultimately in its entirety, common to both. And so also are the practical conclusions and applications. Thus, much of the electronics production must of necessity be planned as an integral part of communications services.

XIII

Recapitulation and the First Sum of Consequences

In the vast, turbulent sea of technological activity in contemporary times, certain well-directed potentialities can be envisioned. In the forefront is the extraordinary dynamism of industrial technology. Science and engineering are rapidly becoming the overwhelmingly important source of the germinal ideas and the practical methods for realizing at once resource expansion, basic product innovation, and significant gains in low-cost production. In continuing success along these three converging lines lies the main hope of rising material standards of living for a rapidly growing global population.

The principal burden of the material expectations of the future, that is to say, is no longer on "Martha's sons"; it is laid instead at the laboratory door. The "Second Industrial Revolution" is becoming what might simply be called the "Scientific Revolution in Industry." And as rapidly as the shift to the new foundations occurs, the question arises: Can production be genuinely "scientifically organized"? This is a dominant question in our time.

It is already dominant in all the older industrial countries, where there are enormous handicaps to be overcome. Industrial development has carried with it habits, institutions, and forms of organization rooted in earlier methods. Plants and populations have been located without reference to the new criteria. Vast urban conglomerates have been built, agricultural lands cultivated, transportation facilities laid out, interdependent plant-processes organized, marketing and other policies generalized, and many practices grown up which cannot easily be squared with the requirements of the emerging industrial order of the future.

But the newly developing countries—India, China, Indonesia, the Arab world, virtually all of South America and Africa—are able, so to speak, to adopt, adapt, and develop Western scientific and industrial methods without these handicaps. Or, where analogous handicaps are faced, they may be able to proceed without building into their industrial systems, as they develop, the flaws and shortcomings which we face in our own. However important, accordingly, some of the developments dealt with in this book may be for the older countries, they may be many times as significant for those countries just launching industrialization plans.

Can industry—can the scientific and engineering foundations, the substratum upon which all superstructures of civilization and culture must rest—truly be organized along scientific lines, or at least consistently with scientific technology?[1]

A PRELIMINARY PROBLEM: ORGANIZATION TO AVOID CHAOS IN SCIENCE ITSELF

The problem begins at the doors of science itself. Ibsen's Peer Gynt found that the search for the secret of life, peeling off experience by experience like the layers of an onion, revealed at the end nothing intelligible at all. But science seems to discover in nature a new source of widening inquiry with each successive layer, and no practical or theoretical end to the layers in sight. For every problem solved, two new problems, or a dozen, spring up to take its place. To change the figure, the condition is, as Vannevar Bush has termed it in a now memorable paper, literally a case of "science—the endless frontier."

But the frontier is, withal, one of a special sort. Its pioneers are now under the stimulus of a driving force of unparalleled power resulting from the concurrence of the apotheosis of science at the hands of industry and the public with the capture by the laboratory of much of the talent, adventurous spirit, and prodigious energy that went into the discovery, exploration, and development of the physical frontiers of the past. This *élan*, however, spawns something entirely new to all frontiers: a complexly interwoven body of knowledge whose rapid proliferation is promoted through cumulative differentiation into ever more numerous and highly specialized disciplines.

On the one hand, such continuing specialization seems to be a necessary precondition to further advance in each sector. Yet, on the other, the very fact of specialization tends to mean that each researcher understands less of what is going on elsewhere in science, and is there understood less in turn. And this paradox is found at the very time when the continued viability of each sector is also clearly, and possibly increasingly, dependent upon its sustained and close interlinkage with the main body of scientific knowledge as a whole. The conditions of the chances for success in research, in short, risk a hopeless confusion which might in time set these chances to naught.

Public and industrial support has its drawbacks too. It tends, in virtually all fields of research, to promote the sacrifice of basic scientific work, as Norbert Wiener has pointed out in connection with atomic energy, in order to discover immediate practical applications. The foundations of science, accordingly, are in constant danger of being sacrificed to the superstructure. Every step in the direction of more scientific organization of the processes of industry enhances this danger. In this area, as the disposition of funds by American and foreign industries testifies, the immediate short-run gain is always uppermost, and research under this stimulus tends constantly to mine itself out.

The situation is not improved by virtue of the fact that what is a field of "application" from one viewpoint nearly always possesses a number of basic "theoretical" problems of its own. As the problems are influenced, sometimes decisively, by developments in the anterior field, so also do solutions found here tend to throw up new questions which force further reëxamination of basic postulates and conclusions in the field of origin. Any tendency, accordingly, unduly to emphasize "practical applications" in such fields as engineering and economics has somewhat the same effect, for example, of restraining basic research in physics and chemistry as the like emphasis in the latter tends to undermine the future practical applications which may be derived from them for use by the former.

At the same time a further element of paradox is contained in the fact that if the trends have been read correctly, escape from the ever closer kinship of science and practice is no longer possible. Nor, on balance, is it desirable. On the whole, the stimulating power of the two-way flow is too great for each, and in each case too widely recognized on its merits for that. Furthermore, the social stakes in the relationship are now far too high. But balance must be achieved and cumulative confusion avoided. Thus arises the recognized and growing need for the organizing, integrating, and pooling of scientific resources on all levels of theory and practice, and on the widest possible basis. A significant effect (as pointed out in chap. iii) has been the organization of great central national scientific bodies such as the Max Planck-Gesellschaft in Germany, the Department of Scientific and Industrial Research in England, the Academy of Sciences in Russia, and—though to a far lesser extent—the National Research Council and the National Science Foundation in the United States.

On the one side, these bodies, with varying degrees of emphasis, are schematically set up to relate and coördinate all levels of research within national frontiers—academic, industrial, governmental, etc. On the other, each is also becoming, to some extent, a world institution which more or less freely acts as a national or regional correspondent, coöperating with all other national and international scientific research bodies in such a way as to serve as a component of a shadowy sort of world science organization. The ideal, stated by Leibnitz, in founding the Berlin Academy over a century and a half ago, of a world academy of science embracing all fields, theoretical or practical, private or public, domestic or cultivated, and extending into the most remote corners of the earth, is somehow being actually realized.

But also, organization may foster the spirit that kills. While, that is to say, the psychological climate for creative scientific research seems always and everywhere to require the maximum freedom from all external guidance and control, so also may administration of the facilities placed at the disposal of science through this vast new organizational machinery proceed, whether by conscious design or willy-nilly, to take these very freedoms away. Clearly, to avoid anarchy it is necessary to have facilities, simplification of procedures, organization—in a word, *order* on an unprecedented scale; but equally clearly, to have order is to face the possibility, however remote, of authoritative direction and the erosion of individual initiative—not to mention the debilitating effects of the possible redirection of science to war and the destruction of human life itself. The consequences for the future of science are serious; for the future of society they are matters of life and death.

THE LARGER PROBLEM: SCIENTIFIC ORGANIZATION TO PROMOTE MAXIMUM SUSTAINED PRODUCTION

But if each new step in the seemingly inevitable further organization of science presents such problems to its leaders and practitioners in an ever more acute and baffling form, still they are as nothing compared to the analogous problems which these self-same scientists must face in the industrial arena as a whole. Circumstances, to repeat, are forcing them into industrially strategic positions. Yet here every paradox seems more paradoxical still; every complication to be multiplied a thousandfold. While it has its own established orders and rules of law, still, in contrast to science, industry as an organic part of social life is imbued with the philosophies of social life and hence shares with it the hazards of becoming a region of a Babel of tongues;[2] of endless major and minor conflicts of interest; of bewilderingly crisscrossing power blocs of varying and constantly changing size, potency, and capacity or will for union or disunion; of strategies and maneuvers perpetually in flux; of differently blended and constantly reformulated medleys of values and objectives.

In this frame of reference it requires but little knowledge of history and philosophy, and even less of the social and psychological sciences, to appreciate how formidable the task is to organize effectively any part of the life and labor of society along scientific lines. Indeed, few among natural and social scientists alike seem to be quite sure what "scientific organization" means in this context, and if sure, still fewer are able to command a serious following for long. Nevertheless, the belief persists, however vaguely or paradoxically expressed, that scientific organization somehow can and should become effective in the productive "substratum" called industry. More recently there has been added the demand that this must come about if the human species is to ride out its span on this planet in any estate above utter meanness of life. And the operational facts of the "scientific revolution in industry" seem generally to say that, unless science and engineering can answer the run of the basic technical questions which its advance throws ever more persistently to the fore, then it may not be well managed or further advanced at all.

Hence it comes about that by so much as science participates, actively or passively, in the problems of the industrial order, and by so far as policy within this industrial order has at the same time been formulated with an eye to the technologically most rational application of scientific methods and know-how, by so much also are scientific efforts more or less immediately channelized through social imposition of three guiding criteria. These have been mentioned above. To repeat, first, it must seek the useful—useful in terms of productive processes or of end products and services. Second, it must take the long view and thus promote conservation of resources to the maximum. And, finally, it must seek ways and means of maximizing output at lowest over-all net cost. Each of these objectives, furthermore, is to be kept in some sort of balanced relationship with the others, and all are to be visualized as achievable while still reconcilable with the maximum freedom of science, pure and applied. All are, in fact, to be regarded as but different aspects of a single common problem: i.e., the common problem of advancing science so as better to aid the scientific organization of production to effect high and rising output on a sustained basis.

How is this general problem to be approached in practice? We may begin with the more obviously technical problems.

FIRST PARTIAL APPROACH: ESTABLISHING A WORKABLE BALANCE BE-
TWEEN SCIENTIFIC RESEARCH AND AN INDUSTRIAL ORDER ORIENTED
UPON MASS OUTPUT

The technical process called "standardization"—or better (to use the German or French equivalent) "normalization"—begins at the foundations of both theory and practice. It follows each through all subsequent development and growth. On the side of theory formation, the start was taken in the dimly lit centuries of prehistory with the evolution of rules and practices of language formation, and the giving of precise meaning to words. On the industrial side the first steps were taken with the initial selecting, by trial and error, of recognizably clear-cut physical and chemical properties of materials—clays, metals, foodstuffs, drugs—and of the best processes for obtaining determinable results in the production of objects of use.

On such foundations, with the rise of the sciences, each of the several disciplines has developed (*a*) nomenclature for theory formation made up of appropriate systems of classification, words, signs, symbols, formulae, methods of representation, etc.; equivalent efforts on the experimental side have added to the older knowledge (*b*) precise and universally valid techniques of measurement of physical-chemical properties of materials and for aiding the analysis of events occurring in time and space. The one poses the problem of standard nomenclature; the other, of standard measurement. The one has gradually evolved a universal scientific lingua franca, understandable virtually in its entirety by scientists and engineers everywhere, regardless of language or other barriers. In fact, the main outlines of a single world scientific language have already been developed.

The other line of development, standard units and methods of measurement, has provided a solid and, for the most part, also universally valid foundation for comparison and interpretation of the results of scientific experimentation. The two are closely related; each is a continuing problem which accompanies every new advance in research, and every new success in applying research results in the production of goods and services.

Broad social concern over this two-phased problem of standardization was first widely evidenced in commerce with post-medieval efforts to establish national systems of standard coinage, weights, measures, calendars, and units of time and space reckoning. Formal recognition of the need for linking on a comprehensive basis technical supervision of such standards with continuing research has come in two major steps.

The first came with the establishment by seventeen coöperating nations of the International Bureau of Weights and Measures at Paris in 1879, followed shortly by the founding of great national standards-research institutions for the purpose of expanding and refining systems of measurement of interest to both scientific research and industrial practice. The lead was taken by Germany with the establishment of the Imperial Physical-Technical

Institute in 1887 (Physikalisch-Technische Reichsanstalt—now known as the Physikalisch-Technische Bundesanstalt, or Federal Physical-Technical Institute). Shortly afterwards Britain followed with a similar body, the National Physical Laboratory at Teddington, founded in 1899. In 1901 the United States established its National Bureau of Standards. Each of these huge laboratories is engaged in continuous research on the problems of units of reference and techniques of measurement. The entire superstructure of experimental science, and of the mathematical application to natural science, rests of necessity upon these foundations.

Upon the foundations provided by standards research, the second step has been taken, namely that of formulating standards for direct industrial and commercial application. This step has given rise to the various national standards bodies described in some detail in chapter iv. The idea here is to establish standards and draw specifications which define the best known ways of designing, processing, fabricating, testing, rating, and using each and every good produced by industry in terms of specified functions which each is to perform. It makes no difference what the use or objective be, nor whether one is dealing with producers' or consumers' goods and services. Once the use or uses can be more or less precisely defined, the standards and specifications can be drawn. Properly set up, such standards and specifications are subject to change as rapidly as basic scientific research advances on the one hand, and user needs and desires change on the other.

The second step is still only half begun. As indicated in chapter iv, scarcely more than pioneering work has been done in many fields of producers' goods; with respect to consumers' goods the surface has barely been scratched. The possible implications are very wide-ranging indeed. In production, they make possible the change-over to mass-output methods for virtually all types and varieties of commodities, however simple or complex in component materials or parts. In distribution, the combination of producing consumption goods along lines laid down by systems of standards and specifications—especially when these are flexibly drawn to carefully analyzed functions (need, uses, wants)—with vending in terms of inherent qualities, properties, and capacities of such goods would promote revolutionary changes in the methods of representing, promoting, selling, distributing, and using consumers' goods.

Throughout all levels, from the research leading to discovery of new materials or the invention of new processes and on to the uses made of end-product consumers' goods, research and standardization can be maintained in a mutually fruitful relationship. In science at the one end, and human wants at the other—however first expressed in art, design, or by indicia of consumer preference—represent the pathbreaking, innovating, fluidizing, significant product-differentiating forces. To these, standards properly drawn and managed are, at all significant points, complementary.

With each innovation, and given the values in use of individuals and society, standards would then represent the selecting, conserving, arranging, ordering of the *best*[3] known means and varieties. So ordered, science on the one hand appears as a source of variation, discovery, invention; of new ideas, materials, processes, products; of new results through improved control, measurement, checking, proof. On the other hand, standardization then appears as the source of guiding norms, units of reference, methods of procedure, standards of comparison, criteria of fidelity in performance of functional product-differentiation—in a phrase, of "controlled variation." They also define the ease, freedom, and generality with which the multifarious variables in production may be reduced to commensurable form, and hence to mathematical treatment in process control. In the new industrial revolution, accordingly, science and standards are the two sides of a common coin. Each may and should change as the other changes; advance in either is then capable of enormously facilitating advance in the other.

Thus, standardization may be organized to serve as a sort of two-way transmission belt for bringing the results of scientific research immediately into human use, and for conveying back to the laboratory, design, or mathematics departments the problems raised by changes in human needs and tastes. At the same time, it may be made to serve everywhere as a sort of simplifier in the process of "rethinking through" and applying the techniques required to transform production processes onto a more or less fully automatic basis (automation).

But in order adequately to play these roles, standardization itself requires some "rethinking." For one thing, it requires organization on a far more comprehensive basis than any major industrial country—with the possible exception of the Soviet Union—is yet prepared to give it. Certainly, in the United States the work of the American Standards Association has barely scratched the industrial surface; one may doubt if it is even successful in holding its own in the face of the extraordinary changes currently being introduced in methods and materials of production. Its current significance for both production and distribution of consumers' goods is far less still.

A second major need is for finding means for linking standardization work more closely to research laboratories and mathematically formulated decision-controls on the one hand, and to design and consumer-preference systems on the other. In actual industrial practice within the United States, only within the confines of a few great industrial corporations, such as the Bell Telephone System and the General Electric Company, has much significant work been done to keep standards continuously linked with basic scientific research. Even here, with few exceptions, little beyond trial and error has been used to keep standards and specifications in line with buyer—particularly ultimate consumer—preferences. Over the workaday industrial system, neglect in both directions is still the general rule.

SECOND PARTIAL APPROACH: THE INNER RATIONALIZATION OF THE "TECHNOLOGICAL SUBSTRATUM" OF SOCIETY AS A WHOLE

Suppose social policy, by whatever means arrived at, were through some appropriate procedures simply to present each separate industry in detail with what would, if emanating from a court of law, appear at large as a writ of mandamus to this effect:[4]

"So organize the resources at your disposal that while conserving the supply of each to the maximum consistent with long-range economical production, you will still produce the following mix

—whatever it might be—of goods and services at the lowest over-all cost. Make due allowance at all points, in your planning of plant and production for capacity, quickly and most economically to introduce new methods, processes, materials, and products. Never mind the human or social problems involved. Either take the personnel and institutional facts as you find them—wages, hours of work, work force, job seniorities, ownership rights, hierar-chies of command and subordination, individual or group in-terests and conflicts, political authorities, plant and population location—as given,[5] or else assume, if and when you find some of these in conflict with changes which you wish to introduce or raising problems which require solution before you may pro-ceed further, that you may remand such problems back to our policy-shaping bodies with the assurance that we will give them immediate and earnest attention. Otherwise you are to ignore them. In your bailiwick, thus defined, you are to have complete charge at all times."

This might seem to a casual observer a pretty high-handed pro-cedure. Actually it is essentially what any well-run industrial corporation does, in effect, say daily to its production depart-ment. It involves no more nor less than a reasonably clean-cut division of labor within top management circles. It is a division which is recognized by the production department to exist so that it may be freed of the complications of policy formation, the better to go about the business of fulfilling the contracts for de-livery which provides its operational *raison d'être*. The production department, to be sure, is usually represented at top policy levels, but once the decision has been made, with or without its approval, such is its subsequent status, and so it must proceed.

The human and institutional elements involved in the produc-tion process are not to be ignored. On the contrary, they are to be separated out for handling by competent and especially equipped representatives and authorities, and their problems are to be dealt with strictly on their own merits. It is also supposed that decisions made with respect to these personnel and policy matters may from time to time call for numerous, possibly drastic, changes in the otherwise determined routines of production. Vice versa, the opposite would equally be true.

Going back, then, to our supposition above—a supposition, to repeat, which merely applies a very ordinary and everywhere well-accepted procedure in the individual producing plants of industry to the larger organization of production in society as a whole—a further question can be raised. How, at the current level of scientific information and engineering know-how, might such an industrial system now be organized?

There are two aspects to a possible answer. The first has to do with an attitude of mind; the second, with certain rather large matters of fact. The attitude of mind is captured in the phrase used by automation experts: the willingness to undertake a "re-thinking through" of processes and methods, in their entirety and from beginning to end. We now meet this need in the macrocosm of industry as well as in the microcosm of the individual plant. Every leading fact brought to mind by the phrase, "the scientific revolution in industry," seems to enhance the need and desir-ability of undertaking such a mental effort.

When such is attempted and its findings are couched in terms of the widest and most thoroughgoing application of the methods and techniques made available by the new industrial revolution, then it seems that planning must proceed more or less along the lines outlined in the descriptive chapters above. The larger facts are, for the most part at least, fairly obvious once they have been stated. Certain of the implications, however, seem to be as little appreciated as they are revolutionary in impact.

To return briefly to a summary recapitulation of the facts pre-sented in the previous chapters. Beginning with the extractive industries, it seems clear that application of scientific criteria in the sense used in this study would mean the reorganization of mining along the lines pioneered by unitization of oil and gas extraction, namely, the exploitation of each deposit as a single unit of production. In agriculture, plans for production would differentiate land use in terms of basic meteorological and hy-drological cycles, soil types, and topographic features; would adjust crop patterns and fertilization to maintain old or establish new ecological and soil-chemicals balances; would consider farm-ing as merely one of several multiple-purpose uses of water re-sources to be coöperatively developed within river valley profiles as a whole; would specialize land in crops within and among major producing areas in terms of the product mix demanded by society at large; would plan a size and scale of farm operations which approaches, with full mechanization and within the limits set by the agronomic sciences, the conditions of optimal economy in production.

Raw materials would flow in the closest possible approximation to conditions of "continuous passage" from the mines and farms to processing plants and from thence to markets via traffic media that had differentiated and specialized in terms of the specific technical and economic advantages of each when operated at or near full capacity; each medium would be unified as a single operational network within its appropriate geographic frame of reference; each of the several public-service media (rail, road, water, air, pipeline) would be managed *as if* it were at all times a fully coördinated and complementary component of a single unified traffic network; terminal facilities for all lines of each medium, and as far as possible for the several media, would be used in common or at least integrated into a balanced system of interdependent termini, and the routing of (at least) bulk flows would be such as to approximate as closely as feasible, in the supply of interplant and interregional connections of all sorts, the equivalents of continuous-belt flows within the confines of an automated plant—storage, that is to say, at both ends, being minimal or nonexistent.

The materials-processing and manufacturing plants interspersed between the extractive industries and the distribution facilities serving ultimate consumers would then be receiving supplies at the beginning of, and sending processed goods away at the end of, production lines in the closest possible approximation to smooth and even flows; the internal processes of such plants would be as fully automated as production techniques permitted, and materials or components would move from step to successive step in continuous self-correcting flows, the never-quite-attainable ideal being production to rated capacity around the clock and 365 days in the year; in physical-chemical analysis of materials all components found in sufficient quantity to "emit a squeal" would be taken out simultaneously or in successive steps; all physical-chemical components or component parts would be standard and would be produced or further assembled in keeping with rigorously drawn systems of standards and specifications; and these standards and specifications would be drawn functionally to defined use, whether reference be had to industrial application or ultimate consumption.

Except where processing plants were built ahead of market demand, or where plants were relatively small because of raw materials or of markets—i.e., where the diseconomies of smaller than optimum scale were still less than shipping costs from more distant plants—the scale of plants would be optimum for the level of approximation to complete automation, and plants would be located primarily with a view to easy and low-cost integration with plants involved in successive or parallel steps in production, as in the roughly prototypal patterns of the Kanawha Valley and General Motors systems, or of German and Russian "industrial complexes."

Energy supplies would be provided plants and transportation facilities by integrated pipeline or grid power networks, each of which would be fully integrated for each geographic frame of reference; nucleation of plants would be paralleled by denser and higher-capacity lines; all pipeline (gas, oil, coal dust) and power networks would be multi-function, and would be integrated backwards to include the source of supply (oil, gas, or coal field, hydraulic or steam generating station), and forward to include distribution networks; supply in the form of pressures and B.T.U.'s per gallon or barrel, or of voltages, frequencies, or current types (direct, alternating) would be standard throughout the system, and would be fed into user equipment constructed and rated to operate most efficiently with such standard supplies; and all supply networks would stand available 24 hours a day and 365 days a year.

Manufacturing and transportation would then feed into distribution principally standardized and mass-produced materials, finished goods, and assembled products. These products would be fully differentiated according to meaningfully defined wants, needs, and uses. It is conceivable that the ratio of the volume of consumers' goods and (nonpersonal) services which might thus advantageously be subjected to standardization is close to 90 per cent or more of the total consumed. Technical rationalization of the distributive apparatus would extend all the way from the manufacturing plant down to the local retail store. The economies in distribution, with enhanced convenience to customers, would be very large—from reorganization which eliminated excessive duplication and overlapping of outlets, recombined outlets in different patterns (as in many of the new suburban shopping-centers) rerouted supply from shipping points to warehouses and from these to retail stores, unified home-delivery systems regionally, and introduced new methods of handling inventories and showrooms.

In the central system of communications for coördinating and integrating all these complicated movements and processes— itself made up of numerous media, wire and wireless alike—the several services would be rounded out as specialized, nationally (in some instances globally) integrated, and multi-purpose networks, which would stand by to give continuous and well-nigh automatic service 24 hours a day, 365 days a year.

Around the central core of the industrial system as it may thus be described when reshaped and expanded in keeping with current or possible future lines of development, and interlarded at a thousand and one points in its indefinitely numerous interstices, will, no doubt, continue to be a vast number of small and discrete handicraft, arts-and-crafts, special, personal-service, and other enterprises which will reflect few or none of the characteristics outlined above. It is even conceivable, with such changes as shorter working weeks and enhanced leisure time, that the range and volume of these types of activities might greatly increase. Such facts or changes, however, do not seem to require modification of the foregoing picture of the leading trends within the central core of the industrial system; rather, they underscore it.

In this picture of the industrial society in becoming, the *physical* unit of reckoning is typically, even by contemporary standards, very large, and the time span of planning is long. With respect to the over all service systems of scientific research and standards, each is visualized as coördinated and advanced through facilities organized on a national or international basis. The same is true of the great wire and wireless communications systems, and of the leading rail, air, highway, and water transportation facilities. Where these fall short of complete national, or continental, and in a few cases global, unification it is generally clear that the gaps are shortly to be spanned, and the integration completed. Though in some respects the regional pattern is more prominent, the same is generally true of gas and petroleum pipeline networks, and of power grid systems. Given sufficient density of use, the continental land masses, or major segments of such continents, become the units of reference in the actual physical construction of lines, and the management of operating properties.

In the physical planning of water resources, the minimum unit of planning is the river profile system. In agriculture, it is the combination of meteorological, hydrological, topographic, and soil-type patterns. In mining, it is the deposit. In all three cases, circumstances are multiplying the pressures to consider the minimum-sized unit for actual day-by-day management and operation as a mere operational unit in a larger frame of reference. Thus, in England, water resources planning has already sketched out the outlines of a national system as a whole. Other countries are facing a similar problem. The President's Committee on Water Resources visualized the need for water planning for major river systems in the whole of the United States. The planning of water development on such a basis is now multi-purpose. Since one of the purposes is typically hydraulically generated power, water planning is linked with the planning of regional, interregional, and continental grid systems. Since another purpose is water transportation, it is further linked with plans for interregional transportation systems. Since still another is frequently irrigation, as in the western parts of the United States and in many of the more arid underdeveloped areas of the world, water planning is further interlinked with plans for regional agricultural development.

Many further interlinkages are obvious; in virtually all cases they call for expansion of the unit of reference with respect to one or more functions in both physical construction of facilities, and in the routine management of operations. Thus in mining, while the exploitation unit under the rule of "unitization" is the deposit or field of oil, gas, coal, copper, etc., many considerations force still further expansion of the effective management operation. Oil and gas fed into public-service pipelines render each field of supply a coördinate part of a common energy pool. The same type of interlinkage is provided for coal mining, which supplies continuous-process coking and other types of manufactured-gas operations for service to regional grids, as in Germany and England. In iron metallurgy, similar considerations link coal mining, coking, gas supply, iron mining, limestone mining, and interconnecting water, rail, or continuous-belt transmission systems as components of a single unified complex of interdependent operations.

When one turns to chemical processing and manufacturing plants, the trends, while in many respects far more complex and difficult to isolate with confidence, are yet generally the same. At least for the so-called "heavy industries" the effective technological unit of reference, with respect to more and more aspects of production, is typically becoming the industry as a whole. By "industry" is meant not so much a group of plants producing one or more products, but rather plants linked in clear-cut patterns of successive or technically complementary process interdependencies—that is, operations linked together by continuous processing, joint supply, joint product, or by ease of extending operations on through to retail channels. Examples are: of continuous process, the aluminum, magnesium, oil, and gas industries; of joint supply, the heavy metallurgical industries; of joint product, the packing and chemical industries. Other examples of various combinations are forest-products industries, as with the Weyerhaeuser and Long-Bell corporations whose operations extend from logging and forest management on a permanent basis, through handling and milling, and on to finished lumber and to chemical and other by-products; textiles, particularly the synthetic yarn and fabrics division, as with part of the Du Pont and Imperial Chemicals operations; automobiles and airplanes, where assembly is linked backwards with networks of parts-supply plants and forwards with distribution and repair facilities.

In distribution, a few American firms, such as Sears, Roebuck, Montgomery Ward, A. & P., and Safeway, already extend, with

respect at least to part of their business, all the way from growing or processing to the ultimate consumer. In Britain and many
other places, the same result is effected through the combination
of the wholesale and retail coöperatives. At the retail end, such
developments as the supermarket, chain department-stores, and
unified metropolitan delivery systems—particularly when supplemented by pressures stemming from community planning
which includes shopping centers—are tending to make a common
management problem of large sections, and in a few cases of the
bulk, of distribution outlets serving the general public.

All of this seems fairly obvious. To be sure there are visible
many, and at certain points seemingly irreconcilable, crosscur-
rents. Yet, in the main, private as well as public enterprise is
slowly extending to interplant and interfirm routine processes the
same interest in technical rationalization which has long characterized internal reorganization schemes of the better-run plants
and firms. Many of the trade associations reflect this interest.
In England the iron and steel industry, immediately after the
war, proposed a plan for complete, long-range reorganization of
the industry as a whole. The various Working Party Reports and
Development Schemes proposed for postwar British industry
visualized, notably in the case of the virtually prostrate Lancashire cotton textile industry, reorganization of the entire industry.
For Germany the RKW (Rationalisierungs-Kuratorium der deutschen Wirtschaft) is attempting to promote simultaneously the
reorganization of all aspects of virtually all types of German economic activity. In six countries of Western Europe, the Coal and
Steel Community has brought together all private and public
bodies in an organization which has literally undertaken to plan
top policy and to integrate investment and plant operations for
the coal, iron, steel, and allied industries.

Most of the various postwar nationalization schemes of England, France, and Italy, as well as those of the countries in the
Soviet bloc, anticipate the complete technical overhauling of the
industries taken over: coal; electricity; rail, highway, and airways;
telecommunications. The same is found in similar governmentally
sponsored schemes in underdeveloped countries such as India,
Indonesia, Ghana, and Mexico. Many of these schemes, it is inter-

esting to note, have either been initiated or actively supported by private industry. The first national plan for over-all Indian national development was actually advanced by a private group of Indian industrialists (Bombay Plan). Many of the leading postwar European cartels have begun to talk in terms of technical improvement of industries which call for comprehensive government participation. Obvious examples are found in the various British agricultural marketing schemes. Many of the agricultural marketing schemes in the United States, particularly those in California, are moving, however slowly and irrationally, along somewhat similar lines. The unit of reference is the industry; the scope of policies runs from crop planning through marketing and pricing arrangements.

Many of these plans are highly reminiscent of ideas running through the so-called "Rationalization Movement" in Germany in the middle twenties. More clearly than at that time, however, and certainly more generally than before, these current plans for industrial reorganization are coming to focus on problems of size, proportioning, and process or product specialization of all plants in each industry; of location of these plants and their supplies with a view to elimination of crosshauling; of specialization of traffic movements by most economical transport or combination of transport media; of industry-wide pooling of research, technical know-how, and management information about products, markets, costs, and prices; of common promotion, development, and widening use of standards, grades, and specifications.

The possible economies from thoroughgoing reorganization of industrial processes along the lines of the slowly permeating scientific revolution in industry within the individual plant or enterprise have been shown in many instances to be extraordinary. They may well be several times as great when applied on an interplant and interfirm footing.

Can they, however, actually be realized? Or, if realized in whole or in part, may the possible gains be partially or more than partially offset by side effects in the form of the dulling of initiative, or of excessive bureaucratization, or of struggles for power of the sort long familiar among great monopolistic blocs, or of excessive political interference?

Limitations of space prevent consideration of these questions in this study. It may be in order, however, to suggest lines of approach which seem capable of very greatly simplifying analysis, particularly as it bears upon our central problem, that is, that of organization of the processes of industrial production in the period of the scientific revolution in industry which stretches out ahead. This may be done in two parts: first, as it relates to the technical-management problems of production routines, and second, as it relates to the policy-forming administration problems of industrial guidance.

THIRD PARTIAL APPROACH: A MAJOR DIVISION OF LABOR IN PROBLEMS OF THE TECHNOLOGICAL BASE

There is no need here further to comment on the complexity of the technical problems which the fusion of natural-science research and industrial technology has brought with it. Every deepening of this alliance along the lines of the scientific revolution in industry, and every extension of both industrial scope and time reference of the relevant planning, tends also to increase the number and variety of highly specialized experts required to carry through successive changes and to keep the processes of production in running order. All this expertise must of necessity share the bias of natural science for controlled experimentation, precise measurement, logical consistency, mathematical reasoning. But it must also share the social sciences' concern with efficiency in the use of limited resources, and with the satisfaction of human wants.

Between these two lines of emphasis it may be possible to drive a wedge, splitting the organization of scientific and engineering problems from the issues of policy formation. This split, theoretically, might run through the industrial system at large. As in the private industrial plant, or in the conduct of such organizations as the Port of New York Authority, or even of the national military establishment, free rein might be given scientific and engineering personnel in the technical implementation of policy—free rein without direct concern with the policy issues of competition versus monopoly, for instance, or of the loci of power among ownership groups.

Policy issues, substantive and procedural alike, might then be handled on their merits without, necessarily, direct reference to the complexities of implementation of a more purely technical character. There would be bound to be many overlapping cases, many examples of terra incognita.

That it is practicable so to proceed, without reference to type of social philosophy or formal structure of political organization, is evidenced in business and government alike, and in the old and the new industrial systems. The farther such a wedge is driven, and the more clearly the functional line is drawn, the more easily can the best use be made of the two contrasting (yet everywhere mutually complementary and interdependent) "biases" of the natural and social sciences.

The first bias tends to be at once more "positivistic" and freer of value judgments the farther expertise moves along the scale of interdependencies toward purely logical or laboratory problems. The second bias tends to be more "valuistic" the farther one moves toward the other end of the scale—that is, toward the shaping of the larger policies which express the values by which human beings live and act in society. On the one extreme are the mathematicians, physicists, chemists, astronomers. On the other are the political scientists, historians, sociologists, the artists, and the students of humanities.

Engineering and economics are situated in the middle. The one is primarily a natural-science derivative; the other is a social-science derivative. The one deals primarily with objectively determined relationships between things—matter, force, mass, time, energy, machinery, processes, products. The other deals with relationships between human beings, and with the conflicts and adjustments between their multifarious interests, wants, and values. They are joined in the problems of production at the point where instrumentation and policy formation meet most clearly and unambiguously.

This joining (as was indicated briefly in chap. i) suggests a fruitful division of labor. It is a division of labor which, if held to with a full understanding of its implications, could at once enhance the influence of natural science, not merely in the field of economics, but in all the social sciences and the humanities.

And conversely, it is a division of labor which might cause not only economics, but also the fine arts, to exercise a demonstrably fruitful influence on natural science.

But, also, confusion of the two might equally be well-nigh fatal for both. In the setting of the scientific revolution in industry, consider this problem on two levels—first, with respect primarily to what has been referred to in the section just preceding as the "industrial base" in the technological sense of the expression ("technological substratum"). The second level, that of policy formation and administration, will be taken up briefly in the section following.

On this first level the bulk of the problems appears, at least superficially, to be primarily of a strictly commensurable character. Continuous refinement of the essential data makes possible, and industrial practice accordingly then comes to require, more precision, closer control, more resort to objectively valid experimentation, more logical proof, more validations of empirical verification, more reliance on mathematical reasoning. Success all the way up and down the line from basic discovery to continuous, running, operational control depends upon the degree to which the relevant variables and constants, physical and logical alike, are precisely defined and come with properties accurately known in all the necessary detail.

The overriding economy directive in all this necessarily places the businessman or manager in the position of a coördinating officer, and makes the economist a party to the methods and emphasis. Their joint efficiency criteria direct attention throughout to such independent or related problems as lowest cost, best factor mix, optimum scale of operations, capacity utilization, quality control, costs and gains from increased automation and process integration, etc.

On the scientific side, independent developments in the field of economics itself have facilitated the ability of the economist to accept the new role of participation and guidance. The leading facts are matters of common knowledge. From the beginning of the theory of the firm—stemming back to the writings of J. B. Say and the theory of Newtonian general equilibrium, most notably from the restatement of basic propositions and theorems by

Walras, and with increasing emphasis as we come to the rise of the marginalist schools (Jevonian, Austrian, Lausanne, Swedish) and their successors in price theory—the search has been for logical and objectively valid classification, definitional precision, universal commensuration, manipulable parameters, or, in general, for sure footing for mathematical or quasi-mathematical reasoning. Progress here has moved, on the one hand, from theory held valid for a purely competitive economy to modifications and adaptations for conditions of partial or varying degrees of monopoly (oligopoly, oligopsony, bilateral monopoly, etc.), and, on the other, from such mathematically primitive "tools of analysis" as marginalist accounting, opportunity cost determination, net revenue concepts, and the like to such later and mathematically more sophisticated techniques as linear programming and input-output analysis.

While it is doubtless true, as the experts in these more recent technical developments very modestly state, that only a beginning has been made in theory and practice, yet it seems difficult to overestimate their importance for the run of the basic problems to be faced as the scientific revolution in industry spreads out before us. It would seem literally to be true that each and every step in production—from the first survey of ore deposits and farm lands on through the multitudinous and inextricably interwoven decisions involved in all processes leading up to final fabrication or assembly of consumers' goods—poses one or more, and in some cases whole series of, interlocking problems for new mathematical economics to solve. Furthermore, it seems probable that a large percentage, perhaps ultimately the bulk, of these major and minor problems can be classified by type, the appropriate data can be arranged, and the characteristic formulae can be written in such a way that the necessary information can be fed into computing machines. These machines will then serve as efficient surrogates for the human calculations in the routine conduct of the economic order.

When this happens, the new mathematical econometrics will become a part, or at least an aspect, of engineering. In the general area of production, all those economists not engaged in new mathematical formulations will then have ceded pride of place to electronic "brains." But it is also at this very point of maximum success in mathematical solution of economic problems that the most obvious need for division of labor and the contribution of economics as a social science are made evident. In the process just referred to, it is axiomatic that the bulk of the raw data of calculation seems to be firm, factual information about real (tons, yards, B.T.U.'s) or monetary things. Indeed, it is a prime requirement that at all times they do so appear, and are so regarded.[6]

But it is also obvious that in a sense of very great importance, both to production processes and to the society which lives by these means, that none of the data is ultimately firm, and rarely are dimensions purely factual. To be sure, tons are tons, and dollars are dollars. But also important in the commensuration process are the answers to such questions as: "How many tons are available?" "Tons of what material or quality?" "Prices in keeping with what policies?" For example, the number of tons available for various uses is in large part a result of social policies —of conservation, of demand for military and other purposes, of prices. And prices are a result of other social policies in the economy as a whole such as those which bear on the always variable components of the equation of exchange and on each specific price series such as wages, hours, working conditions, credit availability and interest rates, transportation rates, profit rules, tax structures, investment and consumption decisions, government regulations.

The engineer and the mathematical economist, in short, must for working purposes accept as given what the economist as a social scientist knows to be the products of policy formation. Policy, that is to say, may as freely change the parameters of calculation as calculation from these parameters may alter the raw material for policy determination. The more passive role in this relationship is that of the mathematician; the more active that of the policy maker.[7] There is, however, a point which is rarely very sharp, but also not necessarily entirely vague, where the two systems of emphasis divide. This point is more or less identical with what is referred to in the electronics literature, and specifically in the engineering work of such firms as A.T.&T., as "systems engineering." This is the point where new ideas, irrespective of their origins, and new or altered policies and objectives "must be carefully assessed and placed on a quantitative basis in order that yardsticks for system performance can be obtained. The dynamic properties of each element in the system must be formulated and the interaction of one part of the system on another must be evaluated." [8]

From one decision to another, this point may be said to trace a line below which system analysis and engineering take over, while above it policy rules. Even in the individual firm this "policy line" is obviously an ever-changing one, but it is, at any given moment, still recognizable for what it is. Where the issues deal with many plants, or even whole industries, it is bound to be badly blurred. It is, however, the line which separates what we have referred to in the text as the "technological substratum" from what might be termed the "bureaucratic or administrative overlay."

Below this policy line, the range of decisions involves for the most part relatively small transfers of resources. In the staid patois of conventional theory, these are mostly transfers "at the margin." The problem is to see what a little bit more or a little bit less of one or more factors will do to the over-all efficiency of production. While techniques such as linear programming drastically reformulate this problem in detail, yet it is, withal, still the same problem, and the techniques are designed to yield similar results.[9] Input-output analysis, like the Soviet system of "synthetic balances" to which it apparently bears some similarity,[10] attempts to trace similar effects of changes in quantity, or price, or any other commensurable item in any one plant, or firm, or entire industry upon the production schedules or costs of the other plants, or firms or industries, or—even—the economy as a whole.[11] In each case, the general structure of production and the economic system as a whole are taken for granted; the task is to be precise with respect to the continuously appearing problems of effecting over-all optimum conditions of production. The trick is to act *as if* the inevitably imprecise data of calculation were in fact precise.

Optimum economy, or optimum size or location of plants, or optimum efficiency of production—these terms can then have no other meaning than they possess when, e.g., linear or other forms of programming find that no further readjustment or re-combination of given factors (physical units, costs, prices) can, with the given social organization and the known technology, yield larger output or lower cost. For all this multifarious activity of accounting, measuring, and weighing merely amounts to the injunction to management to "be prudent." Prudence means "al-locating scarce resources so as to maximize the attainment of some predetermined objective," and "mathematical programming . . . is designed to be useful in making practical decisions in business and economic affairs." [12] In military terminology, from which source linear programming has drawn so much of its inspiration, these decisions are typically at the tactical level, occasionally at the logistical level, but practically never at the strategical level.

What has just been called the "policy line" is the line that sepa-rates, in military terminology, logistics from strategy. Logistics deals with the arrangement, transportation, and deployment of supplies and resources, including human beings, in the conduct of a military campaign. It involves what the military calls material and physical facilities on the one hand, and manpower on the other. But the manpower is viewed for these purposes as a datum; that is, there is available so much of this resource in terms of regiments, or battalions, or special-utility crews. For the purposes at hand, one regiment counts as much as any other; four men are twice as many as two. Their morale, their willingness to stand and fight, is part of another, different type of problem—the prob-lem of strategies.

In the industrial analogy, the "policy line" separates the pri-marily technological and managerial problems from the primarily social. It may be said summarily that, on the technological side of this line, policy makes four types of decisions which serve either to set the metes and bounds for the play of engineering and mathematical programming, or else to supplement both at the points where conceptually they lack further ability to move.

First, it is necessary for policy to speak before the otherwise squashy data of reference can be firmed up sufficiently to enter into the calculus of control. Policy decides, that is to say, what quantities of factors are to be available and sets limits on how they may be allocated; what classes of costs are to be incurred, and how they are to be borne; what the relative dimensions of costs and prices are to be, and by what means they are to be set. It transmutes thereby the indeterminate into the determinate.

Second, it lays upon all operations the injunction to be "prudent" in economic terms. It requires, in other words, that all reckoning be recast or retranslated into the variables of more or less means on the one hand, and of faithful adherence to the productive objectives—that is, the decision to make certain things and not certain other things—on the other.

Third, it transfers massive resources where the economic effects of transfer are not subject to commensuration or economy calculation, but where also the long-run gain from such actions is, nevertheless, quite obviously of great strategic importance to production. Good examples are the allocation of funds for research, particularly basic research; arbitrary decisions to restrict certain resources, such as native grass or forest lands, or gas and oil pools, to certain specified uses and to deny them to others; resources redistribution for the maintenance of all public activities; regional development programs; establishment of standard-of-living priorities such as minimal health, education, and nutritional requirements.

Finally, policy and policy alone is capable of isolating certain types of large wastages of resources. Examples are found in what might, with a polite nod to the semanticists of monopoly theory, be termed "bilateral futility." Illustrations range from the ridiculous to the sublime; competitive advertising which requires firm *A* to advertise to hold its business against firm *B*, and *B* to advertise to secure advance against *A* ("countervailing pilferage"); armaments for national security of country *X* which must then be duplicated or exceeded by country *Y* for maintaining its national security in turn. Policy only can determine when and by how much these expenditures of resources are wasteful.

Paradoxically, despite the obvious fact that there can be no concept of economy which does not imply a parallel concept of waste, yet the linear programming, input-output, and other experts—of probability theory, mathematical statistics, Boolian algebra, matrix algebra, set theory—seem to be as chary of it as the tongues of Oliver Cromwell's Roundheads were of condoning sin. Yet every effort to think through the implications of the new industrial revolution upon the inner technical rationalization of firms, industries, and the economy as a whole must of necessity raise the question of waste in an ever more insistent form. It becomes important to know what organizations, what activities, what resources are then not necessary, or not useful, or not able to play a functionally significant role in forwarding the processes of production. Numerous parasitisms may parade in the seeming clothes of economic or social respectability; somebody must be able to see when the Emperor is wearing no clothes at all. If, e.g., the linear programmer is able to isolate these losses only in detail, the social scientist must possess the capacity to recognize them at large.

The combination of these four types of essentially social, and hence social-science, decisions greatly enhances the role of these same disciplines in the detailed technological-economic processes of industry. Meanwhile, in thus giving over the body of the highly involved catallactics of what is now variously known as price theory, industrial organization, that is, "monopoly theory," and mathematical economics, and surrendering the bulk of econometrics, along with concern over such techniques as linear programming and input-output analysis, to the sophisticates of engineering and mathematics, economics will have surrendered problems which it has become cumulatively less well equipped to handle. At the same time, its absorption in these types of problems has increasingly compromised its ability to deal with the social-science foundations of policy formation, administration, and the human interests at stake in the solution sought. Increasingly, our technically best-equipped economists have spent their energies in exercises, such as those of Post-Pigovian Welfare Theory, where they manage to say practically nothing at all, and are able to come to conclusions of virtually no importance to empirical events.

Such absorption has compromised the ability of economists to see clearly in the "technological substratum" the four types of decisions outlined immediately above, and has largely nullified their capacity to deal with many of the purely economic problems now cropping up in the administrative sphere. With respect to the latter, political science and, to a lesser extent, sociology are being sucked into this vacuum. Despite the fact that economists tend to give economic desiderata relatively little attention, the scale and complexity of the economic problems encountered at the administrative level are as challenging as those found in the processes of production. Indeed, advance along the lines traced in the preceding chapters threatens to make of bureaucracy the foremost economic problem of the future—failure to deal adequately with it may counterbalance the enormous productive potential of which the newly emerging industrial order seems capable. It is thus of very great interest to economists as well as to other social scientists.

It is important, accordingly, and at the risk of going too far beyond the limits set for this study, to consider briefly the bearing of bureaucracy on the problems of scientific organization for achieving the new possibilities in the changing industrial order.

FOURTH PARTIAL APPROACH: NEW LINES OF COÖPERATION
IN PROBLEMS OF THE ADMINISTRATIVE COMMAND

It seems scarcely necessary to emphasize the importance of this problem. Indeed, while the future may look back at the present era as that of the scientific revolution in industry, it may instead think of it primarily as the period of a marked quickening in a sort of cumulative process of massive bureaucratization. Bureaucracy, however defined and understood, praised or vilified, is yet everywhere on the flow, and nowhere on the ebb. As all experts now recognize, it is not confined to government.

Long ago, Max Weber made it clear that the generalization of bureaucracy throughout modern society was engendered by the rise of capitalist enterprise. Bureaucratization has been, that is to say, consciously undertaken in large-scale organizations, private and government alike. The stimulus has been the need and the laudable desire to divide, specialize, train, regularize (i.e., subject to rational, impartial rules), and coördinate duties, functions, and responsibilities. Bureaucracy has of necessity expanded as large-scale organization has expanded—irrespective of whether one has reference to business, industry, government, or private and professional organizations, institutions, and associations.

Further, every effort to integrate and coördinate more closely such wide-ranging functions as are outlined in the foregoing chapters—particularly when these give rise to, or become a part of, planning on an industry-wide, regional, interregional, national, or international basis—multiplies the bureaucratic problems manyfold. The importance of bureaucratic problems in our society is increasing with the momentum of geometric progression. Giant industrial corporations in recent years have come to pay them a good deal of attention.[13] The reports of the Hoover Commissions[14] on federal organization are essentially studies of bureaucratic problems at the national level. There is a mass of literature to show that the Soviet economy is struggling, like the Laocoön Group in the coils of the serpents, with a complicated medley of strangulating forces of bureaucratic origin—forces which seem to grow in strength and ingenuity with every effort to cut through them.[15]

These two examples serve to highlight the central problem. Though the leading purpose of bureaucratic organization, as Weber pointed out, is efficiency, yet the hazard is always faced that it may encourage routine and unimaginative performance, endless red-tape, the habit of "passing the buck," the tendency to invent duplicating and functionless functions, expansion of staffs beyond functional needs, nepotism, and at its worst a cancer-like spread of petty corruption. If it lacks morale, it breeds what the Germans, with an eye on the great Mendicant and Jesuit inquisitional system of late medieval times, call "*Kadaver Gehorsam,*" or listless and corpselike obedience. At any given time, the economic stakes in such a massive institutional freezing of initiative are apt to be very large. The task forces of the second Hoover Commission estimated annual savings of over $7½ billion to the federal government "in the expenditures of the agencies of the executive branch without injury to the security or welfare of the country" if their recommendations were accepted.[16]

It would seem that such a scale of resource use and abuse would be of great interest to economists. Yet it has, with occasional exceptions to the contrary, almost entirely escaped their attention. In fact, the problems of bureaucracy are almost orphans to the social sciences as a whole. To be sure, a good deal of rather technical discussion is to be found in the business and management literature. Political science, particularly in the branch commonly called "public administration," pays it some attention. More recently the sociologists, after the model of their great mentor, Max Weber, have been scrutinizing some of its more sociological aspects—power drives, hierarchies of command, etc. A student might, however, pass through the entire curriculum of most American universities and never hear the subject of bureaucracy—except, perhaps, as occasion for wisecracks—mentioned at all.

In considering such problems, an initial task is to draw a line, never in practice able to be drawn with too sure a hand, between what constitutes at bottom mostly the routine performance of essential duties requiring special training, skills, and experience —such as law, accounting, statistics, personnel management—and those involving considerable discretion in the shaping of policies, substantive and procedural alike. To accomplish this in government was the purpose of the great civil-service systems set up in Europe and the United States after the middle of the nineteenth century. Most modern industry still ignores this initial problem almost entirely.

The problems of bureaucracy extend over both sides of this line. It is a mistake to suppose, as many experts seem to do, that only the personnel under civil service are involved. Take, however, this side first. Great though the amount of attention devoted to it in government circles may be, it is yet easy to demonstrate how simply and by what easy steps enormous diseconomies creep into operations through the apparent fault of no one. A single example out of hundreds that might be cited must suffice. While drawn from government practice, the illustration has a special significance for economists.

The Hoover Commission's Task Force, noting the failure of the Armed Services to coördinate food purchases, made a special study of the shipments of canned tomatoes by the several Services[17] and revealed such situations as the Army shipping from California to New York 807,000 pounds of canned tomatoes while the Navy shipped 775,000 pounds from the East Coast to California, and the Army shipping 1,120,000 pounds of canned tomatoes into Texas from five Midwestern states at the same time that the Navy was shipping 933,000 pounds out of Texas to its East Coast activities.

The Task Force drew the conclusion that the crosshauling was not the result of inefficient management within the services but rather was due to the fact that requirements and inventory-control operations were independently performed by each without knowledge of the over-all Department of Defense stock positions. The latter part was doubtless correct, but the Commission's own data refute the first. It would take but little knowledge of agriculture to show that the shipment from long distances of canned tomatoes into heavy tomato-growing areas indicated poor warehouse location as well as poor shipping arrangements. Some good linear programming or other appropriate econometric analysis of the shipping and warehousing by each of the Services would have revealed the desirability of general reorganization, not only among the several Services, but also for each alone.

In private industry, however—and here the importance for economics is of overriding significance—the equivalent of what the Task Force discovered in the tomato incident is general throughout the system as a whole. From thousands of producing or warehousing points, small-lot shipments of identical or near-identical products are made in all directions. The economies that can be effected by the elimination of duplications of warehouses and of crosshauling have been demonstrated in detail within their own systems by such corporations as Western Electric, General Electric, and General Motors. These are but a drop in the bucket compared to what might be effected by technical rationalization on an industry-wide basis. While a rich country like the United States may, so to speak, be able to afford preventable wastage of this order, poor and underdeveloped countries cannot. But in any case, it represents a spreading curtailment of efficiency and a mounting drain on resources.

Leaving aside for the moment all questions of competition and monopoly—which are resolvable, if at all, on the basis of their effects on prices and production, and hence require the same sort of independent reëxamination as does technological reorganization itself—the point of the tomato illustration in this connection is the need for presenting routine administrative staffs with scientifically acceptable criteria of adequate performance. These criteria cannot be supplied without careful preëxamination of the functions to be performed. When this effort is undertaken a number of quite surprising facts are apt to come to light.

For example, a large part of the more repetitive aspects of routine administrative jobs could be mechanized or otherwise cut back by the application of communications engineering. A further curtailment might follow from asking whether or not part, or on occasion even all, of certain types of record keeping were required. During the Second World War a West Coast shipyard had a so-called "gold form," gold being the color of the last of eleven copies of differently colored paper to be filled out in requisitioning materials from the stock room. Upon inspection of the "gold form," not only it but five or six other copies proved to be going nowhere at all. A wisecrack had it that if all the "paper work" involving a 20,000-ton troopship were loaded on when it was launched, the ship would sink.

The details are endless; in one manifestation or another, the stories are known to all.[18] It may be doubtful whether the case for metering services for gas, electricity, and water is strong enough, as against rational flat-rate systems, to justify the enormous labor involved in producing, installing, and reading meters, and in billing and maintaining the additional records. (Certainly monthly billing in these and perhaps many other cases might be supplanted by quarterly or even semiannual billing.)

Again, if, as some believe, the economic justification for the bulk of installment selling is lacking, it also imposes on the economy swiftly multiplying swarms of personnel in credit agencies, retail credit offices, credit life-insurance companies, collection and "skip-tracing" agencies, debt-consolidation services, legal offices, etc., who must eat and be housed and clothed like everyone else. In the economy as a whole these become the modern equivalents of the gentlemen and ladies in waiting, the butlers and footmen, the doormen and countless other flunkies, who attended the whims of the old wastrel nobility, but who also continually threatened to eat them out of house and home.

From various data it may be estimated that upwards of two-thirds or more of the tonnage load of the Post Office is in the form of direct-mail and other advertising which is never read, and is promptly chucked into wastebaskets. Yet the social mills for grinding out this puffery fill offices, use typewriters and other office equipment, employ personnel, and load transportation facilities and the backs of mailmen.

These are bureaucratic phenomena. They are part and parcel of the administration of the economic system as a going affair. When uncovered in government by the watchful eye of an investigating committee, they are condemned as evidences of an inefficient civil service, or irresponsible policy making, or careless administration, or as boondoggling. Every step in the tightening up of the organization and internal scientific rationalization of industrial processes, of the sort heralded by the scientific revolution in industry, will throw these excesses and wastages into sharper relief. The economic stakes amount to this, that we may well be witnessing the building-in of identifiable inefficiencies on a scale and with a speed which very nearly match the fantastic economies which the newer techniques of production seem eventually able to deliver.

But to come to grips with such problems, administrators and economists must acquire both the capacity to see and the courage to tackle them. When they do, it now seems inescapable that they will have to reëxamine not only the formal structures of economic organization, but also the general range of incentives, motives, interests, values, and power blocs which animate and guide the people who make the strategic decisions. If the old competitive theories can no longer serve them well, the newer monopoly theories will prove but little better. History has already moved beyond.

What were previously problems about the market behavior of an indefinitely large number of small concerns, and then of smaller groups of more powerful combinations, are now being transmuted into quite different types of problems, and for them new frames of reference and new methods of description, new propositions, new theories, and new types of analysis must be found. In all the national-development planning schemes abroad —whether in developed or underdeveloped areas, whether communist, socialist, fascist, or capitalist—as the locus of policy formation and execution is moved from discrete, separate, independent business units over to an economic region, or to an industry or group of related industries taken as a whole, or over to national or international economic blocs, or authorities, or business combinations, then *so also must former market phenomena now be looked upon as bureaucratic problems.*

An analogy may be useful. The rise of the great national states enveloped regions which from time immemorial had been swept repeatedly by invading migrations, or had been split into small feudatories or warring principalities, or had experienced conflicts between constantly changing familial, clan, tribal, or other groupings. The national states domesticated these interests and conflicts; drastically altered the rules of the game; rechanneled energies; aroused new interests; stressed new motives or gave new expressions to old ones. And then, in turn, the international conflicts and looser forms of alliance and mutual coöperation began to undergo a like *process of domestication;* first tentatively with the evolution of theories of international law from the time of Grotius and Pufendorf on, and subsequently with a growing variety of international conventions leading finally to the great initial experiments in world government of the League of Nations and the United Nations.

Something like this is happening to much of the so-called "market phenomena" with which business and economics deal. Open conflicts, market competition, and loose informal alliances and interfirm compacts are gradually being transmuted. Interfirm problems are being domesticated as intrafirm problems—in some places rapidly, in others more slowly. Sometimes under the stimulus of collusive and other types of power pressures; sometimes in keeping with the exigent facts of the new industrial revolution. The structures of both compact and looser forms of organization are widening; the climate of opinion is undergoing a change in favor of administrative controls; the mental attitudes and the acceptable rationales of the policy makers are being subtly transformed in the direction of stability, order, security; and, with these changes, external (to the firm) "market phenomena," in short, are becoming internal—interfirm, or interassociation—bureaucratic problems.

Thus domesticated, the new problems are essentially the same at the lower bureaucratic levels—the routine policy-implementing or "civil-service" levels—whether the larger units of references be private industrial corporations such as Bell Telephone, General Motors, Imperial Chemicals, or Montecatini; or nationalized industries like the European railway systems, the British Coal Board, and the TVA; or mixed public and private general coordinating bodies like the European Coal and Steel Community; or state industrial establishments like the Soviet trusts. It may, of course, well be the case that eventually large, or even on some occasions increasing, percentages of the national economy will be left in private hands. It may be that a fairly high degree of decentralization will be effected for many autonomous groups. But even here, as in the patterns of organization for the General Motors and A.T.&T. systems,[19] the meaning of autonomy is more apt to be a product of regulated *internal* policy decisions, and less the product of *de facto* independence modified by external governmental-umpire decisions. In any case, the run of problems faced by personnel at and below the "civil service" level will be essentially the same.

These are essentially problems of training; of schedules of pay and rates of advancement; of work councils and grievance committees; of individual and group commercial and noncommercial incentives; of conflicts and harmonies between internal and external social life and organization. The problems range from the types dealt with in the pioneering studies of Roethlisberger and Dickson at the Western Electric plant during the late 1920's[20] to those taken up more recently in *group dynamics;*[21] from issues of psychiatric personality adjustment to the right through representation to participate in top policy decisions (e.g., "co-determination"); from the sense of "anomie" of which Durkheim, Mayo, and others have written with such telling effect, to the life values which lead to preference for more leisure time over increase in income.

In broad summary, *below the beginning of the "civil-service line"* there is a great deal that engineering and mathematical programming may be able to do by way of simplifying many manual and routine labors such as typing, filing, recording, and handling the mechanics of communication. They will be of little or no use in identifying the existence of wastages of resources involved in what has been referred to above as the process of "domesticating" market relations to become matters of internal policy decisions. But once the wastages are identified, it is quite conceivable that those methods may be of very great assistance in providing at least the mechanical criteria for the efficient discharge of routine duties.

Even here, however, the major problems of maintaining an effective *esprit*—which may reinforce, not counteract, the productive effectiveness of the industrial order in becoming—are rapidly swelling to proportions of central and overshadowing importance. Along with the issues of policy formation above the "civil-service line" they share the characteristic of being, in the words of George Santayana, problems of "dominations and powers." [22] Thus the meaning as well as the possibility of life is caught up with the objectives being pursued by the larger units of administration and of management, and is bound more closely with the purposes which desire so to plan that something worth while may come out of the more exacting disciplines when these are enmeshed with the problems of closer technical integration and coördination permeating the productive system as a whole.

"Life and spirit," Santayana writes, "are not the cause of order in the world but its result." In human affairs no such degree of order since the theocratic corporativism of the medieval world has appeared to encompass the lives and knit together the common fate of so many human beings as that forecast by the dominant trends in the scientific revolution in industry. But the contrasts between the two great systems of order could not be more striking. This new order is as dynamic as the medieval was static;

as material as that was spiritual; as freedom-oriented as that was authority-minded; as life-affirming and worldly as that was death-asserting, pessimistic, and otherworldly. Every one of these basic differences provides a multiplier of unknown dimensions to the scale and complexity of the emerging social order. The rewards of success are material plenty, new freedoms, new creative powers, more leisure, unparalleled cultural opportunities; but among the dangers are those caricatured by Aldous Huxley in *Brave New World* and George Orwell in *1984*—not to mention the intellectual underworld of technocracy and science fiction.

The conditions for the "life and spirit" of the future course of events dealt with in this study, in short, are apt also to force a "rethinking through" in all of the social sciences. This reëxamination may well be as fundamental to the social disciplines as is that which, under stimulus of closely allied influences, is already driving natural science and engineering to reëxamine the entire physical structure of production. In both the social and the natural sciences, there is call for a *tour de force* no less momentous than that which overthrew the medieval system. But in neither can this new effort bear much fruit alone. The degree of their mutual interdependence has already become far too great for that. Hence the condition for the success of each is a large measure of success in the other. They both will succeed in the scientific effort to shape the material conditions for human existence or, along with the human life which now depends almost wholly upon them, go down together.

Such seems to be the complex character of the larger problems of the scientific organization of production that appear already to have come tumbling upon us. It is no longer an issue of "plan or no plan" that now confronts the great industrial nations. The facts of technological development have moved, along with a radical change in human aspirations, as though in some grand historical conspiracy to force the human hand—not in a few isolated spots, but everywhere. It is now a problem of plan or cumulative breakdown; plan on a wider basis, or a breakdown that will bring disaster to all.

NOTES

CHAPTER I. INTRODUCTION: CHARACTERISTICS OF THE SCIENTIFIC
REVOLUTION IN INDUSTRY
(Pp. 3-37)

[1] The President's Materials Policy Commission (Paley Commission), *Resources for Freedom*, (5 vols.; Washington, June, 1952).

[2] See, e.g., the *Proceedings* of the United Nations Scientific Conference on the Conservation and Utilization of Resources (UNSCCUR), Department of Economic Affairs, 1950, E/Conf. 7/7 (8 vols.; Lake Success, 1950-53).

[3] *The Theory of Business Enterprise* (New York, 1904), p. 16.

[4] California Institute of Technology, *Resources of the World: A Speculative Projection*, as reported in *Business Week*, May 26, 1956, p. 114.

[5] *Lectures on the Industrial Revolution in England* (London, 1884).

[6] See chapter iii below; also, Dickson Reck, ed., *National Standards in a Modern Economy* (New York: Harper, 1956).

[7] E. H. MacNiece, *Industrial Specification* (New York: Wiley, 1953), p. 1.

[8] Council for Technological Advancement, *Automation and Job Trends*, Pamphlet No. 3 of a series on "Technology and Employment" (Chicago, October, 1955), pp. 4-6.

[9] Advertisement of the United States Steel Corporation in *Business Week*, October 16, 1954, p. 87.

[10] Francis Bello, "The Information Theory," in the Editors of *Fortune, The Mighty Force of Research* (New York: McGraw-Hill, 1956), p. 270 ff.

[11] Norbert Wiener, *The Human Use of Human Beings: Cybernetics and Society* (2d. ed., rev.; Garden City, New York: Doubleday, 1954).

[12] *Business Week*, May 26, 1956, p. 114.

[13] Some scientists believe that direct conversion of sunlight to electricity may become a cheaper source of energy than fission or even fusion. Some hope has been held out that the same might be true of cosmic rays.

[14] Stuart Chase, "New Energy for a New Age," *Saturday Review*, January 22, 1955, p. 14. These data check closely with figures compiled by Palmer C. Putnam in his monumental *Energy in the Future* (New York: Van Nostrand, 1953), especially pp. 214-215.

[15] Proceedings of the International Conference on the Peaceful Uses of Atomic Energy held in Geneva 8 August-20 August 1955 (Atoms for Peace). See especially Vol. I, "The World's Requirements for Energy: The Role of Nuclear Energy," A/Conf. 8/3, and Vol. VI, "Geology of Uranium and Thorium," A/Conf. 8/6 (New York: United Nations, 1956).

[16] John Diebold, *Automation: The Advent of the Automatic Factory* (New York: Van Nostrand, 1952), pp. 45-46.

[17] Some have seen the next "short step to be the automatic or 'push button' office—a fast and entirely integrated system into one end of which one could feed raw business data and receive from the other, without human intervention, such finished documents as invoices, paychecks, statements and reports, all in usable form." This may be too optimistic, but banking is already moving rapidly in this direction. John S. Coleman, President, Burroughs Corporation, "Electronics and Banking," an address before the Illinois Bankers Association Convention, Chicago; June 18, 1954. [Mimeographed.]

[18] *The Cambridge Modern History* (New York: Macmillan, 1910; Cambridge, England: Cambridge University Press, 1934), XII, 766.

[19] As, e.g., in Lionel Charles Robbins, *An Essay on the Nature and Significance of Economic Science* (London: Macmillan, 1932); and Milton Friedman, *Essays in Positive Economics* (Chicago: University of Chicago Press, 1953). For a much more temperate statement, see Oscar Lange, "The Scope and Method of Economics," *Review of Economic Studies 1945-46*, Vol. XIII (1), No. 33, pp. 19-32. See also, J. R. Weinberg, *An Examination of Logical Positivism* (London: Routledge and Kegan Paul, 1950).

[20] See in particular, Rudolf Carnap, *Logical Foundations of Probability* (Chicago: University of Chicago Press, 1950), pp. 3 ff.

[21] Mr. Leslie C. Edie, engineer for the Port of New York Authority, Tunnels and Bridges Department, and an authority on operations research and systems engineering, points out that C. West Churchman, in *The Theory of Experimental Inference* (New York: Macmillan, 1948) has put his finger on "one of the basic dilemmas of science from a philosophical standpoint; namely, that the taking of data presupposes the existence of some data. Whatever you start with may be in error and all the logic in the world would help little. Moreover, it has been shown that useful systems can be logically induced from contradictory hypotheses; therefore, continual review in the light of historical change is necessary to establish which set of hypotheses produce the most useful body of theory at any given time . . . even in physics, chemistry and mathematics, basic data and fundamental relations can and do of course change." Letter to the author, August 13, 1956. Very well, the dilemma described for science in general is shared by the social sciences, but in addition thereto human nature, as a self-motivating force, changes, and human society, as the product of cumulative qualitative as well as quantitative changes, changes even more. On top of that, the fact that human activity, in detail and at large, is constantly and differently purpose-oriented introduces new and indefinitely complex variables in social-science problems for which there are no truly meaningful parallels in the natural sciences.

[22] John Maurice Clark, *Studies in the Economics of Overhead Costs* (Chicago: University of Chicago Press, 1923).

[23] Herbert Joseph Davenport, *The Economics of Enterprise* (New York: Macmillan, 1935), pp. 135-136.

[24] Alfred North Whitehead, *Essays in Science and Philosophy* (New York: Philosophical Library, 1948), p. 69.

[25] In the writing of this volume, it has been the author's intention to follow it up with a study of the growth of bureaucracy, considered as the "problem of flexible organization," as it might be designed to manage the type of emerging industrial order outlined here, and, finally, to conclude with a second follow-up study of the manner of formulating and the content of the types of policy which might (1) make most rational use of the new industrial apparatus, while (2) surmounting the dangers of bureaucratic arteriosclerosis, and (3) yet be most consistent with both democratic institutions and the values of individual personality.

[26] Fritz Machlup, *The Political Economy of Monopoly* (Baltimore: Johns Hopkins University Press, 1952), pp. 239-240.

[27] William John Fellner, *Competition Among the Few* (New York: Knopf, 1949).

[28] See, e.g., M. W. Reder, "A Reconsideration of the Marginal Productivity Theory," in Richard V. Clemence, ed., *Readings in Economic Analysis* (Cambridge, Mass.: Addison-Wesley Press, 1950), II, 251-259.

[29] For a rapid survey see, British Information Services, *Western Co-operation, A reference Handbook*, I.D. 1184 (revised, November, 1955; London: H.M.S.O.).

[30] Kenneth Bradley, *Britain's Purpose in Africa*, Central Office of Information pamphlet (London: H.M.S.O., 1955), pp. 12-13.

[81] For an example, see Yale Brozen, "Entrepreneurship and Technological Change," in Harold Francis Williamson and John A. Buttrick, eds., *Economic Development: Principles and Patterns* (New York: Prentice-Hall, 1954), pp. 196 ff.

[82] *Ibid.*, pp. 236-241.

CHAPTER II. THE HANDICAP RACE WITH NATURE
(Pp. 38-71)

[1] As defined by S. V. Ciriacy-Wantrup, *Resource Conservation: Economics and Policies* (Berkeley and Los Angeles: University of California Press, 1952).

[2] Most notably the report by the President's Materials Policy Commission (Paley Commission), *Resources for Freedom*, (5 vols.; Washington, June, 1952), and the *Proceedings* of the United Nations Scientific Conference on the Conservation and Utilization of Resources (UNSCCUR), Department of Economic Affairs, E/Conf. 7/7 (8 vols.; Lake Success, 1950-53); hereafter cited as, respectively, *Resources for Freedom* and *Proceedings*, UNSSUR. See also the comprehensive study by Erich W. Zimmermann, *World Resources and Industries* (rev. ed.; New York: Harper, 1951), and the more recent *Resources of the World: A Speculative Projection* (limited circulation; Pasadena: California Institute of Technology, 1956).

[3] *Resources for Freedom*, I, *Foundations for Growth and Security*, p. 2.

[4] *Ibid.*, I, 17.

[5] *Proceedings*, UNSCCUR.

[6] Sumner H. Slichter believed that American production would double between 1950 and 1980, while Harold G. Moulton thinks that the American standard of living in 2050 may be "eight times as high as in 1950." Cited in Eugene Ayres and Charles A. Scarlott, *Energy Sources—The Wealth of the World* (New York: McGraw-Hill, 1952), p. 158.

[7] *Resources of the World*, pp. 5-7.

[8] *World Population*, p. 42, quoted in *Historical Outline of World Population Growth*, U.N. Economic and Social Council, Population Commission, E/CN. 9/89 (New York, October 23, 1951), table 2, p. 19. [Mimeographed.]

[9] W. F. Willcox, *Studies in American Demography* (Ithaca, N.Y., 1940), pp. 37-45. Quoted in *Historical Outline of World Population Growth*, table 2, p. 19. According to Spengler, "the annual rate of world population growth continues to rise, moving from 0.29 per cent in 1650-1750, through 0.63 in 1850-1900, to 0.9 in 1920-1950." Joseph J. Spengler, "Demographic Patterns," in Harold F. Williamson and John A. Buttrick, eds., *Economic Development, Principles and Patterns*, (New York: Prentice-Hall, 1954), p. 92.

[10] *Resources for Freedom*, I, 17.

[11] *Ibid.*, I, 155.

[12] *Planes* (Official Publication of the Aircraft Industries Association of America), Vol. 10, No. 3 (March, 1954), p. 3.

[13] See data cited by President Eisenhower in an address to the American Society of Newspaper Editors, New York *Times*, April 17, 1953.

[14] I am unable to support this estimate by citation of evidence; yet though the variables involved are numerous and extremely difficult to compute, even in detail, I am satisfied on the basis of personal conversations with military experts that the figures cited are on the conservative side.

[15] The "problem" of programming operations for resource planning in the event of war is "to extract that last unit of war material from the economy without seriously impairing the capacity of the economic machine to produce either armament or those goods and services needed to maintain the health and morale of the people." George A Steiner, "Resource Allocation in Mobilization," in

Current Economic Comment (Urbana: University of Illinois, August, 1954), p. 3.

[16] *Resources for Freedom*, I, 4-5.

[17] At the 126th national meeting of the American Chemical Society, Dr. Clifford C. Furnas estimated that if world population increases threefold, and the present per capita increase in energy output continues, then by the year 2050 the world need for annual energy output will have increased by "between ten and 100 times the yearly demand." New York *Times*, September 15, 1954.

[18] *Resources for Freedom*, I, 5.

[19] *Ibid.*, I, 156.

[20] Derived from Standard Oil Company of New Jersey, *Facts about Oil Imports* (April 15, 1953), table 6, p. 40. [Brochure.]

[21] "Petroleum output (plus imports) increased from 382 trillion B.T.U. in 1900 to 12,462 trillion in 1948" and the "increase in the output of natural gas was from an estimated 254 trillion B.T.U. in 1900 to 5543 trillion in 1948." Zimmermann, *World Resources and Industries*, p. 483.

[22] Ayres and Scarlott, *Energy Sources*, p. 279.

[23] *Proceedings*, UNSCCUR, II, *Mineral Resources*, p. 4.

[24] To illustrate, the item on "potential" iron ore allows only 15 billion tons for the U.S.S.R., "whereas official Russian reports now claim 250 billion." All data are compiled from estimates made at different times, and upon the basis of data of greatly varying quality. Again, the figures included in the above make no allowances for losses in mining of coal.

[25] *Resources for Freedom*, I, 5.

[26] *Ibid.*

[27] *Ibid.*

[28] *Resource Conservation*, p. 3.

[29] *Ibid.*

[30] Hugh Hammond Bennett, *Soil Conservation* (New York: McGraw-Hill, 1939), p. 9.

[31] *A Water Policy for the American People*, Report of the President's Water Resources Policy Commission (Washington, 1950), I, 124.

[32] Bennett, *Soil Conservation*, p. 9.

[33] *Ibid.*, p. 10.

[34] *A Water Policy for the American People*, I, 124.

[35] H. S. Person, *Little Waters: A Study of Headwater Streams and Other Little Waters, Their Use and Relations to the Land*, Soil Conservation Service, Resettlement Administration and Rural Electrification Administration (Washington, November, 1935), p. 30.

[36] Cited in G. V. Jacks and R. O. Whyte, *Vanishing Lands: A World Survey of Soil Erosion* (New York: Doubleday, Doran, 1939), p. 35.

[37] *Ibid.*

[38] *Ibid.*, p. 5.

[39] *Last Chance in Africa* (New York: Harcourt, Brace, 1950).

[40] R. M. Gorrie in *Herbage Reviews*, V (1937), cited in Jacks and Whyte, *Vanishing Lands*, pp. 77-78.

[41] Bennett, *Soil Conservation*, p. 914.

[42] United Nations Food and Agriculture Organization, *Soil Conservation: An International Study*, FAO Agricultural Studies, No. 4 (Washington, 1948), p. 43.

[43] *Ibid.*, pp. 47-49, for details on Venezuela, Brazil, and the Andean region.

[44] *Proceedings*, UNSCCUR, VI, *Land Resources*, p. 17.

[45] See, e.g., Lesley Byrd Simpson, *Many Mexicos* (New York: Putnam, 1941).

[46] Cited in Morris L. Cooke, *Groundwork for Action*, No. 3 of the "Bold New Program" series of the Public Affairs Institute (Washington: Public Affairs Institute, 1950), p. 28.

[47] Jacks and Whyte, *Vanishing Lands*, p. 33.

[48] See, e.g., William T. Hornaday, *Our Vanishing Wild Life: Its Extermination and Preservation* (New York: Scribner, 1913).

[49] *Resources for Freedom*, I, 8.

[50] In the late 1930's the National Resources Planning Board estimated that "a billion cubic feet of natural gas is being blown into the air daily." This is equal to 143,000 barrels of oil daily, or more than one-tenth of total American daily oil production in 1952 (1,260,000 barrels). It is also "the equivalent to forty thousand tons of coal" or "gas enough to supply the United Kingdom twice over. It is forty times as much gas as all the Scandinavian countries use together. It is almost enough to supply regularly every householder in the United States now consuming either natural or manufactured gas." Cited in Richard Lieber, *America's Natural Wealth* (New York: Harper, 1942), p. 44.

[51] Letter to author from E. P. Carman, Acting Chief, Branch of Bituminous Coal Research, United States Department of the Interior, Bureau of Mines, August 28, 1956.

[52] George S. Rice, "Coal—Pillar Drawing Methods," AIME *Abstracts*, Vol. 66, 1921, cited by Mr. Carman. See also Zimmermann, *World Resources and Industries*, pp. 470 ff.

[53] Harry E. Flynn and Floyd E. Perkins, *Conservation of the Nation's Resources* (New York: Macmillan, 1941), p. 209. See also *Resources for Freedom*, IV, *The Promise of Technology*, p. 5.

[54] Glen Lawhon Parker, *The Coal Industry: A Study in Social Control* (Washington: American Council on Public Affairs, 1940), p. 2.

[55] Ayres and Scarlott, *Energy Sources*, pp. 54-55. For Utah the 1907 federal survey estimate was 196 billion tons; the 1936 estimate was 93 billion; the 1945 estimate, by the National Coal Association, showed 46 billion; the "opinion of coal operators" showed 2 billion. *Ibid.*, p. 55.

[56] *Ibid.* This may be compared to a British estimate which places England's total underground coal at something like 150 billion tons, of which it is expected that only 48 billion tons—enough to last at the current rate of usage about 750 years—is economically recoverable. *Ibid.*, pp. 51-52.

[57] *Ibid.*, p. 56.

[58] Parker, *The Coal Industry*, pp. 2-3.

[59] *Ibid.*, p. 4.

[60] *Ibid.*

[61] Robert A. Brady, *Crisis in Britain* (Berkeley and Los Angeles: University of California Press, 1950), pp. 77 ff.

[62] Kenneth Leith and Donald M. Liddell, *The Mineral Reserves of the United States and its Capacity for Production*, prepared for the Planning Committee for Mineral Policy (Washington: National Resources Committee, March, 1936), pp. 98-99.

[63] As cited in *Home Affairs Survey*, July 13, 1954, p. 29.

[64] *Resources for Freedom*, I, 14.

[65] *Ibid.*, I, pp. 1, 5, 13.

[66] *Business Week*, May 26, 1956, pp. 112-118, reporting on a study made by the California Institute of Technology.

[67] A dramatic example is offered by the case of oil shale, where the handicaps in production of oil from shale do not end with the mere problem of crushing the rock and refining the oil. In many cases the overlay is very heavy and underground mining methods must be used. Many seams are relatively thin and undulating. Refining requires enormous quantities of water, while most of the deposits (in America at least) are found in arid regions. Disposal of the residual ash is itself an enormous problem. This ash "is material without fertility. It contains salts

that can be leached out by rain waters of flash floods. It contains 'fines' that could be carried by erosion into river beds. And it is not a matter of dumping it in some unused valley. If all of the rich oil shales of Colorado were retorted, enough ash would be left to cover the entire state of Colorado to a depth of ten feet. Much of the ash could be dumped into the huge canyons of the oil-shale regions, and it would seem that the first billion tons might not be impossible to manage. The disposal of 500 billion tons will require extraordinary ingenuity." Ayres and Scarlott, *Energy Sources,* p. 70.

⁶⁸ Professor A. V. Hill, as cited in *Home Affairs Survey,* September 16, 1952, p. 19.

⁶⁹ Cited in *Business Week,* May 26, 1956, p. 114.

⁷⁰ Particularly in chap. 50, on "Resource Adequacy."

⁷¹ Ayres and Scarlott, *Energy Sources,* p. 279.

⁷² *Resources for Freedom,* IV, *The Promise of Technology,* particularly chap. i, "Tasks and Opportunities."

⁷³ W. F. P. McLintock, "Outlook for Mineral Discovery in Great Britain," *Proceedings,* UNSCCUR, II, 44-47.

⁷⁴ Mario Carta, "Lead and Zinc Resources in Sardinia," *Proceedings,* UNSCCUR, II, 70-75.

⁷⁵ Stojan Pavlovic, "Development of Mineral Wealth in Yugoslavia," *Proceedings,* UNSCCUR, II, pp. 95-96.

⁷⁶ *Resources for Freedom,* I, 25, 28 (map), 29.

⁷⁷ *Ibid.,* I, 27.

⁷⁸ National Resources Committee, *Energy Resources and National Policy* (Washington, January, 1939), p. 137.

⁷⁹ See, e.g., the "List of Minerals in Descending Order of Knowledge of their Available Reserves" given by Leith and Liddell, *Mineral Reserves,* p. 5. As the authors indicate, most of the estimates are little more than intelligent guesses upon the basis of scattered data supplied by various experts who agree but little among themselves. While these figures are some years out of date, the picture today remains essentially unaltered.

⁸⁰ W. E. Wrather, "Outlook for Future Mineral Discovery in North and South America," *Proceedings,* UNSCCUR, II, 48-50.

⁸¹ M. S. Krishnana, "Mineral Resources in India," *Proceedings,* UNSCCUR, II, 67.

⁸² *The Coal Resources of the USSR,* prepared under the direction of M. M. Prigorovsky for the XVIIth Session of the International Geological Congress, Leningrad, 1937, p. 8. [Pamphlet.]

⁸³ Chauncy D. Harris, "Industrial Resources," in Abram Bergson (ed.), *Soviet Economic Growth* (New York: Row, Peterson, 1953), p. 163.

⁸⁴ O. E. Baker, "Agriculture and the Future of China" *Foreign Affairs,* Vol. VI, No. 3 (April, 1928), pp. 484-489.

⁸⁵ O. E. Baker, "The Population Prospect in Relation to the World's Agricultural Resources," *Journal of Geography,* September, 1947, pp. 218-219.

⁸⁶ Alfred Bonné, "Land and Population in the Middle East," *Middle East Journal* (Winter, 1951), pp. 42-43.

⁸⁷ Alfred Bonné, "The Resources and their Potentials," in Harvey P. Hall, ed., *Middle East Resources, Proceedings of the Eighth Annual Conference on Middle Eastern Affairs* (Washington: Middle East Institute, 1954), pp. 32-33.

⁸⁸ Zimmermann, *World Resources and Industries,* p. 704.

⁸⁹ The Johannesburg area of South Africa has undergone a tremendous postwar boom largely as a result of the discovery of uranium salts in the tailings from the gold mines in sufficiently high concentrations to make possible extraction at costs which are, apparently, competitive with all but the richest known uranium ores.

A similar possible source of uranium is found in connection with uranium in oil shales.

[90] The ways: water suspension, or "sink-and-float"; "Dutch-State Cyclone," or water suspension plus centrifugal force; "Humphreys Spiral," a variation on the second method; "froth flotation," using oily reagent and air-ore-water mix plus forced air draft and temperature control; "electrostatic" and "magnetic," using respectively electric current and magnets to separate ores; and "radioactive," depending for separation on different degrees of radioactivity. *Fortune*, April, 1953, p. 154.

[91] *Resources of the World*, p. 17.

[92] *Resources for Freedom*, IV, 23.

[93] *Ibid.*

[94] *Resources of the World*, pp. 17-18.

[95] Sir Francis Simon, "Nuclear Energy and the Future," *Lloyds Bank Review*, April, 1955, p. 5.

[96] *Saskatchewan News*, May 1, 1956.

[97] "To get an idea of relative amounts, compare the tonnage of residues (say, 250 million tons) with figures for some other natural products. The total growth of timber for 1944 was reported as 13.7 billion cubic feet, equivalent to approximately 218 million tons of dry material. About 592 million tons of coal was produced in 1946. The production of petroleum amounted to 1,733 million barrels, equivalent to 291 million tons. The average annual consumption of food in the United States is approximately 110 million tons—not more than 55 million tons on a dry basis." S. I. Aronovsky, L. E. Schniepp, Elbert C. Lathrop, "Using Residues to Conserve Resources," in United States Department of Agriculture, *Crops in Peace and War*, Yearbook of Agriculture, 1950-1951 (Washington, 1951), pp. 829-830.

CHAPTER III. SCIENCE AS THE KEY TO RESOURCE INNOVATION
(Pp. 72-107)

[1] L. Kowarski, "Psychology and Structure of Large-Scale Physical Research," *Bulletin of The Atomic Scientists*, Vol. V, Nos. 6-7 (June-July, 1949), p. 186.

[2] "Philosophy of Science," in Dagobert D. Runes, ed., *Twentieth Century Philosophy* (New York: Philosophical Library, 1943), pp. 109, 115, 118.

[3] *Ibid.*, pp. 118-19.

[4] "Science and Civilization," in Dexter Masters and Katharine Way, eds., *One World or None: A Report to the Public on the Full Meaning of the Atomic Bomb* (New York: McGraw-Hill, 1946), p. x.

[5] W. H. Harrison, Vice-President of the American Telephone and Telegraph Company, "Technology in the Bell System with Particular Reference to Employment," in Hearings on Public Res. No. 113, Temporary National Economic Committee, 76th Cong., 3rd Sess., Part 30, "Technology and Concentration of Economic Power," Exhibit 2572 (Washington, 1940), p. 17398.

[6] Herbert George Wells and Julian S. Huxley, *The Science of Life* (New York: Doubleday, Doran, 1931), II, 1022.

[7] "Ought Science to be Planned? Two Opposing Views: The Case for Collective Research," *Bulletin of the Atomic Scientists*, Vol. V, No 1 (January, 1949), pp. 17-18.

[8] A. Wolf, *A History of Science, Technology and Philosophy in the 16th and 17th Centuries* (2d. ed.; London: Allen and Unwin, 1950), pp. 54 ff. Most of the following summaries of the origin of the academies are taken from this excellent source.

[9] Quoted in Sir Henry George Lyons, *The Royal Society, 1660-1940: A History*

of its Administration under its Charters (Cambridge, England: Cambridge University Press, 1944), p. 41.

[10] Wolf, *History of Science, Technology and Philosophy*, pp. 63, 68-69.

[11] *Ibid.*, p. 70.

[12] *Ibid.*

[13] E.g., the Organization for European Economic Cooperation study, *The Organization of Applied Research in Europe, the United States and Canada*, Vol. II, *Applied Research in Europe* (Paris, 1954), pp. 176-177, lists associations for such widely varying industries as baking, boots and shoes, cast iron, ceramics, cutlery, gas, gelatin and glue, iron and steel, lace, laundry, linoleum and felt base, rayon, coil springs, welding, and wool. Hereafter cited as OEEC Study.

[14] Henry S. Pritchett, "The Function of Scientific Research in a Modern State," *Bulletin of the National Research Council*, Vol. I, Pt. 1, No. 1 (October, 1919), p. 11. Council of the National Academy of Sciences, Washington.

[15] A situation which is described by a word coined by Horace Walpole: ". . . serendipity—this faculty or fact of accidentally finding a result of superior significance while searching for something else . . . occurs frequently. . . . Serendipity operated while the geochemist measured the ratio of lead to uranium in various old strata of rocks and while the paleontologist pondered the structures of fossil plants. For they found results that forced the astrophysicist, in searching vigorously again for a sufficient explanation of constant sunlight, to make a speculative invasion of nuclear physics and to find there a clue to the coming of a terrestrial atomic era. There could be no better example of the intermingling and advisable cooperation of the various highly specialized sciences." Harlow Shapley, Director of the Harvard College Observatory, "It's an Old Story with the Stars," in Masters and Way, eds., *One World or None*, p. 8.

[16] OEEC Study, II, 79-80.

[17] *Ibid.*, II, 81.

[18] It is impossible to summarize in a short space the scope, comprehensiveness, and intensity of the work supervised by the VDI. See, however, Verein Deutscher Ingenieure (VDI), *Geschäftsbericht, 1954* (Düsseldorf).

[19] D.S.I.R., *A Description of the Work of the Department of Scientific and Industrial Research* (London: H.M.S.O., 1949), p. 2. [Brochure.]

[20] Central Office of Information, London, Reference Division, R.2911, 7.10.54, *The Promotion of the Sciences in the United Kingdom*, p. 7. [Mimeographed.]

[21] *Ibid.*, p. 8.

[22] Federation of British Industries, *Scientific and Technical Research in British Industry* (London: F.B.I. Industrial Research Secretariat, July, 1947), pp. 4-5. [Brochure.]

[23] Federation of British Industries, *Research and Development in British Industry* (London, July, 1952), quoted in Central Office of Information, *The Promotion of the Sciences in the United Kingdom*, p. 3.

[24] *Ibid.*, p. 5.

[25] "Russian Science Threatens the West," *Nation's Business*, September, 1954, pp. 42-43.

[26] Nicholas DeWitt, *Soviet Professional Manpower* (Washington: National Science Foundation, 1955).

[27] Waterman, in *Nation's Business*, September, 1954, p. 46.

"The Soviet Union may soon be turning out more than twice as many scientists and engineers as the United States." A pilot study at the Center for International Studies at M.I.T. indicates that, "judging strictly on technical grounds one must conclude that high-quality scientific education seems to be taking place." "Soviet Science: Unfathomed Threat," *Quarterly Report*, Carnegie Corporation of New York, Vol. III, No. 1 (January, 1955), p. 4.

Notes

[28] Alexander Lipski, "The Foundation of the Russian Academy of Sciences," *Isis*, Vol. 44, No. 138, Pt. 4 (December, 1953), pp. 349 ff.

[29] Eric Ashby, *Scientist in Russia* (New York: Penguin Books, 1947), p. 20.

[30] Ashby, *Scientist in Russia*, pp. 22-23.

[31] *Ibid.*, p. 23. This figure, cited by Ashby, should be compared with the figures given by Sidney and Beatrice Webb, *Soviet Communism: A New Civilization?* (New York: Scribner, 1936), II, 961, as follows: for 1928, 3,903,000 roubles; for 1932, 16,746,000 roubles; and the estimate for 1934, 44,500,000 roubles.

[32] Ashby, *Scientist in Russia*, p. 212.

[33] *Ibid.*, pp. 39-40.

[34] S. and B. Webb, *Soviet Communism*, pp. 961-962.

[35] Eric Hodgins, "The Strange State of American Research," *Fortune*, April, 1955, p. 224.

[36] Estimates vary widely. A preliminary report of the National Science Foundation suggested that "the national total for scientific research in 1953 was in the neighborhood of $5 billion, of which more than $2 billion was spent by Government agencies." F. Emerson Andrews, *Scientific Research Expenditures by the Larger Private Foundations* (Washington: National Science Foundation, 1956), p. 5.

[37] Calculated from data supplied by the National Science Foundation, *Federal Funds For Science*, IV, *The Federal Research and Development Budget* (Washington, 1955).

[38] OEEC Study, III, 17.

[39] Research supported by the federal government but conducted by private firms, universities, etc., is referred to as *extramural*, as distinguished from *interdepartmental* research. Most of the civilian agencies conduct their own research programs (*intramural research*) while the defense agencies contract a very large percentage of their research work. The Atomic Energy Commission has only extramural programs. In the latter case, e.g., "The contractor for Brookhaven National Laboratory is Associated Universities, Inc., an organization made up of nine eastern universities; Oak Ridge National Laboratory is operated by the Carbide and Carbon Chemicals Company; Argonne National Laboratory by the University of Chicago; Los Alamos by the University of Chicago; Los Alamos by the University of California; Hanford by the General Electric Company." OEEC Study, III, 24-25. The Office of Naval Research, "With a 1955 appropriation of $60 million . . . has some 360 projects under investigation, and farms its work out to some 217 universities and laboratories, in addition to maintaining a 4,500 staff of its own." Hodgins, *op. cit.*, p. 216.

[40] As a typical opinion, Hodgins comments as follows: "Industry has been on an increasing research binge ever since World War II, but it still remains 99 per cent devoted to the linkages between applied research and the immediate needs of its sales departments . . ." *Ibid.*, p. 219.

[41] *Ibid.*, p. 222.

[42] These and similar data from this source (National Science Foundation, *Federal Funds for Science*, IV, p. 17) do not agree at all points with those given by the OEEC Report, Vol. III, cited above. The writer is unable to account for the differences—which are at some points rather large.

[43] Estimated expenditures for the year 1956, in millions of dollars: physical sciences, 1,720; life sciences, 244; social sciences, 32; and collection of general-purpose statistics, 29. National Science Foundation, *Federal Funds for Science*, IV, 7.

[44] George Ellery Hale, "The Purpose of the National Research Council," *Bulletin of the National Research Council*, Vol. I, Pt. 1, No. 1 (October, 1919), p. 3.

[45] National Research Council, *Organization and Members, 1940-1941* (Washington, December, 1940), p. 4.

[46] "The Steelman Report estimated that the Federal research budget in 1930 amounted to $25 million out of a total national research budget of $166 million." OEEC Study, III, 15.

[47] "The members of the Board are the Secretaries of Agriculture, Commerce, Interior, War, and Navy, the Chairman of the Atomic Energy Commission, the Federal Communications Commission, the National Advisory Committee for Aeronautics, and the Tennessee Valley Authority, the Administrators of Federal Loan, Federal Works, Federal Security, and Veterans Affairs, and the Director of the Office of Scientific Research and Development." Philip N. Powers, "The Organization for Science in the Federal Government," *Bulletin of the Atomic Scientists*, Vol. 3, Nos. 4-5 (April-May, 1947), p. 122.

[48] "The International Geophysical Year is undoubtedly one of the most significant scientific undertakings in the history of man. For a period of a year and a half, beginning July 1, 1957, thousands of scientists from many nations will be making simultaneous observations of the earth's interior, its crust and oceans, of the complex atmosphere reaching from the surface to the heights of several hundred miles, and of the sun, which virtually controls life and events on our planet. At the present time 46 nations are participating in the International Geophysical Year and still more are expected to take part." Alan T. Waterman, Director, National Science Foundation, in the Preface to *A Special Report on the International Geophysical Year to the Senate Committee on Appropriations*, 84th Cong., 2d Sess., *Congressional Record*, p. vii. It was anticipated that the total expenditure of all participating nations might run to around $2 billion.

[49] Letter to the author from C. E. Sunderlin, Deputy Director, National Science Foundation, July 27, 1956. See also the Foundation's *Fifth Annual Report, 1955* (Washington: G.P.O.), p. 95.

[50] E.g., Divisional Committees for Mathematical, Physical and Engineering Sciences; Biological and Medical Sciences; for Scientific Personnel and Education; and Advisory Panels for Anthropological and Related Sciences; Astronomy; Chemistry; Environmental and Systematic Biology.

[51] OEEC Study, III, 47.

[52] See, e.g., Francis Bello, "Industrial Research: Geniuses Now Welcome," *Fortune*, January, 1956, pp. 96 ff.

[53] Wang Ging-Hsi, "UNESCO and International Scientific Organizations," *Bulletin of the Atomic Scientists*, Vol. VI, Nos. 8-9 (August-September, 1950), p. 283.

[54] For a compact résumé see Esther C. Brunauer, "International Council of Scientific Unions Brussels and Cambridge," *Department of State Bulletin*, Vol. XIII, No. 324 (September 9, 1945), pp. 371-376.

[55] *Report of the United States Delegation to the Seventh General Assembly International Council of Scientific Unions, Oslo, Norway, August 9-12, 1955* (Washington: National Research Council), p. 2.

[56] "Boundaries of Science," presidential address by Robert B. Brode to the Pacific Division of the American Association for the Advancement of Science, Seattle, Washington, June 12, 1956. See also, e.g., International Union of Pure and Applied Physics, *Report of the Eighth General Assembly* (1954), (Paris: Office of the Secretary, November, 1954).

[57] For further details see League of Nations Secretariat, Information Section, *Essential Facts About the League of Nations* (10th rev. ed.; Geneva, 1939), pp. 265 ff.

[58] Wang, *op. cit.*, p. 283.

[59] Charles S. Ascher, *Program-Making in UNESCO, 1946-1951: A Study in the Processes of International Administration* (Chicago: Public Administration Service, 1951).

[60] UNESCO, *Report of the Director General from April 1950 to March 1951,* UNESCO Publications No. 973 (Paris, 1951), p. 44.

[61] A more precise and detailed grasp of the work of these agencies may be had by consulting any annual *Yearbook of the United Nations.*

[62] See, e.g., the breakdown of the average National Science Foundation research grant, by type of expenditure, in National Science Foundation, *Fifth Annual Report, 1955,* p. 49.

[63] National Science Foundation, *Federal Funds For Science,* IV, 8-9.

[64] National Science Foundation, *Science and Engineering in American Industry: Preliminary Report on a Survey of Research and Development Costs and Personnel in 1953-54,* National Science Studies (Washington, 1955), p. 17.

[65] UNESCO, *Trade Barriers to Knowledge* ("A manual of regulations affecting educational, scientific, and cultural materials"), UNESCO Publication 847, (Paris, 1951).

[66] "One of the most formidable obstacles to the international circulation of informational materials is the complexity and variety of trade regulations in force in different countries, and the inaccessibility of information concerning them. Confronted with this maze of restrictions, many organizations and individuals are discouraged from embarking on international exchanges of such materials or even their sale in countries abroad." *Ibid.,* p. 5.

[67] The following list of Special Agencies is taken from the United Nations *Yearbook* for 1956:

Abbreviation	Full title	Field	Number of members	Headquarters
ILO	International Labor Organization	Labor and social problems	77	Geneva
FAO	Food and Agriculture Organization of the United Nations	Food, its production and distribution	74	Rome
UNESCO	United Nations Educational, Scientific, and Cultural Organization	Education, science, and culture	79	Paris
ICAO	International Civil Aviation Org.	Civil air transport	70	Montreal
WHO	World Health Organization	Health	84	Geneva
BANK	International Bank for Reconstruction and Development	Lending for progress	60	Washington
IFC	International Finance Corporation	Investment for economic development	47	Washington
FUND	International Monetary Fund	Keeping national currency stable	60	Washington
UPU	Universal Postal Union	Postal services between nations	96	Berne
ITU	International Telecommunication Union	Communication by telephone, radio, and telegraph between nations	91	Geneva
WMO	World Meteorological Organization	Weather reporting	95	Geneva

[68] *The Budget of the United States Government for the Fiscal Year Ending June 30, 1956*, Special Analysis H, Federal Research and Development Programs (Washington, 1955), p. 1195.

[69] The amount so classified increased from 30 per cent in 1940 to 68 per cent in 1942, 78 per cent in 1943, and 94 per cent in 1945. For 1956, 84 per cent was so classified. *Ibid.*, table 2.

[70] For example, the *Physical Review* increased in size "from about 2,000 pages annually during World War II, to about 5,000 pages in 1951," and is continuing to grow at the rate of an additional 700 pages a year. As for one of the highly valuable abstracting services, *Chemical Abstracts*, which "attempts to cover all papers containing new knowledge in the field of chemistry," has increased its abstracts from 43,000 papers in 1948 to 79,000 in 1954. National Science Foundation, *Fifth Annual Report, 1955*, p. 77. These examples appear to be typical of the general run of scientific journals. Serious efforts are being made by the National Science Foundation, in coöperation with the Library of Congress, to master this problem of growing volume. But "keeping up," nevertheless, is bound to become a steadily more difficult problem.

CHAPTER IV. THE DELICATE MOVING BALANCE BETWEEN ORDER AND INNOVATION
(Pp. 108-142)

[1] "In a work entitled *A Treatise on the Steam Engine* published in 1827, a John Farey described a particular difficulty that plagued James Watt and Matthew Boulton for nearly ten years in their manufacture of the first rotary steam engines. They simply could not buy or build pistons and cylinders that fitted each other. 'The borer,' Farey explains, 'was not guided in its progress, and therefore followed the incorrect form given to the cylinder in casting it . . . ; it was scarcely ensured that every part of the cylinder should be circular; and there was no certainty that the cylinder should be straight.' To make the piston tight in such a cylinder, Watt 'wrapped it round with cork, oiled rags, tow, old hats, paper, horse-dung and other things, but still there were open spaces left, sufficient to let the air in and the steam out.' On one occasion Watt measured a cylinder 18″ in diameter and found that at the worst place the long diameter exceeded the short by ⅜″. Thus at the very birth of the modern industrial age men ran head-on into the basic problem of procuring standard component parts that fitted and worked. The example, of course, is an extreme one; but even in this age of mass production we are not quite so far removed from those early conditions as we may like to think." Thomas D. Jolley, Vice-President, Aluminum Company of America, "Coordinating Suppliers and Purchasers Through Standard Purchase Specifications," in Dickson Reck, ed., *National Standards in a Modern Economy* (New York: Harper, 1956), p. 118. Hereafter cited as *National Standards*.

[2] "The Government gave him a contract in 1793 for 10,000 stands of arms, although he had no plant for their manufacture. He built a small factory in New Haven and began work but found a great obstacle in the difficulty of getting good workmen, especially those capable of acting as foremen under his novel methods. His plan was to make of his factory a single huge machine. . . . In an armory before Whitney's day each man, highly skilled, produced by himself a distinct part of a musket. This division of labor Whitney supplanted by so apportioning work that little or no skill was demanded. He separated the various tasks and at each of these operations kept a group busy. For their assistance he simplified each operation and introduced three aids, since indispensable in manufacture—drilling by templates or patterns, filing by jigs or guides, and milling irregular forms. From first to last a model musket was copied with precision so that every lock for example, was exactly like every other among thousands. When all the parts needed to form a weapon were assembled, they united much superior

to a musket formed on any other plan. . . . In case of repair a new part exactly fitted the place of the old part and at a trifling cost." New York *Sun and Globe,* March 29, 1928. Today, while we take the Whitney methods for granted, one is frequently astonished by how much practice lags behind. In the 1930's an American Cadillac automobile was assembled in London entirely out of prefabricated parts taken at random. The British were astounded. According to a member of the staff of the British Standards Institution (in conversation with the author, 1948), during World War II a repair garage on the British front lines in France which had to stand prepared to fit with new parts any lorry brought in, the lorries being of five basic sizes and having around 2,000 parts each, was required to stock not 10,000 parts but 400,000. This is illustrative of a good deal of the industrial backwardness of Britain since the turn of the century.

[3] From ASA *Yearbook,* 1945-1946 (New York: American Standards Association), p. 11. The last column has been added.

[4] Vol. III, Pt. II (Munich and Leipzig, 1927), pp. 698 ff., 712 ff.

[5] "The Role of Company Standards in Industrial Administration," *Advanced Management,* April, 1954, p. 20.

[6] *Ibid.,* p. 22.

[7] American Standards Association, *Dollar Savings Through Standards* (New York, n.d.). [Brochure.]

[8] "Company and National Standards in Interchangeable Parts Manufacture," in *National Standards,* pp. 91 ff.

[9] Directory of Members of the American Standards Association (New York, June, 1956). [Pamphlet.]

[10] Paul Arnold, Assistant to the Technical Director and Standards Coordinator for ANSCO Division, General Aniline and Film Corporation, and Chairman of the Photographic Standards Board, ASA, "American Standards in Complementary Industries," in *National Standards,* p .125.

[11] *Directory of Members of the American Standards Association.*

[12] *Standards are Your Business* (New York: American Standards Association, n.d.), p. 11. [Pamphlet.]

[13] *Ibid.,* p. 16.

[14] ASA *Yearbook,* 1945-1946, p. 13.

[15] National Bureau of Standards, *Standardization Activities of National Technical and Trade Associations,* Misc. Publ. M169 (Washington: G.P.O., 1941), p. 34.

[16] *Standards are Your Business,* p. 13.

[17] *Ibid.,* pp. 15-16.

[18] "The lack of common standards on screw threads and fasteners faced by the Allies in World War II cost hundreds of millions of dollars and nearly resulted in the loss of North Africa. American-made tanks remained immobilized because British-made fasteners in Egyptian stores were not interchangeable and hence not usable for repair of battle damage. It took two world wars and the current needs for mutual defence to stimulate necessary action." H. W. Robb, "Significance of Company and National Standards to Industrial Management," in *National Standards,* p. 295.

[19] E. C. Crittenden, "The Contributions of Government and Private Agencies to National Standards," in *National Standards,* p. 33.

[20] The procedure is explained in a pamphlet entitled "Voluntary Standards Adopted by the Trade," obtainable from the Commodity Standards Division, Office of Technical Services, Washington 25, D.C.

[21] The procedure is explained in "Simplified Practice, Its Purpose and Application," Letter Circular LC-590, obtainable from the Commodity Standards Division, Office of Technical Services, Department of Commerce, Washington 25, D.C.

[22] Policies and Procedures governing development of Federal Specifications and

Standards are covered in Regulations of the General Services Administration, Title I, Personal Property Management, chap. vi.

[23] *ISO: The International Organization for Standardization* (New York: American Standards Association, n.d.), p. 3. [Pamphlet.] Hereafter cited as ISO pamphlet.

[24] "This Commission was organized in 1906 as an outgrowth of a resolution adopted by the St. Louis Electrical Congress in 1904, stating the desirability of taking steps 'to secure the cooperation of the technical societies of the world by the appointment of a representative commission to consider the question of standardization of nomenclature and rating of electrical apparatus and machinery'." Robert A. Brady, *Industrial Standardization* (New York: National Industrial Conference Board, 1929), p. 151. This Commission has subsequently participated in, and is largely responsible for, development of a standard international nomenclature, standard and uniform methods of rating machinery and equipment, standard rules, regulations, and codes, etc., for the world electric-power industries, telecommunications networks, and countless related products and industries.

[25] ISO pamphlet, p. 5; ISO *Journal* (Geneva: ISO General Secretariat), No. 33 (July, 1956), pp. 6 ff.

[26] ISO *Journal*, No. 33 (July, 1956), pp. 6-7.

[27] *Research, The Prime Mover of Industry* (Washington: National Research Council, 1927), p. 1 (reprinted from *Scientific Monthly*, April, 1926).

[28] *The Place of Standardization in Modern Life* (Washington: Inter-American High Commission, 1924), pp. 2-3.

[29] William S. Kinne, Jr., cited in "Standards—Engineering Tools for Industry," *Proceedings of the Third National Standardization Conference* (New York: American Standards Association, 1952), pp. 36-37. (Italics in the original.)

[30] Arthur Bohnen, of the J. L. Simmons Company, and representative of the National Association of Housing Officials and the National Association of Real Estate Boards, *ibid.*, p. 31. See also *Modular Measure*, edited by Charles R. Koehler, Building Research Institute, Division of Engineering and Industrial Research (Washington: National Academy of Sciences–National Research Council, June, 1955).

[31] Standardization of pigments—how it was carried out is not known—appears to have been responsible for the magnificent tonal effects of late classical, in contrast to early, Renaissance painting. The fourteenth- to eighteenth-century perfection of musical notational system, arrangements of scales and chords, and construction and qualities of most musical instruments involved similar, and in many cases extraordinarily exacting, standardization.

[32] The writer saw, at a model housing exhibit in Los Angeles, a bathroom done eleven different shades of a dominant color. Few of them matched, while several "clashed" badly. Standards in color would have made possible proper matching of color tones without in any way diminishing the possible number of color tones to be matched.

CHAPTER V. THE PRINCIPLES OF UNITIZATION IN MINING
(Pp. 145-157)

[1] ". . . I am like the Frenchman, who being shown the Empire State Building for the first time, was much impressed and stated to his American host that it reminded him of a beautiful woman. His friend was frankly puzzled and said that while he agreed that the Empire State Building was truly magnificent, he could not understand what there was about it that made the Frenchman think of a beautiful woman. The Frenchman shrugged his shoulders and said, 'Oh, everything does.' Similarly, regardless of the subject, I always seem to find an excuse for discussing conservation." William J. Murray, Jr., Member, Railroad Com-

mission of Texas, "Engineering Aspects of Unit Operation," *Proceedings of the Third Annual Institute on Oil and Gas Law and Taxation as it Affects the Oil and Gas Industry,* Southwestern Legal Foundation (New York: Matthew Bender, 1952), p. 1.

[2] H. L. Keenleyside, Deputy Minister of the Department of Mines and Resources in Canada and Commissioner of the Northwest Territories, Ottawa, "Critical Mineral Shortages," in the *Proceedings* of the United Nations Scientific Conference on the Conservation and Utilization of Resources (UNSCCUR), Department of Economic Affairs, 1950, E./Conf. 7/7 (8 vols.; Lake Success: 1950-53), I, *Plenary Meetings,* p. 41.

[3] Fernand Blondel, Directeur du Bureau d'Études géologiques et minières coloniales, France, "Mineral Discovery," in *Proceedings,* UNSCCUR, I, 170-171. Oil is a major exception to this general rule because of "its liquid or semi-liquid state which is the cause why petroleum is found concentrated under conditions very different from those of other minerals and in particular is the cause why the large deposits of petroleum do not touch the earth's surface—but for which fact they would by now, in the course of geological time, have either exhausted themselves or become oxidized as bitumen." *Ibid.,* p. 171.

[4] The NUSCCUR *Proceedings* (I, 43) give the "following tabulation of the comparative abundance of metals in the upper 10 miles of the earth's crust:

341.	Silicon	0.05	Zinc
100.	Aluminum	0.05	Lithium
62.	Iron	0.04	Hafnium
45.	Calcium	0.04	Tantalum Columbium
35.	Sodium	.025	Lead
32.	Potassium	.025	Thorium
26.	Magnesium	.012	Beryllium
8.	Titanium	.012	Cobalt
1.25	Manganese	10^{-3}	Tin, Arsenic, Molybdenum, Rubidium
0.61	Barium		
0.45	Chromium	10^{-4}	Mercury, Cadmium, Antimony, Calcium
0.32	Zirconium		
0.25	Nickel	10^{-5}	Silver, Bismuth, Celenium
0.23	Strontium	10^{-6}	Gold, Platinum, Tellurium
0.21	Vanadium	10^{-7}	Osmium, Iridium, Thallium
0.18	Rare earths	10^{-8}	Indium, Palladium, Germanium Gallium, Ruthenium, Rhenium
0.12	Copper		
0.10	Uranium	10^{-9}	Radium
0.06	Tungsten		

The justification for aluminum as a base ratio is that it is the most plentiful of all the metals used by man—nearly double in supply to the next largest, iron.

[5] Robert H. Randall, United States Bureau of the Budget, "Resource Surveys," in *Proceedings,* UNSCCUR, I, 177. (Italics in the original.)

[6] *Ibid.,* I, 176.

[7] A. E. Dunstan *et al.,* eds., *The Science of Petroleum: A Comprehensive Treatise of the Principles and Practice of the Production, Refining, Transport, and Distribution of Mineral Oil* (London: Oxford University Press, 1938), I, xi. This huge compendium, consisting of four large volumes, contains over 3,000 pages of closely packed materials relating to the oil industry.

[8] *Oil For Today and Tomorrow* (Oklahoma City: Interstate Oil Compact Commission, 1953), p. 16.

[9] *Ibid.,* pp. 20-21.

[10] *Ibid.,* pp. 24 and 26.

[11] R. M. Williams, "The Negotiation and Preparation of Utilization Agreements," *First Annual Institute on Oil and Gas Laws,* Southwestern Legal Foundation (1949), pp. 43, 60, cited by David T. Searls in "Antitrust and Other Statutory Restrictions of Unit Agreements," *Proceedings of the Third Annual Institute on Oil and Gas Law,* pp. 80-81.

[12] Sir John Cadman, Chairman, Anglo-Iranian Oil Company, "Conservation of Petroleum," in the *Transactions* of the Third World Power Conference (Washington, 1936), VI, 758.

[13] *Ibid.*

[14] "Excessive rates of withdrawal lead to rapid decline of reservoir pressure, to release of dissolved gas, to irregularity of the boundary between invaded and non-invaded sections of the reservoir, to dissipation of gas and water, to trapping and by-passing of oil, and, in extreme cases, to complete loss of demarcation between the invaded and non-invaded portions of the reservoir, with dominance of the entire recovery by inefficient dissolved-gas drive. Each of these effects of excessive withdrawal rates reduces the ultimate recovery of oil." *Oil For Today and Tomorrow,* pp. 27-28.

[15] Cadman, *op. cit.,* VI, 758-759.

[16] This matter has been examined in some detail with mining engineers. The main objection to use of the term outside the oil and gas producing industries is the lack of analogy between deposits which flow and move and those fixed *in situ.* Aside from this, there seems to be no serious objection, agreement being general that the underlying facts of deposit-wide, comprehensive, long-term exploitation found in oil and gas utilization are found in virtually all other fields of mining.

[17] Ministry of Fuel and Power, *Coal Mining: Report of the Technical Advisory Committee* (Reid Committee), Cmd. 6610 (London: H.M.S.O., 1945), p 122. In contrast, in 1943 there were in Britain 966 mines of less than 50,000 tons annual output, and 816 with a capacity of more than 50,000 tons—having an average capacity of 228,000 tons. Most of these mines had actually been opened before the turn of the century and could not be successfully mechanized at all.

[18] Letter to the author from M. H. Gidel, Geological Department of the Anaconda Copper Mining Company, February 11, 1955. The Kelley mine involves a capital expenditure of around $25 million before a ton of ore is extracted. When in operation it will be able to handle copper ores down to 0.6 per cent copper, and will literally scavenge the entire copper-bearing mountain range underneath and around the city of Butte.

[19] For an interesting example of how far these processes have gone in a much smaller concern, see the extensive description of the Colorado Fuel and Iron Corporation, *Journal of Metals,* Vol. 5, No. 10 (October, 1953), pp. 1308-1366.

[20] See, e.g., James E. Lawver, "What Automatic Controls Can the Mill Operator Use?" *Mining Engineering,* Vol. 5, No. 10 (October, 1953), pp. 982-984.

CHAPTER VI. DETERMINANTS AND PROSPECTS OF INDUSTRIALIZED AGRICULTURE
(Pp. 158-201)

[1] "Civilization's Race with Famine," a speech given by Walter C. Lowdermilk on the Third Programme of the British Broadcasting Corporation; reproduced in *The Listener,* April 15, 1948, p. 605. Lowdermilk is the author of the plan for the Jordan Valley Authority.

[2] Lowdermilk finds only two minor exceptions, England and Egypt. It is no longer true of England, particularly since the rapid postwar expansion of cereal and row crops. In Egypt the exception is due to the bounty of the Nile in the form of silt deposits during the annual flood season—a free dividend to the Egyptians at the cost of continued denudation of the Sudan, Abyssinia, and other upland areas whose soils the Nile steadily moves towards the sea.

[3] L. C. Gray, *Evolution of the Land Program,* Conference on Agricultural Plan-

ning, Bureau of Agricultural Economics (Washington: Department of Agriculture, March 22, 1939), pp. 10-11.

[4] "Although twice as many people are engaged in agriculture as in all other occupations combined, two thirds of the people of the world have never had enough of the right kinds of food." Howard R. Tolley and Leroy D. Stinebower, in The Department of State *Bulletin,* Vol. XII, No. 295 (February 18, 1945), p. 226.

[5] "Inter-Relations of Living Creatures," in *The Outline of Science* (New York and London: Putnam, 1922), III, 669-670.

[6] Martin R. Cooper, Glen T. Barton, and Albert P. Brodell, *Progress of Farm Mechanization,* United States Department of Agriculture, Misc. Publ. No. 630 (Washington, October, 1947), p. i.

[7] United States Department of Agriculture, Agricultural Marketing Service, *Agricultural Outlook Charts, 1956,* (Washington, 1955), p. 17.

[8] Henry Wallace, "The Impact of Technology," speech, August 11, 1936, at the centennial celebration of the city of Council Bluffs, Iowa.

[9] E. A. Gutkind, *Creative Demobilisation Principles of National Planning* (London: Kegan Paul, Trench, Trubner, 1942), I, 126.

[10] E.g., Sir Charles Fielding, *Food* (London: Hurst and Blackett, 1923); Arthur Smith, *Agriculture's Challenge to the Nation* (London and Toronto: Heinemann, 1942); and George P. Pollitt, *Britain Can Feed Herself* (London: Macmillan, 1942).

[11] *The Colombo Plan for Co-Operative Economic Development in South and South-East Asia,* Report by the Commonwealth Consultative Committee, Cmd. 8080 (London: H.M.S.O., September-October, 1950), pp. 10-11. See also, *The First Five Year Plan,* a draft outline of the Government of India Planning Commission (New Delhi, July, 1951).

[12] This is of course somewhat misleading, for depletion of these resources may be (a) slowed down by improved use—higher thermal efficiencies, "revolving funds" of basic metals, etc., (b) capacity to use lower-quality and more widely scattered deposits, and (c) substitutes of less exhaustible nature.

[13] H. S. Person, *Little Waters: A Study of Headwater Streams and Other Little Waters, Their Use and Relations to the Land,* Soil Conservation Service, Resettlement Administration, Rural Electrification Administration (Washington; November, 1935), p. 3.

[14] The term "cycle," as Professor James J. Parsons has pointed out (letter to the author, September 25, 1956), must be used with caution in this context. In contrast with the other "cycles" referred to here, meteorological "cycles" refer to *time,* not to *processes,* and might more accurately be "thought of as a part of the hydrological cycle." Furthermore, the "whole concept of 'cycles' in climatology . . . as [it] relates to regularly recurring, long-run climatic periodicity . . . is, of course a controversial one." With this caution, however, the term as used here still has some limited use and serves to point up a set of interdependencies of very great importance for future land planning.

[15] The Water Resources Development Corporation claims to make "surveys and field operations for scientific rain induction, rain suppression, and related water problems" (*Business Week,* August 5, 1950, p. 28), but the possibilities of cloud seeding seem, as subsequent research has brought out, very doubtful and at best very limited.

[16] *International Telecommunications* (London: Oxford University Press, 1943), p. 42.

[17] *Ibid.*

[18] *Ibid.,* p. 43.

[19] *Ibid.,* pp. 43-44.

[20] Letter from Professor Parsons.

[21] Person, *Little Waters*, pp. 6-8. (Italics in the original.)

[22] "Land Available for Agriculture Through Reclamation," *Supplementary Report of the Land Planning Committee to the National Resources Board* (Washington, 1936), pt. 4, pp. 5, 39.

[23] *A Water Policy for the American People*, Report of the President's Water Resources Policy Commission (Washington, 1950), I, 177.

[24] National Association of Manufacturers, *Water in Industry*, Economic Policy Division Series, No. 36 (New York, December, 1950), p. 14.

[25] E.g., "The Beautiful Ohio can become a pretty ugly river from a sanitation standpoint. The reason: Each year for more than 20 years, more and more tons of untreated sewage and industrial waste have been dumped into the Ohio and its tributaries. It's so bad now that when the water is low, one quart out of every gallon of it is from a sewer. Yet, more than 1.5 million people get their drinking water from the Ohio River." *Business Week*, July 31, 1948, p. 26. Eight states in the Ohio area have combined to clean up the river by signing the Ohio River Valley Water Sanitation Compact, calling for a $400-million sewage-control program which is coextensive with the entire Ohio River basin.

[26] *Overdraft on Ground Water Basins*, Bull. 53 of the California Department of Public Works, Division of Water Resources, 1947.

[27] "The use or misuse of water is so extravagant and public demands are so insistent that many important towns in England and elsewhere in the world have been compelled to carry out expensive projects that involved long-distance transmission of water impounded in regions where rainfall or other factors favoured a surplus. New York suffered an unexpected scarcity this year; while such demands on the great Colorado River have been made by California and other states which have abstracted water that limitations have been placed on withdrawals. Even the Great Lakes of North America have suffered a serious fall of level from removals, especially by Chicago, which takes its water from Lake Michigan and discharges the city effluent into the Mississippi drainage system. Abstractions have led to a diminution of flow over Niagara Falls of between 50,000 and 60,000 cusecs, or about 25 per cent of an average year's flow, mainly since 1904. Great artesian basins in the United States have long since ceased to yield flowing wells, and a falling static level is upsetting the economies of ground water irrigation, thereby indicating the extent to which abstractions have exceeded intake." A. Beeby-Thompson, "Recharging London's Water Basin," *The Times* (London) *Review of Industry*, November, 1950, p. 20.

[28] J. Kenneth Allbeiter, "Soil Maps and Their Use," in United States Department of Agriculture, *Soils and Men: The Yearbook of Agriculture, 1938* (Washington, 1938), p. 1003.

[29] The Division of Soils, Bureau of Plant Industry, was, in the summer of 1946, about eight years behind on publication on account of shortage of funds. The situation has not materially improved since.

[30] That is, contour maps which exist have not been related to soil maps where these are complete, nor have either been broken down extensively by major regional crop areas.

[31] W. J. McGee, *Wells and Subsoil Waters*, Department of Agriculture, Bureau of Soils, Bull. No. 92 (Washington, March, 1913), p. 8.

[32] David E. Lilienthal, *TVA: Democracy on the March* (rev. ed.; New York: Harper, 1953), p. 62.

[33] Person, *Little Waters*, p. 6.

[34] John T. Curtis, "The Modification of Midlatitude Grasslands and Forests by Man," in William L. Thomas, Jr., *et. al.*, eds., *Man's Role in Changing the Face of the Earth*, Wenner-Gren Foundation for Anthropological Research and the National Science Foundation (Chicago: University of Chicago Press, 1956), pp. 726-727.

[35] Lilienthal, *TVA*, p. 63.

[36] Person, *Little Waters*, p. 45.

[37] G. V. Jacks and R. O. Whyte, *Vanishing Lands: A World Survey of Soil Erosion* (New York: Doubleday, Doran, 1939), pp. 12, 14.

[38] Person has estimated that the average yield of 35 bushels of corn per acre on land showing "no erosion" will decrease to 15 bushels on "partially eroded" soil, and to 5 bushels on "badly eroded" land. See figure 32 in *Little Waters*, p. 36.

[39] Soil stability is to some degree dependent upon soil type, but erodability is found to be primarily dependent upon the combination of cropping methods and slope, and soil types as such are largely determined by whatever determines resistance to erosion in native plant and animal life. See Jacks and Whyte, *Vanishing Lands*, pp. 87-88.

[40] *Ibid.*, p. 19. Here is a case where "an ounce of prevention is worth a pound of cure" holds with a vengeance.

[41] Person, *Little Waters*, p. 33.

[42] Robert M. Salter and C. J. Schollenberger, "Farm Manure," in United States Department of Agriculture, *Soils and Men*, pp. 445-461.

[43] See, e.g., Wheeler McMillen, "How Far Can We Go in Chemurgy?" in United States Department of Agriculture, *Crops in Peace and War: The Yearbook of Agriculture, 1950-1951* (Washington, 1951), pp. 10-13.

[44] Myron S. Anderson, "Wastes That Improve Soil," *ibid.*, p. 882.

[45] "Statisticians have calculated that France alone makes a deposit of half a milliard [francs] every year, in the Atlantic, through the mouths of her rivers. . . . The cleverness of man is such that he prefers to get rid of these five hundred millions in the gutter. It is the very substance of the people that is carried off, here drop by drop, there wave after wave, the wretched outpour of our sewers into the rivers, and the gigantic collection of our rivers into the ocean. Every hiccough of our sewers costs us a thousand francs. From this spring two results, the land impoverished, and the water tainted. Hunger arising from the furrow, and disease from the stream . . . the public wealth flows away to the river, and leakage takes place. Leakage is the word. Europe is being ruined in this manner by exhaustion." Les Misérables, Book Second of Jean Valjean, "The Intestines of the Leviathan." (New York, 1887), pp. 84-85.

[46] John Lossing Buck, *Land Utilization in China*, International Research Series, Institute of Pacific Relations (Nanking: University of Nanking, 1937), p. 265.

[47] Myron S. Anderson, "Wastes that Improve the Soil, in United States Department of Agriculture, *Crops in Peace and War*, p. 881.

[48] United States Department of Agriculture, *Technology on the Farm: A Special Report* (Washington, August, 1940), p. 31.

[49] Cited by Luna B. Leopold, in "Land Use and Sediment Yield," in Thomas et al., eds., *Man's Role in Changing the Face of the Earth*, p. 642.

[50] Hug H. Bennett and W. C. Lowdermilk, "General Aspects of the Soil-Erosion Problem," in United States Department of Agriculture, *Soils and Men*, pp. 595-596.

[51] Herbert George Wells and Julian S. Huxley, *The Science of Life* (New York: Doubleday, Doran, 1931), II, 1031.

[52] Spectacular as these possible increases may appear in individual instances, they are brought about primarily by supplying chemicals which were previously mined out of the soil, or which it lacked originally, and by improving the potentialities of the natural ecological balance.

[53] Carl O. Sauer, "The Agency of Man on the Earth," in Thomas et al., eds., *Man's Role in Changing the Face of the Earth*, pp. 67-68.

[54] Edward H. Graham, *Natural Principles of Land Use* (New York: Oxford University Press, 1944), pp. 24-25.

[55] *Soils and Men,* p. 602.

[56] *Evolution of the Land Program,* p. 11.

[57] Carl T. Schmidt, *American Farmers in the World Crisis* (New York: Oxford University Press, 1941), p. 57.

[58] United States Department of Agriculture, *Food and Life: The Yearbook of Agriculture, 1939* (Washington, 1939), p. 400. See also "Per Capita Consumption of Farm Products," in *Supplementary Report of the Land Planning Committee to the National Resources Board* (Washington, 1936), pt. 3, pp. 1-113.

[59] If, according to a U.N. estimate, the population of Asia, Africa, South America and Central America were to increase between 1950 and 2000 from 1,625 to 2,936 millions—possibly a conservative figure—to feed them (*a*) at the same per capita level as now would require bringing into cultivation "over 394 million new hectares" (975 million acres) in these areas, and (*b*) at the level of 2,800-3,000 calories per capita daily would require increasing the productivity of *old and new* land over present efficiency by 41 per cent. Stephen Raushenbush, "Economic Considerations in Conservation and Development," in the *Proceedings* of the United Nations Scientific Conference on the Conservation and Utilization of Resources (UNSCCUR), Department of Economic Affairs, 1950, E/Conf. 7/7 (8 vols.; Lake Success: 1950-53), I, *Plenary Meetings,* p. 202.

[60] In some areas, loss of agricultural land to other uses—urban and industrial construction, highways, airfields, public parks and recreation areas—has begun to cause alarm. Between 1927 and 1939, for example, Britain lost from its small total of some 16½ million acres of agricultural land an average of over 66,000 acres a year. During and since the war the rate has been considerably increased. *Country and Town: A Summary of the Scott and Uthwaitt Reports* (London: Penguin Books, 1943). In the United States, 40 million acres were absorbed by expanding cities between 1910 and 1950, a rate of 1 million acres per year. Another 10 million acres have been covered by impounded waters. "A single modern airport requires 5,000 acres or more," while a two-lane highway and a parallel railroad track will take out of agricultural production 50 acres to the mile. Expansion of suburban areas, highways, street networks, and similar developments threaten further to increase such demands on agricultural lands. See William A. Albrecht, "Physical, Chemical, and Biochemical Changes in the Soil Community," and Edward H. Graham, "The Re-creative Power of Plant Communities," in Thomas *et al.,* eds., *Man's Role in Changing the Face of the Earth,* pp. 648, 684.

[61] From William D. McFarlane, *A Survey of Canadian Research on the Utilization of Farm Products,* National Chemurgic Committee of the Canadian Chamber of Commerce (Montreal, May, 1941), pp. 44, 45. Similar estimates have been made for use of wastes from corn, starch, sugar beets, noxious farm weeds, wheat and other straws, scrub brush, etc.

[62] Person, *Little Waters,* p. 47.

[63] Lilienthal, *TVA,* p. 69.

[64] Luther Gulick *et al.,* eds., *Papers on the Science of Administration,* Institute of Public Administration, Columbia University (New York, 1937), p. 10.

[65] It is the general thesis of this book that the two are reconcilable throughout, but, as indicated in the prefatory chapter, examination of the manner in which this reconciliation may be effected is so important, and involves such wide-ranging issues that the problem, *sui generis,* must be omitted from the present study.

[66] *Vanishing Lands,* p. 311.

[67] See, e.g., Robert A. Brady, *Crisis in Britain* (Berkeley and Los Angeles: University of California Press, 1950), chap. x, "Town and Country Planning," and chap. xi, "Agriculture and Marketing." See also Central Office of Information, *Agriculture in Britain* (London, 1950). [Pamphlet.]

[68] Jacks and Whyte, *Vanishing Lands,* pp. 307-308.

[69] See, e.g., the Introduction by E. E. Edwards to *Washington, Jefferson, Lincoln and Agriculture*, Bureau of Agricultural Economics, United States Department of Agriculture (Washington, November, 1937), a publication in celebration of the 75th anniversary of the Department.

[70] C. A. Bonnen and A. C. Magee, "Some Technological Changes in the High Plains Cotton Area of Texas," *Journal of Farm Economics*, Vol. XX, No. 3 (August, 1938), p. 615.

[71] The method can be used for seeding range lands at half the former cost per acre, of grain lands in units of 500 acres or more at 75 cents (as against 90 cents) per acre, etc. *Fortune*, June, 1945, p. 166.

[72] E. A. Starch, "Farm Organization as affected by Mechanization," *Bulletin*, No. 278, Agricultural Experiment Station, Montana State College (Bozeman, May, 1933), p. 11.

[73] A. P. Brodell and James W. Birkhead, "Work Performed with Principal Farm Machines," *Farm Management*, No. 42, Department of Agriculture, Bureau of Agricultural Economics (Washington, May, 1943), p. 9.

[74] A. O. Parsons and Kenneth Sire, *The Cost of Using Modern Farm Machinery*, Circular, No. 29, Department of Agricultural Economics, Montana State College Agriculture Experiment Station (Bozeman, October, 1940), p. 4. [Mimeographed.]

[75] R. W. Trullinger, "Science in the Agriculture of Tomorrow," in United States Department of Agriculture, *Crops in Peace and War*, p. 1.

[76] Martin R. Cooper, Glen T. Barton, and Albert R. Brodell, *Progress of Farm Mechanization*, Department of Agriculture Misc. Publ. No. 630 (Washington, October, 1947), p. 16.

[77] The necessity for county boards of agriculture was recognized when it was seen that the various activities of the federal and state agencies did not add up to a comprehensive and adequate agricultural program and the needs of farm families were not being met. Some method was needed to spread the leadership base and reach a larger proportion of the people, and bring them more directly into the determination and execution of programs, and to correlate the work of all the various agencies. "And so the apparent drift away from democracy led inevitably back to this democratic process which now extends into 47 states and more than 1,600 counties. It is estimated that 17,000 county, state and regional employees of public agricultural agencies and over 90,000 farm men and women are participating in program planning activities in leadership capacities. The farm families affected by the resulting changes and developments in programs run well into the millions. Farm people are now having the most direct and active part in determining what programs shall be and how they shall be administered, of any time since the government provided substantial assistance to agriculture. . . . With a committee man and woman for every small neighborhood area of 25 to 40 families and with these committee members grouped under the leadership of community committee chairmen we have the most complete organization of farm people that we have ever had in America." B. L. Hummel, "County Boards of Agriculture," in *Proceedings* of the National Conference on Planning, held at Philadelphia, May 12-14, 1941 (Chicago: American Society of Planning Officials), pp. 130-131.

[78] Attempting to answer the question, what should be the best "scale of operations" for farming in the Canadian Great Plains areas of the central-western provinces, the Saskatchewan government was unable to find any data except that the religious sects of the Hutterites allowed their farm colonies to reach the size which could be cultivated by 20 to 25 families, while the "Mennonite villages as a rule had eight or sixteen families as a basic unit of size." *Guide to Co-operative Farm Planning*, issued by the Consultation Committee on Co-operative Farming of the Province of Saskatchewan (n.d., but of the middle 1940's), p. 13. [Mimeographed.]

CHAPTER VII. THE CHEMICAL REVOLUTION IN THE MATERIALS
FOUNDATION OF INDUSTRY
(Pp. 202-231)

[1] Enquete Ausschuss zur Untersuchung der Erzeugungs und Absatzbedingungen der deutschen Wirtschaft, *Die Deutsche Chemische Industrie* (Berlin: E. S. Mittler, 1930), p. 1.

[2] Watson Davis, ed., *The Advance of Science* (New York: Doubleday, Doran, 1934), p. 45.

[3] Harrison E. Howe, "The Chemical Industries," in *Technological Trends and National Policy*, Report of the Subcommittee on Technology to the National Resources Committee (Washington, 1937), p. 290.

[4] Unless, of course, there were important conservation reasons for utilizing an otherwise waste material at a commercial loss. This was the basis upon which the Farm Chemurgic Council proposed to utilize farm and forest wastes—a recurring resource—for the making of alcohol to be mixed to a fixed percentage of gasoline derived from petroleum—a limited, nonrenewable, and shrinking resource.

[5] "Optimum," of a plant or process, is taken to mean such a size that, given the closest possible approximation to continuous processing, any changeover to smaller or larger size would raise processing cost. The cost parameters are, for this purpose, assumed to be constant.

[6] See chap. viii.

[7] See chap. vi.

[8] An outstanding example of collapse of an iron and steel industry because of failure to plan upon the basis of adequate geological data is found in the case of the exhaustion of the Pilot Knob ores in Missouri. See Victor S. Clark, *History of Manufacturers in the United States* (New York: McGraw-Hill, 1929), Vol. II.

[9] Eliminating, of course, those heat changes at the billet-casting and soaking-pit stages. The first lowers the heat of the molten metal by creating a cooled shell, and the latter evens the heat to the point required for rolling. Heat losses, here, are not, however, very important. Newer methods—continuous casting—now make it possible completely to bypass the soaking-pit stage.

[10] *Home Affairs Survey*, April 12, 1951, p. 5.

[11] There are other by-products from the steelmaking process itself. For example, fertilizers (Thomas meal), portland cement (from slag), stack gas.

[12] Erich Zimmerman, *World Resources and Industries* (rev. ed.; New York: Harper, 1951), p. 491.

[13] *Business Week*, April 10, 1948, p. 30.

[14] The so-called "petrochemicals" were valued in that year at $3,500,000,000; they supplied from oil and natural gas some 2,500 chemical compounds. Chemists believe some 2,500 may be added within the next 15 to 20 years. Petrochemicals supply the principal raw materials for the new synthetic rubber industry, and in addition are important materials for the manufacture of "synthetic fibers, as detergents in soap, for fertilizers, plastics, refrigerants, anti-freeze, paints, insecticides and medicines. In fact, chemicals made from petroleum enter into nearly every phase of modern living." New York *Times*, January 3, 1955.

[15] "Commercial Solvents," *Fortune*, October, 1944, p. 135.

[16] Benjamin I. Weitz, ed., *Electric Power Development in the USSR*, U.S.S.R. Committee for International Scientific and Technical Conferences (Moscow: INRA Publishing Society, 1936), p. 302.

[17] *Ibid.*, pp. 303-304, 308.

[18] "Carbide & Carbon Chemicals," *Fortune*, September, 1941, p. 57.

[19] *Ibid.*, p. 59.

[20] In *Fortune's* colorful terminology, "Carbide's South Charleston Works, with gases as raw materials, out-Wellses H. G. The 800 operators who run this mam-

moth are dwarfed under giant tanks and columns. They read gauges, turn valves, push buttons, and see neither the raw materials nor the end products until they gush out as water-white liquids." *Ibid.*, p. 57.

[21] *Business Week*, October 29, 1949, p. 54.

[22] National Resources Planning Board, *Regional Planning, Part XI, The Southeast* (Washington, 1942), p. 86.

[23] The possibilities here may be visualized when it is realized that in the southeastern states surveyed in the NRPB report (*ibid.*, p. 82), "6 acres out of every 10 acres are under forest cover," and that the bulk of this forest land can eventually be made to sustain commercially valuable stands. The same holds for many other sections of the United States, once denuded of forest, but which may once again be advantageously reforested.

[24] *Iron Age*, January 11, 1951, p. 71.

CHAPTER VIII. THE PERMEATION OF AUTOMATION PROCESSING
(Pp. 232-266)

[1] Thorstein Veblen, *The Theory of Business Enterprise* (New York, 1904), p. 16.

[2] Stuart Chase, "Danger at the A. O. Smith Corporation," *Fortune*, November, 1930, pp. 62-67, 102; also "A. O. Smith at War," *Fortune*, October, 1941, pp. 86-89, 134-140.

[3] Hearings, Temporary National Economic Committee, Congress of the United States, on Public Resolution No. 113, *Investigation of Concentration of Economic Power*, Part 30, "Technology and Concentration of Economic Power," 76th Cong., 3rd sess., (Washington, 1940), p. 17338.

[4] *Ibid.*, p. 17339.

[5] "Cybernetics is the general theory of machines that can deal with changing situations the way a human operator would." *Business Week*, "Machines That Think," February 19, 1949, p. 44.

[6] *Making the Automatic Factory a Reality*, a special study by a Harvard Business School Group under the leadership of John T. Diebold, in a partial reprint by Griffenhagen and Associates, management consultants (Boston, May 15, 1951), p. 36.

[7] It is not, of course, here implied that the making of the reservations solves the problem of how to avoid virtual enslavement of masses of human beings with such a technology. It is, however, to imply that the problem of avoiding mass regimentation is not more difficult—as is assumed in such a gross misunderstanding of the course of events as Orwell's *1984* or Ortega's *Revolt of the Masses*—but less difficult by virtue of the possibilities opened up by trends in contemporary technology.

[8] It is not necessary, in this connection, to summarize the range and proportions of these net gains in productivity. No such attempt can have any meaning except when evaluated in terms of definite policies leading to full production, proper cost accounting, etc.

[9] *Business Week*, "Pushbuttons Run Pipeline," July 29, 1950, p. 42.

[10] *Business Week*, "Electrical Arithmetic for Quality Control," February 4, 1950, p. 58.

[11] Hartley W. Barclay, *Ford Production Methods* (New York: Harper, 1936), p. 9.

[12] See, in particular, *Production and Engineering Bulletin*, a monthly publication of the Ministry of Labour and National Service and the Ministry of Production, London, particularly for the years 1944-1945. Of special interest was the work of the Regional Boards and the Regional and District Capacity Offices. Their functions were to mobilize all productive capacity in all of England by districts and localities, control and regulate the "Load of the Regions," unify the production

schedules of confluent industries, modernize—as far as appeared possible under wartime conditions—all production processes and thus, to unify, in effect, all production by localities, regions, and the nation with respect to materials flow, production schedules, manpower, housing facilities, etc.

[13] See, e.g., the series of articles on conveying and lifting in *Production and Engineering Bulletin*, May-November, 1945.

[14] That is, including costs which must be borne by all individuals and groups involved—housing, moving, etc., included.

[15] *Business Week*, "An Electronic 'War Production Board,'" October 9, 1948, pp. 22-24.

[16] Gregory Bienstock, Solomon M. Schwarz, and Aaron Yugow, *Management in Russian Industry and Agriculture* (London and New York: Oxford University Press, 1944), p. 7.

[17] See, e.g., *Iron and Steel Industry*, Reports by the British Iron and Steel Federation and the Joint Iron Council to the Minister of Supply, presented by the Minister of Supply to Parliament (London: H.S.M.O., May, 1946).

[18] See Robert A. Brady, *The Rationalization Movement in German Industry* (Berkeley: University of California Press, 1933).

[19] Working parties were organized to study problems of efficiency and productivity in the following industries: cotton, boots and shoes, carpets, china clay, heavy clothing, light clothing, rubberized clothing, cutlery, furniture, domestic glassware, hosiery, jewelry and silverware, lace, linoleum, pottery, wool, and jute. Development councils for implementing the recommendations of working parties include the Furniture Development Council, the Jewelry and Silverware Council, the Clothing Industry Development Council, and the Cotton Board.

[20] Industry reports cover vegetable production, animal production, power, textiles, construction materials, interior transport, fuels, steel, and handwork.

[21] *Iron and Steel Industry*, p. 14.

[22] *Ibid.*, pp. 23, 35.

[23] *Ibid.*, Part II, "Report on the Ironfounding Industry."

[24] It is virtually impossible, however, to separate "purely technical modernization" from the over-all plan even in the case of such a comparatively simple problem as fuel consumption, as the following quotation shows: "The possibility of reducing fuel consumption depends in the main on (*a*) the full use of available scrap; (*b*) the use of high grade ores; (*c*) the preparation of ores; (*d*) an increase in the size and efficiency of blast furnaces; (*e*) full integration of blast furnaces, steel melting and rolling plant; (*f*) utilization of waste heat." *Ibid.*, p. 29.

CHAPTER IX. THE PROBLEM OF INTER-MEDIA TRAFFIC UNIFICATION
(Pp. 267-295)

[1] In a message to Congress on June 7, 1935, recommending extension of the Emergency Railroad Transportation Act of 1933, President Roosevelt said: "It is high time to deal with the Nation's transportation as a single, unified problem." House Doc. 221, 74th Cong., 1st sess. The Motor Carrier Act of 1935 made this policy the law of the land. See the opinion of the United States Supreme Court in McLean Trucking Co. *v.* United States, 321 U.S. 67, 80-83.

[2] Harry Schwartz, *Russia's Soviet Economy* (New York: Prentice-Hall, 1950), pp. 331-332.

[3] List saw this more clearly than any of his contemporaries. "The railroad system and the Zollverein," he wrote in 1841, "are Siamese twins. They were born at the same time, have grown bodily together, of a single spirit and understanding, they mutually support each other and strive after one and the same great objective—towards unification of the German peoples in a great, cultivated, rich, mighty, and unassailable nation. Without the Zollverein a German railway system

is only a figure of speech, impossible of realization. Only with the aid of a German railroad system is it possible for the social economy of the German nation to reach true national greatness, and only following this advance can the railroad system achieve its full significance." Friedrich List, *Schriften zum Verkehrswesen, Werke,* Vol. III, chap. 15, "Das Deutsche Eisenbahnsystem als Mittel zu Vervollkommnung der deutschen Industrie, des deutschen Zollvereins und des deutschen National-berbandes überhaupt" (Berlin: Reimar Hobbing, 1929), p. 347.

⁴ See, e.g., Cheng Ch'eng-K'un, "Regionalism in China's Postwar Reconstruction," *Social Forces,* Vol. 22, No. 1 (October, 1943), pp. 14-18; also "Railroads for Asia," *Fortune,* November, 1943, pp. 28 ff.; also H. J. von Lochow, *China's National Railways* (Peiping, 1948).

⁵ Mr. Robert S. Henry of the Association of American Railroads thinks (letter to the author, March 7, 1956) that the estimate requires modification on the grounds of (1) estimated stand-by capacity for defense needs, and (2) the volume and variety of American consumption and the competitive structure of transportation and the economy it serves.

⁶ Federal Coordinator of Transportation, Section of Car Pooling, *Report on Freight Car Pooling* (1934), p. 35.

⁷ For electricity, see H. Parodi, "Développement de l'Electrification des Chemins de Fer," in *Transactions of the World Power Conference,* sectional meeting, Scandinavia (Stockholm: Svenska Nationalkommittén för Världskrafkonferenser, 1933), *Railways—Urban and Suburban Traffic,* pp. 337-371.

⁸ "As regards Diesel and electric traction it may be pointed out that these traction systems will give the best results only when they are used separately so that such stationary plants and staff as are required for steam traction only can be entirely given up. Nevertheless, a combination of different kinds of traffic can in certain cases be the most suitable solution: for instance the use of Diesel motor coaches on lines for steam traction or Diesel electric shunting locomotives at harbours, connected to electrified railway lines." *Ibid.,* pp. 27-28.

⁹ Federal Coordinator of Transportation, *Second Report on Economy Possibilities of Regional Coordination Projects* (1935), p. 2, cited by the National Resources Planning Board in *Transportation and National Policy* (Washington, 1942), p. 166. This estimate, it is worth noting, was made for the low-volume years of 1932 and 1933, and at the price levels prevailing then. Data drawn on a comparable basis for the postwar period, and at prevailing prices, might well run from three to four times this figure.

¹⁰ *Rail Freight Service Costs in the Various State Territories of the United States,* Letter from the Chairman of the Interstate Commerce Commission to the Senate, June 8, 1943, p. 29.

¹¹ 78th Cong., 1st sess., Senate Document No. 63, p. 94.

¹² Letter from Mr. Henry.

¹³ The Conservative government subsequently denationalized the road hauler service.

¹⁴ "Restoration of European Transport," *The Times* (London) *Review of Industry,* April 1950, p. 66. Also *International Road Transport—Further Problems and Developments,* Transport and Communications Commission, U.N. Economic and Social Council, E/CN. 2/54, March 21, 1949.

¹⁵ *Automobile Facts,* June, 1951, p. 3.

¹⁶ National Research Council, Highway Research Board, Special Report 4, *Final Report on Road Test One-MD: Effect of Controlled Truck Axle Loadings on Concrete Pavement* (Washington, 1952), p. 7.

¹⁷ Robley Winfrey, "Gasoline Consumption, Weight and Mileage of Commercial Vehicles," in *Highway-User Taxation,* Bull. 92, National Research Council, Highway Research Board (Washington: National Research Council, 1954), p. 43.

[18] Memorandum from Mr. Richard Carll, Institute of Transportation and Traffic Engineering, University of California, Berkeley, August 20, 1956.

[19] From data supplied by Mr. Leslie C. Edie of the Port of New York Authority, Tunnels and Bridges Department, in a letter to the author, August 13, 1956.

[20] To compare with somewhat earlier data: a surface streetcar line can handle 13,500 persons per hour, while a subway with one track for local and one track for express trains in each direction can handle 100,000 passengers per hour. International City Manager's Association, *Local Planning Administration* (2nd. ed.; Chicago, 1948), p. 133.

[21] In 1955, the State Highway Departments and the Bureau of Public Roads estimated that federal, state, and local governments must spend $101 billion to bring inadequate highways up to standard by 1965. *Automobile Facts*, April, 1955, p. 1.

[22] These systems, of course, are in the main not integrated with the rail networks and may conceivably involve large-scale and (to the economy as a whole) uneconomic duplications.

[23] The Union Railroad Freight Terminal, opened in 1932, costing $19 million; the New York Union Motor Truck Terminal, opened in 1949, costing $10 million; and the Newark Union Motor Truck Terminal, completed in 1950, costing $8.2 million. The first is leased to eight trunk railroads; the second is designed to reduce truck street traffic by consolidation of less than truckload hauls. The third, temporarily leased to the United States Air Force, is to facilitate "interchange of over-the-road, less-than-truckload freight." *The Port of New York Authority Facilities* (New York: Port of New York Authority, February, 1954). [Brochure.]

[24] Erich W. Zimmermann, *World Resources and Industries* (rev. ed.; New York: Harper, 1951), p. 529.

[25] New York *Times*, July 17, 1955.

[26] Cited in Zimmermann, *World Resources and Industries*, p. 531. The comparable figures for railroad costs were $0.01695 (twenty times the water shipping cost) and by truck $0.06125 (eighty times the water shipping cost). Pipeline costs per barrel decline rapidly with increase in the size of the pipe. One estimate has shown the cost of pumping oil 1,000 miles through 8-inch pipe to be 3.7 times as expensive as through 24-inch pipe (23.6 cents vs. 7 cents). P. Harvey Middletown, *Oil Industry and Transportation—Prewar and Postwar* (Chicago: Railway Business Association, 1943), p. 20.

[27] For the railroads' case for such integration see Association of American Railroads, Railroad Committee for the Study of Transportation, *Transportation in America* (Washington, 1947), chap. xxi, "Pipe-Line Transport."

[28] Association of American Railroads, *Quiz on Railroads and Railroading* (11th ed.; Washington, 1956), sec. 211.

[29] Zimmermann, *World Resources and Industries*, p. 556.

[30] *Business Week*, February 17, 1951, p. 25. Professor Arthur Gray, California Institute of Technology, in a personal communication to the author, points out that propane gas can be successfully carried along with the oil in a crude oil pipeline in suspension in the oil, and has little if any more volume.

[31] Association of American Railroads, Railroad Committee for the Study of Transportation, Report by Subcommittee on Pipe Line Transport, May 1, 1944, p. 249.

[32] Interstate Commerce Commission, Sixty-Eighth Annual Report on *Transport Statistics in the United States* for the year ended December 31, 1954 (Washington, 1955), pt. i, table 1, p. 3. Prior to January 1, 1956, the ICC classified railroads according to annual revenue: Class I above $1,000,000; Class II, $100,000 to $1,000,000; Class III, below $100,000. Since that date Class III has been eliminated; Class II includes all roads earning annual operating revenue up to $3,000,000; Class I includes all lines above that figure. Thus at the end of 1956

there remained 113 Class I companies operating 223,336 miles of track and 309 Class II companies operating 10,173 miles of track. Interstate Commerce Commission, Seventieth Annual Report on *Transportation Statistics in the United States* for the year ended December 31, 1956 (Washington, 1957), pt. i, table 1, p. 3.

[33] There are a few partial exceptions such as that of the Railway Express Agency —a national and wholly owned subsidiary of the railroads—which does an extensive contract business with the major airlines.

[34] A 1947 review of 25 leading railroads showed coördinated rail-highway service for the l.c.l. (less-than-carload) freight as approximately 69,000 routed miles. For coördinated bus-rail service the corresponding figure was 74,000 miles. Association of American Railroads, *Transportation in America*, p. 308.

[35] The Prince plan was a variation on the ICC plan which was promulgated in 1929, for consolidation into 19 systems.

[36] National Resources Planning Board, *Transportation and National Policy*, p. 163.

[37] *Ibid.*, quoted, p. 164.

[38] This general class of costs amounts to about 3 per cent of the total cost of operating railroads. Robert S. Henry, letter, March 7, 1956. Mr. Henry remarks, however, that even if the cost could be halved "without loss of quality of supervision and intimacy of contact, the saving would not be as great as it might seem to the uninformed reader."

[39] "This comes about," testified J. H. Parmelee, Director of the Bureau of Railway Economics, before the T.N.E.C., "through the fact that they have a standard gauge of track, they have completely interchangeable locomotives and cars, not only as to the complete units of equipment but also as to the various accessories, two of the most important of which are the standard coupler and the standard air brake, which are interchangeable on all cars; and finally they have an arrangement by which freight cars travel, regardless of their ownership, over the lines of all railways freely from one end of the country to the other." Temporary National Economic Committee, Hearings, 76th Cong., 3d sess., Pursuant to Public Resolution no. 113 (75th Cong.), Part 30, "Technology and Concentration of Economic Power" (Washington, 1940), p. 16548.

[40] Not to mention a few of the ancient and many of the medieval towns, as pointed out by Lewis Mumford, *The Culture of Cities* (New York: Harcourt, Brace, 1938).

[41] See Vernon Sommerfield, *London Transport, A Record and Survey* (London, 1935). Sommerfield describes the Board as the greatest urban transport system in the world. "The L.P.T.B.," writes the British Information Service, "is the largest urban transport undertaking in the world. It has a capital investment of about £150,000,000, operates every mechanical form of public passenger transport except the taxicab and the airplane in an area of nearly 2,000 square miles containing about one-quarter of the total population of England and Wales." *Labor and Industry in Britain*, Vol. III, No. 8 (August, 1945), p. 123.

[42] See, e.g., the various reports of the American Society of Planning Officials, The American Planning and Civic Association, Town and Country Planning, The *Quarterly Review* of the British Town and Country Planning Association, and The *Journal* of the American Institute of Planners.

[43] *The Port of New York Authority Marine and Inland Terminals* (New York: The Port of New York Authority, 1950). [Brochûre.]

[44] *Newark Union Motor Truck Terminal* (New York: The Port of New York Authority, December, 1949). [Pamphlet.]

[45] K. G. Fenelon, *Transport Co-ordination* (London: P. S. King and Son, 1929), pp. 37-38.

[46] Sir Osborne Mance, *International River and Canal Transport*, Royal Institute of International Affairs, London (New York: Oxford University Press, 1945), p. 13.

⁴⁷ See, e.g., "Old Man River Has a Fine Young Boom," *Business Week*, October 21, 1950, pp. 69 ff.

⁴⁸ See, e.g., Harold G. Moulton, "Inland Waterways," in *Encyclopaedia of the Social Sciences*, Vol. 15, pp. 377-384, and the two Brookings Institution publications by Moulton *et al.*, *The St. Lawrence Navigation and Power Project* (Washington, 1929), and *The American Transportation Problem* (Washington, 1933), pt. v., "Water Transportation." See also the criticism of the railroad industry in Association of American Railroads, *Transportation in America*, chap. xix, "Water Transport."

⁴⁹ Eli F. Heckscher, *Mercantilism* (London: Allen and Unwin; New York: Macmillan, 1935), I, 45 ff., 110 ff., 137 ff., 221 ff.

⁵⁰ M. Slade Kendrick, *Public Finance, Principles and Problems* (Boston: Houghton Mifflin, 1951), pp. 325-326.

⁵¹ F. Eugene Melder, *State Trade Walls* (Public Affairs Pamphlets, 1939).

⁵² United States Dept. of Agriculture, Bureau of Agricultural Economics, *Interstate Barriers to Truck Transportation* (Washington, December, 1950).

⁵³ Harmer E. Davis, Director, Institute of Transportation and Traffic Engineering, University of California, "Developments in the Western States Relating to Reciprocity Agreements," paper delivered before the Session on Economics, Finance and Administration at the 35th annual meeting of the Highway Research Board, Washington, D.C., January 18, 1956.

⁵⁴ For a historical summary of the early agreements see "Die Internationalen Beziehungen der Eisenbahnen," in *Handwörterbuch der Staatswissenschaften*, III; the excellent summary by Sir Ralph L. Wedgwood, *International Rail Transport*, Royal Institute of International Affairs (London: Oxford University Press, 1946); and the reports of the various subcommittees of the Transport Commission of UNESCO.

⁵⁵ For details of the original plan see "Proposed Inter-American Highway," prepared by the United States Department of Agriculture, Bureau of Public Roads, 73d Cong., 2d sess., Sen. Doc. No. 224 (1934).

⁵⁶ Abraham Berglund, "Shipping," in *Encyclopaedia of the Social Sciences*, Vol. 14, p. 38.

⁵⁷ See, "Seeschiffahrt," in *Handwörterbuch der Staatswissenschaften*, VII, 303-423; also, Sir Osborne Mance, *International Sea Transport*, Royal Institute of International Affairs (London: Oxford University Press, 1945).

⁵⁸ Mance, *International River and Canal Transport*, p. 3.

⁵⁹ See the list in Sir Osborne Mance, *International Air Transport* (New York: Oxford University Press, 1944), pp. 14-16.

⁶⁰ Joe D. Walstrom, "The Chicago Air Conference," Department of State *Bulletin*, December 31, 1944, Vol. XI, No. 288, p. 844. The U.S.S.R. was not represented at the conference, though the way was opened for her subsequent participation.

⁶¹ Vilhjalmur Stefansson, "Arctic Supply Line," *Fortune*, July, 1942, pp. 65 ff.

⁶² British Information Services, *Labor and Industry in Britain*, Vol. III, No. 8 (August, 1945), p. 125.

⁶³ Association of American Railroads, *Transportation and National Policy*, p. 1.

⁶⁴ A valid precondition is that the advantages enjoyed should be revealed in the rates and tariffs charged, and to this end, indubitably, "prices paid should reflect true cost." But what does this mean? Take the case of subsidies. Among others, *Transportation in America*, pp. 355-362, cites the following as illustrative: subsidy land grants to railroads, valued at about $125 million "when granted," paid back in land-grant rate reductions to the government ninefold by 1945. Throughout American history federal government subsidies to waterways amounted to "more than $2.8 billion in cash for the construction, improvement, and maintenance of waterways . . . for navigation purposes"; subsidies to road carriers (in part),

$34 billion for the 20-year period ending in 1940; subsidies to air navigation, around $1 billion for air terminals alone up to 1944. Such subsidies, no doubt, along with differential tax rates, supply of "free services" (as, e.g., meals on scheduled air flights, etc.), distort "true cost." So also does the manner of reckoning subsidy. For example, if subsequent real estate value, and not original grant value, be taken as the basis for reckoning railroad subsidies, the figure would be many times as high as the one cited above. Rivers and harbors are maintained partly for military purposes. Recent air navigation subsidies are stated in terms of depreciated dollars. There are many other complicating variable factors.

CHAPTER X. EVOLUTION OF THE UNIVERSAL ENERGY POOL
(Pp. 296-325)

[1] Sir Francis Simon, "Nuclear Energy and the Future," *Lloyds Bank Review,* April, 1955, p. 1.

[2] Oscar von Miller, *Gutschten über die Reichselektrizitäsversorgung* (Berlin: VDI Verlag, 1930).

[3] E. h. Oskar Oliven, in *Transactions,* Second World Power Conference, Berlin, 1930, XIX, 30.

[4] See *Electric Power Development in the USSR* (English translation), a series of papers submitted by the Russian delegation to the Third World Power Conference, Washington, and published by the INRA Publishing Society, Moscow, 1936.

There is an interesting chapter to be written on the origin of Goelro. Apparently it was largely based on a sketch elaborated from certain proposals made by von Moellendorf in 1919 for postwar planning in Germany. Von Moellendorf was an electrical engineer serving with the German General Electric (A.E.G.) who became understudy to and collaborator with Walter Rathenau, the head of the famous materials-supply division—Kriegsrohstoffabteilung (KRA)—of the German war machine during 1915-1918. Von Moellendorf's program consisted, in effect, of carrying the wartime planning of Rathenau over into the postwar era as a means for full industrial and economic mobilization. This became the Russian pattern.

[5] Electricité de France was established under the nationalization law of 1947, and has since evolved a comprehensive national power development plan. For a survey of work in progress, see *Travaux,* January, 1951.

[6] Cited by Joseph Sirera Ransmeier, *The Tennessee Valley Authority* (Nashville: Vanderbilt University Press, 1942), p. 14.

[7] Commission on Organization of the Executive Branch of the Government (Hoover Commission), *Task Force Report on Water Resources Projects* (Washington, January, 1949), p. 32.

[8] *Ibid.*

[9] David E. Lilienthal, *TVA—Democracy on the March* (New York: Harper, 1935), p. 55.

[10] *Ibid.,* pp. 56-57.

[11] *Ibid.* (rev. ed., 1953), pp. 12-13.

[12] See *Electric Power Development in the USSR,* pp. 441 ff., for a sketch of such development in the Dnieper, Don, Volga, Lake Sevan, Chirchik, Ili, Irtysh, Ob, and other Russian systems.

[13] There may be some cases where low gravity flow is preferable for irrigation purposes, but even here the net advantage lies with high dams because of the fact that the amount of current that may be generated with any given stream flow rises, in a power curve relationship, with increase in the waterhead.

[14] *Electrical World,* January 23, 1956, pp. 158, 160.

[15] Ph. Schereschewsky, "Le Chauffage Urbain," in the *Transactions* of the World Power Conference (Sectional Meeting, Scandinavia), 1933, IV, 202.

[16] *Electric Power Development in the USSR,* p. 246.

[17] John Pearce Hardt, *Economics of the Soviet Electric Power Industry*, Documentary Research Division, Research Studies Institute, Air University, 1955 (unpublished doctoral dissertation, Columbia University, 1955), p. 184.

[18] For a list of such advantages, see Schereschewsky, *op. cit.*, pp. 203-204.

[19] For a very careful summary of costs in an experimental plant constructed by General Electric at Schenectady, see A. R. Smith, "Co-ordinated Production of Industrial Steam and Utility Power," in the *Transactions* of the World Power Conference (Sectional Meeting, Scandinavia), 1933, IV, 251-273, and in particular the tabular data summarized on p. 254.

[20] Hardt, *op. cit.*, p. 217.

[21] *Electric Power Development in the USSR*, p. 89.

[22] There appear to be several counterbalancing costs. Thus, while a 25,000 kilowatt plant will save 30,000 tons of conventional fuel over steam-condensing stations of equal capacity, it will also require some 1,500 to 2,000 tons of additional low-grade metal for construction purposes. Hardt, *op. cit.*, p. 218. A British estimate has it that "if the use of steam and electric power were combined to the maximum extent," this would save the country 20 million tons of coal, or nearly 30 per cent of its entire coal requirements for steam generation in stationary industrial plants and electric power production. *Science and the Nation* (Harmondsworth, Middlesex: Pelican Books, 1947), p. 45.

[23] "Conditions as to the degree of simultaneousness and the relative magnitude of the power and heat consumptions respectively are of fundamental importance in considering the feasibility and economy of combined heat and power supply schemes. The first technical consideration in the planning of such combined plants is to obtain a sufficiently reliable picture of the actual requirements of heat and power respectively for almost every moment of the year. The requirements are generally found to vary considerably, for not only are there one or several erratic daily cycles of variation due to the demands of the individual consumers, but the seasonal variations in daylight and in the air temperature (and that of the water in nature) exercise also, in most cases, a great influence on both the heat and the power requirements." T. Nordensson, in *Transactions*, World Power Conference (Sectional Meeting, Scandinavia), 1933, I, 353-354.

[24] *Ibid.*, IV, see the article by S. Kaniewski, of Poland, on by-product electricity from sugar factories (p. 117), and the articles by J. P. Spangenberg and by P. A. Halberg and K. Morch, of Denmark, on steam-electric plants in the brewing industry (pp. 151,160).

[25] Edison Electric Institute, *Statistical Bulletin for 1955*.

[26] F. Marguerre, "Stand und Entwicklungsaussichten der Abfallkraftnutzung in Deutschland, insbesondere Heizkraftbetriebe," in *Transactions*, Second World Power Conference, Berlin, 1930, IV, 256.

[27] The same principle will hold for utilization of otherwise waste or low-grade solid fuels, such as anthacite culm, by-product coal dust from underground mechanized operations, peat, and lignite.

[28] *New York Times*, April 8, 1955.

[29] Sam H. Schurr and Jacob Marschak, *Economic Aspects of Atomic Power*, Report of the Cowles Commission for Research in Economics (Princeton: Princeton University Press, 1950).

[30] *Ibid.*, p. 19.

[31] *Ibid.*, p. 21.

[32] A. C. Monteith of Westinghouse has estimated that Latin America possesses only 30 billion tons of the world's known resources of coal, and only 10 per cent of the world's known oil resources—most of the latter in Venezuela.

[33] The percentages given were: aluminum, 20; chlorine-caustic soda, 8; phosphate fertilizer 33; cement, 15-26; brick, 20; flat glass, 7-10; iron and steel, 12; railroads, 8. Schurr and Marschak, *Economic Aspects of Atomic Power*, pp. 86-87.

[34] Central Electricity Board, *Eighth Annual Report, 1935* (London: Whitehead Morris, 1936), p. 3.

[35] See especially the diagram "The Electricity Transmission Systems of Europe," *Economic Bulletin for Europe,* Vol. 4, No. 3. (Geneva: United Nations, November, 1952), p. 24.

[36] There are but two limited possibilities: one is storage batteries, and the other is the pumping of otherwise unusable water into storage basins, using off-peak or otherwise waste current. Limited experiments along the latter line have been undertaken in Germany and Britain.

[37] In technical language, capacity factor equals the ratio of current generated to rated capacity for any given time-interval. Expressed in terms of hours, the maximum is the rated capacity times 8,760 hours per annum. As an average, this would be total units generated divided by the sum of the rated average capacities of the generating units.

[38] Technically defined as the ratio of kilowatt-hours generated to peak demand, multiplied by total hours of the period (day, month, or year), or the ratio of current to the maximum usage for any given time-interval.

[39] In engineering terms, the sum of separate maxima loads divided by total maximum load, or the ratio of the total of separate peaks (e.g., agricultural and industrial, summer and winter) to the combined simultaneous peak.

[40] Especially noteworthy, in this connection, is the effect of low-cost current in the development of continuous processing in both manufacturing and chemical industries, and their reciprocal effect upon the structure of electric rates.

[41] Federal Power Commission, *Electric Utility Cost Units: Steam Electric Power Generating Stations* (Washington, 1947), pp. 2, 10, 2nd *Electric Utility Cost Units: Hydroelectric Generating Stations* (Washington, 1948), pp. 3, 10.

[42] Federal Power Commission, *Electric Utility Cost Units: Steam Electric Power Generating Stations,* pp. 9, 12.

[43] See, e.g., J. Tobolla, "The Influence of Load Factor on the Economy of Power Production," in *Transactions,* World Power Conference (Sectional Meeting, Tokyo), 1929, II, 1251-1283, particularly the résumé on the last page. Also, L. A. Doggett, "Cost of Power in the United States—1938," in *Proceedings,* Midwest Power Conference (Chicago: Illinois Institute of Technology), 1942, V, 174-176.

[44] United States Department of Commerce, *The St. Lawrence Survey,* pt. vi, "The Economic Effects of the St. Lawrence Power Project" (Washington, 1941), pp. viii, ix, 97.

[45] *Transactions,* World Power Conference, Berlin, 1930, Vol. XIX.

[46] Simon, *op. cit.,* p. 10. The American figure seems to be too high. Data supplied by the *Electrical World,* January 24, 1955 (p. 154), indicate a national plant capacity-factor in the United States for 1954 of approximately 55 per cent.

[47] *Business Week,* October 4, 1947, pp. 68, 70.

[48] As is the case in various sections of New York City and until recently throughout metropolitan London.

[49] *The National Power Scheme of Great Britain, The Constitution and Functions of the Central Electricity Board,* April 4, 1934, p. 35. [Mimeographed.]

[50] See, for example, the huge three-volume report of the President's Water Resources Policy Commission, 1950, particularly Vol. I, *A Water Policy for the American People.*

CHAPTER XI. THE POSSIBLE IMPACT ON GOODS DISTRIBUTION
(Pp. 326-360)

[1] James B. Jefferys, Simon Hausberger, and Göran Lindblad, *Productivity in the Distributive Trade in Europe, Wholesale and Retail Aspects,* (Paris: Organization for European Economic Cooperation, 1954), pp. 13-14.

[2] *Ibid.,* pp. 15-16.

³ Distribution, of course, is made up of much more than the moving, storing, and handling of goods. It is also contracts, payments, bookkeeping, information, etc. In what follows, however, it is mostly the former that will be covered. It is possible that the economies possible in the latter may be no less impressive. But to consider them in this brief review is out of the question.

⁴ Throughout the following pages attention will be focused primarily on distribution of consumers' goods—to the general neglect of producers' goods.

⁵ From personal investigations by the writer; estimates made by and checked with a wholesale drug house and a leading drug retailer.

⁶ Robert A. Brady, *The Citizen's Stake in Price Control* (Paterson, N.J.: Littlefield, Adams & Company, 1952), p. 38.

⁷ Testimony given before the Subcommittee of the Committee on Military Affairs (Kilgore Committee) in hearings on a bill (3.702) to mobilize the scientific and technical resources of the nation.

⁸ As reported in personal conversation with the author by a member of the technical committee, then on the staff of the University of California.

An engine mounted above the rear wheels can be completely removed in 20 minutes and completely replaced in less than one hour. Other commonly repaired parts are equally accessible. Engineers have known how to do this for 40 years. The only place where the practice of rear-engine mounting has become common in the United States is on busses. And here the same economies are effected.

⁹ Dickson Reck, *Government Purchasing and Competition* (Berkeley and Los Angeles: University of California Press, 1954), pp. 130-131.

¹⁰ See Willis S. MacLeod, "Standards in the Federal Supply System—Civilian Goods," and C. R. Watts, "Standards in the Federal Supply System—Military Goods," in Dickson Reck, ed., *National Standards in a Modern Economy* (New York: Harper, 1956), pp. 220, 247.

¹¹ Dewey H. Palmer, "Standards for Medical, Surgical, and Hospital Supplies," *ibid.*, p. 207.

¹² It need not be emphasized, perhaps, that this special use of the word "utility" means not mere "satisfaction-yielding" but "functional to defined use."

¹³ *Industrial Standardization*, written for the National Industrial Conference Board in 1929; in charge of standards work in connection with the Code Authorities, National Recovery Administration, 1934; Standards Unit of the Consumers' Division, Office of Price Administration, 1940-41; acting editor, *National Standards in a Modern Economy* (1956).

¹⁴ M. Edwin Green, "Modular Construction—The Building Block Principle in Architectural Design," in Reck, ed., *National Standards in a Modern Economy*, p. 82.

¹⁵ *Ibid.*

¹⁶ MacLeod, *ibid.*, p. 221.

¹⁷ Watts, *ibid.*, p. 247.

¹⁸ Harry C. Trelogan and Kenneth J. McCallister, "National Standards for Agricultural Products," *ibid.*, p. 157.

¹⁹ George P. Larrick, "The Role of Food and Drug Regulation," *ibid.*, p. 174.

²⁰ T. Richard Witmer, "Consumer Goods Standards and the Sherman Act," *ibid.*, p. 319.

²¹ Comfort A. Adams, "National Standards Movement—Its Evolution and Future," *ibid.*, p. 21.

²² Various articles in *National Standards in a Modern Economy* give details on company standards.

²³ A number of examples have been gone over with practicing physicians in a large hospital. The cases are few where the trade-branded item sells for less than 50 per cent above the retail price of the drug as a chemical item.

[24] Sydney R. Elliott, *The English Coöperatives* (New Haven: Yale University Press, 1937), p. 138.

[25] *Business Week*, October 28, 1950, p. 41.

[26] Donald W. Paden, *Delivery Pooling for Retail Stores*, Department of Commerce, Bureau of Foreign and Domestic Commerce, Economic Series, No. 37 (Washington, May, 1944), p. 3.

[27] For an early study, see William F. Bristol, "Operating Costs of Service Grocery Stores in Iowa for the Year 1927," in *Iowa Studies in Business*, No. VI (Iowa City: State University of Iowa, February, 1930).

[28] Cited in Paden, *Delivery Pooling*, from Management Service Division, Wartime Prices and Trade Board, *Pooling of Retail Deliveries* (Ottawa: February 20, 1943), pp. 5, 6.

[29] *Ibid.*, p. 4.

[30] *Ibid.*, pp. 7-10.

[31] Conducted under the auspices of R. G. Bressler, Jr., of the University of Connecticut, in 1942.

[32] There are some notable exceptions. The familiar "automobile row" of most cities permits some degree of interproduct comparison, though far better would be a series of automobile shopping-centers where the different makes could be seen and demonstrated on a single lot, with supply from central storage places. A better example is the suburban shopping-center where significant efforts are being made to face up to the problem more or less as posed in the text above. These, however, have the great drawback that they do little by way of selection in terms of meanigful product-differentiation, or adequate delivery services, and hence are unable to make use of otherwise potential economies.

[33] Conducted under the auspices of the author; data taken from notes and reports in his possession.

[34] M. M. Zimmermann, *The Supermarket Grows Up* (Super Market Publishing Co., 1938), p. 14. It must be kept in mind that these figures were presented to make a case for the supermarket, yet they are supported by various investigations of the Federal Trade Commission, and they are consistent with the results of studies of the bearing of size upon distribution economies and of the "distribution cost unit" published by the Department of Commerce.

[35] Dorthea Braithwaite and S. P. Dobbs, *The Distribution of Consumable Goods* (London: Routledge, 1932), pp. 75, 80.

[36] Dollar volume, of course, makes the increase seem much greater than actually is the case. Deflation of 1954 figures by 50 per cent in order to put them on a roughly real-value basis with 1935 would give for 1954 a figure of around $4,500 million. Contrariwise, the 1935 figure compares with a previous advertising high of $3,426 million for the year 1929 when, again, the price level was much higher than 1935. Again, the relative size of advertising outlays may be compared with changes in gross national product. When such adjustments are made, it appears that media outlays have increased fairly steadily along with growth in national product, rising possibly a little more rapidly until the late forties, and much more rapidly thereafter.

[37] Data as cited in *Modern Medical Topics*, August, 1955, and in an address before the Pharmaceutical Advertising Club of New York by Dorthy Noyes, Vice-President and Treasurer of Noyes and Sproul, Inc., on "Your Share of Disposable Professional Time," April 5, 1956.

[38] Clark-O'Neill, Inc., a commercial house specializing on drug trade promotion, in a letter, "To the Professions," dated June 3, 1955.

[39] Noyes address, April 5, 1956. (Italics in the original.)

[40] "673 specialties were offered to the physician this year—170 of them for the first time. The 170 replaced the 172 that dropped out of the picture since last

year." At the same time the physicians "received almost 500 more mailings." Clark-O'Neill, Inc., in a letter, "Addressing the Profession," dated June 5, 1956.

[41] From *Housewives United Newsletter*, April-May, 1952.

[42] It needs to be added, however, that (*a*) the existence of standards does not, per se, inhibit high-pressure advertising, and (*b*) the existence of brand names does not of necessity promote high-pressure advertising. Examples of the first are fluid milk and many drugs (such as aspirin). Examples of the second are the Hershey chocolate products, the Volkswagen automobile, and, until the middle nineteen-twenties, the Ford automobile.

[43] *Printers' Ink* Advertisers' Guide to Marketing for 1957, October, 1956, sec. ii, p. 76.

[44] Walter F. Crowther, Bureau of Foreign and Domestic Commerce, 1942. This statement, it should be noted, is made by an official who was thoroughly familiar with the rise of supermarkets, chain-store and mail-order distribution, automatic (machine) selling, and other similar developments in the field of distribution.

[45] Dr. Julius Klein, Assistant Secretary of Commerce, New York *Times*, May 4, 1929. Such a statement needs to be compared with similar estimates, such as the famous report of the Federated American Engineering Societies, *Waste in Industry*, (New York: McGraw-Hill, 1921) which places "preventable waste" in production at a far higher figure.

[46] Robert T. Haslam, "The Need for Research in Marketing," a speech delivered before the American Marketing Association in December, 1949. It is, of course, difficult to evaluate such an estimate. It could mean many, and widely differing, things. For example, it could be taken to mean that distribution in 1870 was relatively efficient when compared to production, and that production subsequently was engaged in catching up. It could mean that the possibilities inherent in one were much greater than in the other. It could mean that increased manpower and resources in distribution made possible large-scale production economies that otherwise would not have come about.

[47] *Ibid.*

[48] In 1954, T. V. Houser, Chairman of the Board of Sears, Roebuck said that only 47 per cent of the retail price charged goes for raw materials and production, and that distribution takes the remaining 53 per cent. *Printers' Ink*, November 5, 1954, p. 20.

[49] S. J. Lengyel and R. M. Beecroft, *The Cost of Distribution* (Melbourne: University of Melbourne, 1949, p. 21.

[50] A. M. Carr-Saunders, P. Sargant Florence, and Robert Peers, *Consumers' Co-operation in Great Britain* (London: Allen & Unwin, 1938), p. 357.

[51] *Distribution: The Case for a National Census*, Fabian Publications, Research Series, No. 108 (London, 1946), p. 9.

[52] Examples where freight costs have induced such relocation of plants are local automobile parts-production and assembly, bakeries, soft-drink bottling.

CHAPTER XII. INTEGRATION OF TELECOMMUNICATIONS NETWORKS
(Pp. 361-386)

[1] T. A. M. Craven and A. E. Giegengack, "Communications," in National Resources Committee, *Technological Trends and National Policy* (Washington, 1937), p. 211.

[2] A. B. Clark, *The Development of Telephony in the United States*, Bell Telephone System Technical Publications, Monograph No. 2045 (1952), p. 1.

[3] Regular foot-courier or mounted service for conveyance of official documents was used by the Chinese under the Chou Dynasty (1122-255 B.C.), the XVIIIth Dynasty in Egypt (around 1400 B.C.) and the Achaemenid emperors of Persia. The Roman postal service, the *cursus publicus*, though originally intended only

for official documents, subsequently came to carry both public and private communications through all parts of the empire, by land and by sea. *Encyclopaedia of the Social Sciences,* Vol. 12, pp. 269-273.

[4] In 1949 independents had 7.2 million out of 40 million telephones, served two-thirds of the nation's area (mostly in rural areas), employed in excess of 90,000 persons, and had assets of over $1 billion. (Bell Telephone assets were then listed at $7.5 billions.) *Business Week,* October 29, 1949, p. 84.

[5] In 1955, General Telephone Corporation had "a network of 16 phone companies operating in 21 states, plus a minority interest in six small operating companies." It had some 2.5 million telephones, assets close to $1 billion, and a large telephone-equipment manufacturing company in Automatic Electric. In comparison, the Bell System had 44 million telephones, assets of nearly $13 billion, and a huge equipment company in the Western Electric Company. *Business Week,* September 10, 1955, p. 158.

[6] This and the following description are taken from *Your Career in Bell Telephone Laboratories,* a company promotion pamphlet (New York, January, 1952), supplemented by conversations with company officials.

[7] *The Story of Western Electric,* a company promotion pamphlet (New York, 1955), p. 22.

[8] "The United States Independent Telephone Association . . . is vitally interested in the standardization of operating procedures and the technical aspects of the interconnections among the various properties involved." It works very closely with Bell Telephone on the standardization of signals and tones, uniform quality of transmission, "coordination of area and exchange numbering plans within a nation-wide master plan," etc. William H. Harrison, President of the International Telephone and Telegraph Corporation, "Standards for Telecommunications" in Dickson Reck, ed., *National Standards in a Modern Economy* (New York: Harper, 1956), p. 141.

[9] The Post Office manages all domestic telephone, telegraph, and common-carrier wireless communications; Cable and Wireless, Ltd., all overseas cable and wireless networks owned by British nationals. The Commonwealth Telecommunications Board is a coördinating body between Cable and Wireless and the Dominion networks, publicly or privately owned. An External Telecommunications Board coördinates all British interests in connection with the Commonwealth Telecommunications Board or in the signing or making of agreements with member organizations of the International Telecommunications Union. Its powers, however, are not exclusive; agreements may be signed by any of the participating bodies.

[10] The British owned 170,000 miles of their own cable and operated over half of that owned by American interests—50,000 out of 95,170 nautical miles. In addition the British operated over 200,000 miles of wireless circuits under the same administration. Together they made up the largest telecommunications system in the world. *Labor and Industry in Britain* Vol. XI, No. 3 (September, 1953), p. 141.

[11] Clark, *op. cit.,* p. 8.

[12] This cable, it is interesting to note, is a joint project of Bell Telephone, the Canadian Overseas Telecommunications Corporation, and the British Post Office.

[13] "Switching at Its Boldest," by J. Meszar, *Bell Laboratories Record,* Vol. XXXII, No. 12 (December, 1954), p. 445.

[14] The Chief Engineer of A.T.&T. has speculated on the "ultimate." The time may come when, "whenever a baby is born anywhere in the world, he is given at birth a number which will be his telephone number for life. As soon as he can talk, he is given a watch-like device with ten little buttons on one side and a screen on the other. Thus equipped, at any time when he wishes to talk with anyone in the world, he will pull out the device and punch on the keys the number of his friend. Then, turning the device over, he will hear the voice of his friend and see his face

on the screen, in color and in three dimensions. If he does not see him and hear him, he will know that the friend is dead." Harold S. Osborne, "Communication Sets Its Sights Ahead," *Bell Telephone Magazine*, Summer, 1952, p. 73.

¹⁵ As of October, 1950, Western Union, floundering on the edge of bankruptcy from absorption of the run-down plant of Postal Telegraph, and losing business through lower telephone rates on the one hand and improved airmail service on the other, reported the "percentage utilization of plant available for message business" during daily peak periods (one half-hour) to be 32 per cent; over a 24-hour weekday, 11 per cent; and over the Saturday-Sunday weekend, 4 per cent. *Telecommunications: A Program for Progress*, report by the President's Communications Policy Board (Washington, 1951), p. 71.

¹⁶ "In its barest essentials, reperforator switching consists of receiving line signals in printing telegraph 5-unit code on a printer-perforator which records those line signals on a paper tape; passing that tape through an intraoffice transmittor which may be connected through a switchboard or 'turret' to a selected intraoffice path which terminates in a reperforator on the sending terminal of another circuit; the latter reperforator again records the signals in another paper tape which in turn flows through a line transmitter which sends them on to the proper destination. It replaces receiving operators, route clerks, route aides, and transmitting operators with clerks who simply read the destinations of telegrams as they are received, mark off the numbers on number sheets, and connect transmitters to intraoffice circuits at switching turrets. All route clerks and route aides are dispensed with and switching clerks can handle considerably more telegrams per day than receiving and transmitting operators formerly handled." R. F. Blanchard and W. B. Blanton, "Push Button Switching in Telegraph Systems," *Electrical Engineering*, Vol. 68, No. 3 (March, 1949), p. 225.

¹⁷ In a communication to the President's Communications Policy Board, dated November, 1950, Western Union maintained "the advisability, in the interest of national security, that a nation-wide network of telegraph trunking circuits be for reasons of physical security separate from the circuits carrying voice communications." *Telecommunications, a Program for Progress*, p. 71. With capacity automatically to reroute messages, as outlined above, this contention seems to be without foundation. In fact, the very reverse may be true. No other ground is given for a separate system, in effect conceding the argument as outlined above.

¹⁸ *Radio Spectrum Conservation: A Program of Conservation Based on Present Uses and Future Needs*, report of the Institute of Radio Engineers to the Joint Technical Advisory Committee (JTAC) of the Radio-Television Manufacturing Association (New York: McGraw-Hill, 1952), p. 128.

¹⁹ *Ibid.*

²⁰ "The International Radio Conference at Madrid in 1932 had a committee prepare a summary of radio propagation as then known; it was only seven pages long. The International Radio Consultative Committee at Bucharest in 1937 set up a committee to do the same thing; this time it was 42 pages long. In 1943, the Interservice Radio Propagation Laboratory prepared a handbook of only part of the subject (ionospheric propagation); it was 238 pages long and was considered as supplemented by monthly data pamphlets. In 1947 to 1950, efforts to compile the facts of radio propagation needed for their purposes were made by various international radio meetings (Atlantic City Telecommunications Conference, Mexico City and Florence Conferences on High Frequency Broadcasting, Provisional Frequency Board in Geneva); the resulting compendia of radio-propagation . . . amount to so many thousands of pages that they constitute a stack over 3 ft. high." *Ibid.*, pp. 20-21.

²¹ See Appendix by D W. Innis in Harold A. Innis, *The Bias of Communication* (Toronto: University of Toronto Press, 1951), pp. 199, 201.

[22] "Frequency Resources and National Policy," an address before the Armed Forces Communication Association, February 23, 1950.

[23] *Radio Spectrum Conservation,* p. 148.

[24] Cited by George A. Codding, Jr. in *The International Telecommunication Union* (Leiden: Brill, 1952), pp. 147-148.

[25] ". . . ten times the amount of power is required to do the same job of broadcasting on a frequency of 1,500 kc. as would be needed on one of 600 kc., all other factors remaining the same." Cornelia Bruere Rose, Jr., *National Policy for Radio Broadcasting* (New York and London: Harper, 1940), p. 30.

[26] For a complete and exhaustive account see Codding, *The International Telecommunication Union.*

[27] Listed in Sir Harry Osborne Mance, *International Telecommunications* (London and New York: Oxford University Press, 1943), p. xii.

[28] The International Advisory Committee on Telephones (CCIF), the International Advisory Committee on Telegraphs (CCIT), and the International Advisory Committee on Radiocommunications (CCIR). *Ibid.*

[29] *Telecommunications: A Program for Progress,* pp. 40-43, 127.

[30] The idea, however, is not foreign to this country. In 1910 the Navy favored "the passage of a law placing all wireless stations under the control of the Government." Letter from the Secretary of the Navy, March 30, quoted in Report No. 659, "Radio Communication" from the Committee on Commerce (61st Cong., 2nd Sess., U.S. Senate, May 6, 1910), p. 4. In 1914 the Wilson Administration in a report, *Government Ownership of Electrical Means of Communication,* called for government ownership and operation of telephone, telegraph, and radio. When the President assumed control of telegraph, telephone, and cable systems in 1918, Secretary of the Navy Josephus Daniels testified that in his personal opinion the government should "control and own telegraph, telephone and all means of communication permanently." Postmaster General A. S. Burleson concurred. House of Representatives, Commitee on Interstate and Foreign Commerce, Hearings on H. J. Res. 309 (65th Cong., 2nd Sess., July 2, 1918), p. 27.

[31] *Radio Spectrum Conservation,* p. 182.

[32] In the report on the 1944 allocation hearings, *In the Matter of Allocation of Frequencies to the Various Classes of Non-governmental Services in the Radio Spectrum . . . Docket No. 6651, Report of Proposed Allocations from 25,000 kilocycles to 30,000 kilocycles,* January 15, 1955, pp. 19-20.

[33] E. M. Webster, "Implementation, Cooperation and Self-Regulation," an address before the Armed Services Communications Association, January 19, 1955.

[34] According to the *20th Annual Report* (1954) of the FCC (Washington, 1955), there were in use in the United States in that year 117 million radio sets, and 30 million television sets (p. 109). There were also—in addition to 842,000 commercial operators (p. 124)—some 120,000 licensed amateur radio operators (p. 83).

[35] Spectrum Utilization; Frequency Allocation; High Frequency Generation; Standard Broadcasting; FM Broadcasting; Television; Facsimile; Radio Communication; Relay Systems; Radio Range; Direction and Recognition; Aeronautical Radio; Industrial, Scientific and Medical Equipment.

[36] Professor Dallas Smythe of the Institute of Communications Research, University of Illinois, in a letter to the author, adds the following comment: "In the discussion . . . you seem to be saying that standards impede innovation. . . . Innovation in *equipment* is possible in radio even while standards and systems remain unchanged. It is entirely possible to have either the present electronic gun method of presenting color television images in the receiver or an entirely different kind of equipment operating to the same standards as are applicable to existing equipment. In fact this is the point to the delay in developing a low cost color

TV receiver. The cost of the RCA 'color tube is so high that the innovation of color TV has been thwarted to date. And various elements in the industry are attempting to develop equipment which will perform the same function more cheaply. . . . It also seems to me that rather than lay the responsibility for difficulty in innovation in radio principally to standards you might well point out that unwillingness to accept obsolescence because of the capital invested is at least as large a factor making for use of the radio spectrum which is less efficient than it could be in the light of the state of the radio art."

[37] Report on 1944 allocation hearings, p. 19.

[38] *Radio Spectrum Conservation*, p. 189.

[39] The new facility of "forward scatter" constitutes an exception to the former general rule. For example, it was proposed in 1955 to increase the Miami-Havana telephone circuits by adding cables Nos. 7 and 8 using, like existing cables Nos. 5 and 6, deep-sea repeatered solid dielectric submarine cables. This would have provided a maximum of 36 new telephone circuits at a cost of $3.8 million. By using "forward scatter" or "over-the-horizon" radio technique to span the water, the job can be done for an estimated cost of $3.4 million and provide ultimately over 100 telephone circuits plus a television channel. It was decided to go ahead with the job on the "forward scatter" radio basis.

[40] Further progress in narrow-beam microwave relays may supply, in the short run at least, an indefinitely large supply of circuits without further resort to coaxial cables—which are much more expensive to construct and maintain.

CHAPTER XIII. RECAPITULATION AND THE FIRST SUM OF CONSEQUENCES
(Pp. 387-424)

[1] E.g., "The technology that is now developing and that will dominate the next decades seems to be in total conflict with traditional and, in the main, momentarily still valid, geographical and political units and concepts. This is the maturing crisis of technology." John von Neumann, member of the Atomic Energy Commission, "Can We Survive Technology?" in *Fortune*, June, 1955, p. 151.

[2] In philosophy, Hoernle wrote, "[we find] that all new theories do but add to the babel and confusion, that there is no cumulative cooperative advance from generation to generation, no funded stock of philosophical truths which can be taught as its established rudiments to beginners, and which are taken for granted by all experts as the basis of further enquiry. The same problems are ever examined afresh . . . the old problems remain persistently open." R. F. A. Hoernle, *Studies in Contemporary Metaphysics* (New York: Harcourt, Brace, 1920), p 48.

[3] Perhaps it need be added that "best" must be indeterminate unless societal values are known; but to itemize them, and the impact they may have on the narrower problems before us, would lead too far afield. In this context it is necessary to pass such discussion by; the issues involved are too vital for more parenthetical generalization.

[4] It would do equally well to suppose that some such organization as the National Bureau of Economic Research in coöperation, e.g., with the Michigan Survey Research Center, were to present a schedule of demands for goods desired by the general public over some given time-interval—say, six months to a year—and industry were then so to organize (1) to comply with this schedule, and (2) to adhere at each and every step to the rule of least means as indicated in the text.

[5] This division of labor is necessary to get quick results, although the greater the number of subdivisions, the greater the opportunity for "sub-optimumizations" which are deleterious to the whole. On the other hand, if an industry does not give such mandates to specialized departments but attempts to optimize all processes simultaneously, the delay in finding the optimum strategy (if one could be found) would in itself change the optimum. High-speed computers may alter this some-

what so that sales, proceurement, production, and distribution can be better integrated than at present.

⁶ See, e.g., Oskar Morgenstern, "The Accuracy of Economic Observations," in Tjalling C. Koopmans, ed., *Activity Analysis of Production and Allocation* (New York: Wiley, 1951), p. 282-284.

⁷ "Objectives must be stated in terms of basic ends, thus permitting the consideration of alternative means, if they are to be useful in programming operations designed to maximize objectives within resource limitations." Marshall K. Wood and George B. Dantzig, "The Programming of Interdependent Activities: General Discussion," *ibid.*, p. 18.

⁸ Albert Hall, Bendix Aviation Corporation, "Automation in Business and Industry," an address delivered at the University of California, Berkeley, May 4, 1955.

⁹ See, e.g., Koopmans, *Activity Analysis of Production and Allocation*, and the very compact summary by Robert Dorfman, "Mathematical, Or 'Linear,' Programming: A Non-Mathematical Exposition," *American Economic Review*, December, 1953, pp. 797-825.

¹⁰ Maurice Dobb, *Soviet Economic Development Since 1917* (New York: International Publishers, 1948), pp. 341-342.

¹¹ See, e.g., Wassily W. Leontief, *The Structure of American Economy, 1919-1939* (2nd ed.; New York: Oxford University Press, 1951).

¹² Dorfman, *op. cit.*, p. 797.

¹³ See, e.g., the comprehensive survey of the bureaucratic problems of all types of organizations in *Onward Industry*, by James D. Mooney, at the time a vice-president of the General Motors Corporation, and Alan C. Reiley, medieval historian (New York: Harper, 1931).

¹⁴ Usually called by the name of their chairman, Ex-President Hoover, there were two separate Commissions on Organization of the Executive Branch of the Government, one set up under Public Law 162, July 7, 1947, and the second under Public Law 108, July 10, 1953. The first Commission concerned itself chiefly with the reorganization of federal departments and agencies and their relations with each other. The second dealt more extensively with the functional organization of the Executive Branch and with questions of policy. The first Commission produced 19 *Reports to the Congress*, supplemented by 18 *Task Force Reports* of study groups whose work preceded these. The second Commission produced 20 *Reports to the Congress* and 20 *Task Force Reports*.

¹⁵ Gregory Grossman, "In the Land of Paper Pyramids," *Problems of Communism*, Vol. IV, No. 4 (July-August 1955), pp. 18-26.

¹⁶ Commission on Organization of the Executive Branch of the Government (Hoover Commission), *Final Report to the Congress*, June, 1955, pp. 19-20. It should be added that only part—it is very difficult, even after careful reading of the reports to be sure how much (it may be about half)—of the savings would come from transfer of functions now performed by the federal government to state, municipal, or private agencies and would not, consequently, represent net savings to the economy.

¹⁷ See the chart facing page 68 in Commission on Organization of the Executive Branch of the Government, *Task Force Report on Food and Clothing in the Government* (Washington, April, 1955).

¹⁸ During the Korean war, a returning veteran relates, a bored civilian officer noticed flypaper in a barroom, and amused himself by turning in an official report on flypaper efficiency. Receiving no comment, he sent further reports on the subject. Failing to send one in, he received an official reminder from Washington. Shortly, inquiries came from other military quarters asking how to make such reports. In almost no time at all such reports had become standard procedure.

A management expert has estimated that in the United States as a whole, one file-case drawer is filled each year for every man, woman, and child in the country, and that more than half of the total was entirely unnecessary. The manpower used in producing the extra paper and typewriters must be very great; but far greater is the excess labor going into filling the forms and typing, filing, and maintaining the records.

[19] In both these cases, a central policy-forming holding company serves to co-ordinate and integrate the operations of organizationally more or less autonomous operating companies. The original design was that of the Bell System. It has been copied in Germany, notably by I. G. Farben and Vereinigte Stahlwerke. Many others have since followed suit. The Soviet trusts and the major British Nationalized industries—coal, power, transport, airways—seem to have built at least in part on the basis of this early experimentation.

[20] F. J. Roethlisberger and William J. Dickson, *Management and the Worker* (Cambridge, Mass.: Harvard University Press, 1950). See also Elton Mayo, *The Human Problems of an Industrial Civilization* (New York: Macmillan, 1938). These experiments, it is interesting to note, were largely the basis of the TWI—Training Within Industry—programs sponsored by the government for War Production plants during World War II. These same programs became widely used in Britain during the war, and provided the point of departure for the Institute for Industrial Management.

[21] See, e.g., the collection of papers in Dorwin Cartwright and Alvin Zander, eds., *Group Dynamics* (New York: Rowe, Peterson, 1953), especially Part 4.

[22] *Dominations and Powers: Reflections on Liberty, Society, and Government* (New York: Scribner, 1951).

INDEX

480

Index

Technology: science and, 14-19, 72-
79, 85, 90-92, 94-95, 96, 104, 389;
and conservation, 17-18; and natural
resource utilization, 62-71; and qual-
ity-quantity-costs relationships, 64-65;
"complex ores" processing, 65; sea
water mineral extraction, 66-67; use
of agricultural residues, 69-70; and
forest utilization, 69; standardization
and, 108; requisites for, 109-111;
and the "chemical revolution," 202-
231 *passim;* "nuclear chemistry,"
203-204; and "industrial complex"
development, 207-225 *passim;* the
Industrial Revolution, 232-235; *Cybernetics,* 239; and inter-plant integration, 243-253; and plant location,
257-265 *passim;* railroad equipment,
269, 289; transportation equipment,
292-293; aeronautics, 292; and energy
supply, 296-325 *passim;* "breeder
process," 310-312; electricity generation efficiency, 317-318; and "creative" obsolescence, 330-333; and marketing efficiency, 354-360; and role of
communications engineering, 361-386
passim; and telecommunications rates,
364; telephone transmission, 366-369;
and radio spectrum allocation, 370-
377; public policy and, 406-415
passim. See also Automation; Continuous-flow production; Production;
Rationalization; "Scientific revolution"; Standardization, standards and
specifications
Telegraph networks, 363-370. *See also*
Communications
Telephone industry, 76-77, 363-370. *See
also* Communications
Tennessee Valley Authority (TVA):
objectives of, 171; land utilization
planning, 189; individualism vs., 192;
water transport integration, 286; electricity system, 298; multi-purpose
water resource development, 299-303
passim
Thorium sources, 311
Transport Act of 1947 (Britain), 271-
272, 278
Transport and Communications Commission (UNESCO), 267
Transportation: "revolution" in, 10-13;
and productivity, 109-110; and plant
location, 208-210, 227-228; in continuous-flow production, 242; and

industrial integration, 262-264 *passim;* unification of, 267-295; functions
of, 267-268; National Resources
Planning Board (U.S.) report on,
267; land transport, 268-282; rail-
road-highway unification, 271-274;
British Transport Act of 1947, 271-
272; routing inefficiency, 271; competition among media, 272-273; international standardization and unification, 272, 287-293; bus-lines, 273-
274; Port of New York Authority,
274, 281-282; electricity transmission,
275-277, 308, 314-324; continuous-
belt transmission, 276; management
duplication, 277; and city-planning,
279-282 *passim;* London Passenger
Transport Board, 280; land-water
unification, 281-287; inland waterways, 283-287; English and Continental waterways, 284-285; terminal
facilities, 286; and industry, 292-293;
research on, 292-293; of heat, 308;
product duplication and, 330; grid
transmission of energy, 314-324; and
marketing, 339-344; crosshauling,
339-340; consumer delivery, 341-344;
gasoline, 345-346; and retailing inefficiency, 346. *See also* Air transport;
Marketing; Pipelines; Trucking
Trucking: advantages of, 272; unification economies, 281-282; state load
limitations, 287-288

Underdeveloped countries: industrialization and "scientific revolution" in, 34-
37, 387-388, 404-405; standard of
living, 41; geological knowledge of,
61-62; land cultivation, 62-63; agricultural productivity, 161-162
UNESCO: support of science, 81; and
international organization of research,
98-107 *passim;* Transport and Communications Commission, 267, 285
Union of Soviet Socialist Republics
(U.S.S.R.): mineral resources, 61;
organization of science, 88-91; education of engineers, 88; Academy of
Sciences, 89-91; scientific publications, 90; restriction of scientific information, 104-105; water-resource
development, 191; Dnieper industrial
"complex," 219-221; integrated administration and planning, 256-257;
industry-wide planning, 260-264 *pas-*

Date Due